Every mea
banquet,
every night a
honeymoon

To Jilly

Every meal a banquet, every night a honeymoon

UNFORGETTABLE AFRICAN EXPERIENCES

Peter Younghusband

JONATHAN BALL PUBLISHERS
JOHANNESBURG & CAPE TOWN

Published in 2003 by
JONATHAN BALL PUBLISHERS (PTY) LTD
P O Box 33977
Jeppestown
2043

ISBN 1 86842 167 8

Cover cartoon by Dr Jack
Design by Michael Barnett, Johannesburg
Typesetting and reproduction of text by Alinea Studio, Cape Town
Cover reproduction by Triple M Design & Advertising, Johannesburg
Printed and bound by CTP Book Printers

Contents

Introduction

It is widely believed that journalists publish everything they find out. That is simply not true. Every journalist has secrets gathered on the wayside of reporting that can never be told, or told only in part, or revealed only when time has dimmed or healed the past.

I have unlocked some private memories and confidences for the purpose of this book.

It became, I confess, a more tortuous and conscience-challenging process than I had expected. It required a formula to present the facts without revealing identities and circumstances where these could lead to hurt, embarrassment or wrath.

The result is a roller coaster of chapters that leap from straight reporting of events and known people to stories novelette-styled and veiled in form where names have been changed, events juxtapositioned, and some red herrings drawn to protect identities as decently as possible. So much bubble-wrap should leave no cause for lament. And the facts themselves remain intact. That's important because the events you will read about in the following pages really happened.

These are stories about Africa, which means you might laugh or cry, or merely shake your head in wonderment or despair. Because that's the way life is in Africa. Just reading through one edition of a local daily newspaper can take you through all these emotions.

I reported some of the following events when they occurred, for whichever newspaper or magazine I represented at the time. I am telling others for the first time.

Life as a farmer alongside my career as a foreign correspondent has provided its own crop of experiences. How else, for instance, would I ever have been able to tell you that tractors can make love?

Regretfully a lot of what I have to tell deals with death. But death is very much part of life in Africa, and much of its sorrow. Some of this has been personal, such as the deaths of close friends like Howard Lawrence whose life we tried to save by thrusting aside the barrier of apartheid – only to see our defiance seal his fate; and John Edlin whose demons finally struck him down in a Dakar nightclub; and Sarah Barrell who shot herself when her Rhodesian lover was killed in an ambush; and the death of my son in a terrorist bomb attack.

Much of what I have written occurred before the advent of cell phones and the other advances of the new information technology, and this will be noticed. It helps a great deal now to be able to telephone a story to a newspaper from the remotest corner of Africa – certainly an improvement on the days when you might have secured the greatest story of the decade, only to find that the real challenge was to find a way of communicating it. That was the test that often separated the men from the boys.

Peter Younghusband
Spooky Mountain Vineyards
Franschhoek

1

Little brother John

My uncle ordered his farm workers to tie the Italian to a tractor, and then he whipped him with a sjambok until he bled profusely. It was a terrible beating.

Most people knew my uncle by his childhood nickname of Boetie Jan, which means, literally, Little Brother John. That was because he was the youngest of six brothers – none of whom was under six feet in height. But the nickname became a misnomer as Boetie Jan outgrew all of them to become a towering and powerful six feet six inches, black-haired and bearded, with pale-blue eyes. He always reminded me of the hero John Ridd in Blackmore's famous novel, *Lorna Doone*, who once seized a man by his upper arm and tore his muscle out. I could imagine my uncle doing that.

The Italian, whose name was Mario, was a prisoner of war who, together with another POW called Gino, had been allocated to the farm by the South African Defence Department as labourers. Many South African farms acquired Italians to supplement their workforces in the early 1940s after they had been taken prisoner in North Africa by the South African army following South Africa's decision to join Britain in the war against Germany. My uncle's farm, Soetfontein, however, was the only one in the district to receive such prisoners.

Mario and Gino were a great success at first. They harboured no grudges about being prisoners. In fact they seemed happy to be away from the war. They worked hard, which pleased my uncle. They also pleased my aunt, which was where the trouble began.

The women on the farm – my Aunt Milly and my cousins Valerie, Rina and Amelia – were fascinated by the Italians. They had never before met men like these. In the somewhat austere Afrikaner community in the small Swartland dorp of Mooreesburg, the men were a grim lot.

The older men were stern and growly, and went to bed early. They all smoked a strong brand of pipe tobacco called Magaliesberg and smelled heavily of it at all times. Their conversation rarely exceeded the boundaries of politics, religion and rugby. The young men were shy, gauche and clumsy, and they stumbled and fumbled in matters important to women. Their conversation was confined mostly to rugby. Astonishingly, however, these men – both young and old – were graceful dancers, light on their feet, and they could swing a girl around in a manner that left her breathless and excited.

But as the Church frowned on dancing, there wasn't much of it. There was a lot of morality in Mooreesburg in those days and, consequently, some degree of frustration. There must have been a lot of compensatory action after marriage, because families in and around Mooreesburg tended to be large. But whether it was fun or not was hard to gauge because it was rarely spoken about. The only apparent pleasure the women had seemed to revolve around baking bread, making jam and lopping the heads off chickens for Sunday lunch. Not surprisingly the ladies of Mooreesburg always seemed a little pensive, as if yearning for something without quite knowing what it was.

Thus the arrival of the Italian prisoners of war, Mario and Gino, was like a rainfall in a desert. Compared to my dour uncle and his morose son, Barend, they were quite something else. What it was, of course, was that they brought with them a whiff of the romance of Italy.

Their attitude towards the women on the farm was deemed to be amazing. They would open the doors of vehicles for my aunt with courtly gestures. They would present her and the girls with flowers they had picked in the veld.

Gino, the elder of the two, an engineer from Milan, was also a born craftsman. He would carve delightful objects, such as birds and small animals, out of wood, paint them in delicate colours and present them as gifts.

Mario, a teacher from Naples, was the more effusive of the two.

He would greet each female on the farm every morning, from my aunt down to her youngest daughter, Amelia, aged six – even Skattie, the ageing Labrador bitch – as if she were the rising sun.

Every frock that my aunt donned was greeted with exclamations of admiration: *'Aaah, Signora! Bella bella! Fantastica!'* It was soon noticed that my aunt was becoming decidedly more fastidious in the way she dressed and did her hair, and my uncle was heard to express some sour surprise at the increased amount she was spending on clothes and toiletries.

It was also noticed that a lot of women from the village and neighbouring farms, including a few distant matrons who did not usually favour Aunt Milly with visits, were coming to call on various pretexts. The truth was that news of the Italians had seeped through to the village and further afield and everyone was curious.

It had been decided early on that the Italians could not be billeted with the farm's coloured labour force, because they were, after all, white, and clearly men of culture, although my uncle was suspicious of their Catholicism, having been warned of it by the local dominee. So they were housed separately but quite comfortably in a large lean-to at the back of the main house, formerly used as a sweet-potato store, and they were invited to take their meals with the family.

Whereupon it was found that Gino was an outstanding cook – surpassing even my aunt's abilities in the kitchen – and the family was introduced to new dishes of sensational variety and taste, including pasta with delectable sauces. This was appreciated by everyone except my uncle, who had difficulty negotiating spaghetti through his beard, finally cursing and giving up in exasperation, saying: *'Die donderse goed gaan orals!'* ('The bloody stuff goes all over the place!')

It was further discovered that Mario was an accomplished pianist and this provided some wonderful entertainment on many evenings. He also began to give piano lessons to my cousin Valerie, whom he and Gino called 'Valerina'. She liked this version of her name so much that she adopted it.

Mario also possessed an attractive tenor voice and would frequently burst into operatic arias while working, even stopping what he was doing so that he could accompany his performance with the appropriate gestures. Everyone else in the vicinity would usually stop working to listen and watch in enjoyment and appreciation.

While repairing a pump outside the kitchen one sunny morning, Mario launched so passionately into *O Sole Mio* that my aunt came out of the kitchen to listen, wiping flour from her hands with her apron. When he had finished she clapped in delight and exclaimed: 'Bravo, Mario, bravo!' At which Mario stepped over to her, bowed low and, with exaggerated courtliness, kissed her hand with all the tenderness with which he had sung.

Boetie Jan, who had emerged from the nearby tool shed, watched the entire performance with the tolerance one accords the antics of children, and went back into the shed, shaking his head.

Indeed my uncle seemed to accept all these diversions with wintry good humour because, in general, both men were diligent. Gino, especially, was a wizard at everything he did. All the farm vehicles were maintained as never before. Old ploughs and other discarded machinery in the sheds or lying about the farm were repaired and given new life by a man who simply used a blow torch and a welding iron to manufacture new parts from old metal wherever he could find it.

Thus all seemed well at Soetfontein – until Oom Karel, a nearby neighbour, came on one of his periodic visits to indulge Boetie Jan in one of their peculiar non-conversational conversations.

This began, as always, with the two men seating themselves on the stoep and filling their pipes with Magaliesberg, while Boetie Jan called for coffee.

Oom Karel said: '*Ja, ou Jan.*'

Boetie Jan replied: '*Ja, ou Karel.*'

There followed such a long silence that it seemed the two had forgotten each other. Then Oom Karel sighed, and said: '*So gaan dit in die wêreld.*' ('So it goes in the world.')

Boetie Jan agreed: '*So gaan dit in die wêreld.*'

'Aaiee,' lamented Oom Karel, shaking his head.

'Aaiee,' agreed Boetie Jan.

Another long silence, during which old Sinnah, the maid-servant, brought the coffee, and the men blew on it and slurped it.

Oom Karel sighed.

Boetie Jan sighed.

Silence.

'*Nog geen reën,*' ('Still no rain') said Oom Karel, looking at the sky.

'*Nog geen reën,*' agreed Boetie Jan.

'Aaiee.'

'Aaiee.'

Oom Karel sighed.

Boetie Jan sighed.

'*Ja-nee, ou Jan.*'

'*Ja-nee, ou Karel.*'

Then Oom Karel tapped the bowl of his pipe against the heel of his boot to dislodge the ash on the stoep, and stood up. '*Dankie vir die lekker gesels,*' ('Thanks for the nice talk') he said. The two men walked to Oom Karel's bakkie.

Sinnah moved out of the shadows with a broom to sweep up the ash, as she always did after these encounters.

It was she who heard Oom Karel say, as he got into his vehicle: 'How's it going with the Italian labour?'

'Fine,' replied my uncle.

Another long silence as Oom Karel sat gazing through the windscreen of his *bakkie.* Then he said: '*Pasop vir hulle met die vroumense.*' ('Be watchful of them with the womenfolk.') And he started the engine and drove away.

According to Sinnah, as my uncle walked back up the steps to the stoep: '*Sy gesig was donker.*' ('His face was dark.')

Now, it is well known that old retainers like Sinnah are nosy, incurable gossips and troublemakers.

But who knows what emotions had been set in train? Did my uncle deduce something from Oom Karel's words? Had there been talk in the village? Was Oom Karel's comment simply a general observation as one man speaking to another – or was he trying to warn my uncle about something? Or did the remark link up, in Boetie Jan's mind, with the memory of Mario kissing his wife's hand?

My aunt told my mother (her sister) that, before the dreadful event occurred, there was a period of several days when Boetie Jan seemed withdrawn. 'And I used to look up sometimes and find him watching me in a brooding sort of way.'

13

So one might say the atmosphere was already mildly charged on the morning that Boetie Jan walked into the kitchen and found his wife in Mario's arms.

Whether the two were having an affair or whether it was merely an embrace on the spur of the moment has always been a grey area open to speculation and somehow never clarified within our family. My mother, probably out of loyalty to her sister, was always reticent on this point, saying only that my aunt had confided to her that Mario came from a country where people tended to embrace warmly on any pretext, and had merely given her a harmless good-morning kiss. The least that could be said was that he had timed it badly.

Anyhow, all hell broke loose at Soetfontein. Boetie Jan crossed the kitchen in two strides, lifted Mario off his feet by his collar and bore him outside into the morning sun, where he flung him onto the ground and kicked him when he tried to get up.

'Koos! Jakob! Willem! Damoen!' yelled Boetie Jan, summoning the farm workers, who came running.

'*Vat hom waenhuis toe and maak hom vas oor die trekker,*' ('Take him to the wagon shed and tie him to the tractor') ordered my uncle. The workers stood gaping.

'*Ek sê maak hom vas oor die trekker!*' bellowed Boetie Jan.

The frightened workers picked Mario up and dragged him to the wagon shed. In the doorway of the kitchen my aunt and the children stood weeping.

My uncle strode to the tool shed to fetch the sjambok that he kept there, usually for use on recalcitrant livestock.

Gino, who had been working in the tool shed, ran out at that moment to discover what all the noise was about. My uncle knocked him senseless with a single blow, not because he had done anything but because he was in the way, and was an Italian, a nationality now in disfavour.

They tied Mario across the tractor in the wagon shed and my uncle flogged him mercilessly, until the shirt was cut from his back and he bled from wounds that would scar him for life.

Only when Boetie Jan became exhausted was my aunt, with the assistance of the workers, able to drag him away from the shocking deed.

Mario was taken to hospital, where the police were called. The police informed the Defence Department, who sent two officers to the farm, and Mario and Gino were formally removed from Soetfontein.

Boetie Jan had to appear in court in nearby Malmesbury, where he was heavily fined for assault by a magistrate who told him: 'Consider yourself fortunate that you are not going to prison because you have committed a serious offence.'

Boetie Jan protested that Mario deserved to be punished. The magistrate replied that only the courts could punish people – if found guilty.

Boetie Jan retorted: 'On my farm I am the law and I am the court.'

Whereupon the magistrate fined him a further 20 pounds for contempt of court.

Boetie Jan and Aunt Milly are both dead, as is Barend their son, and the three daughters, Valerie, Rina and Amelia, have long married and moved away from Mooreesburg. But there are old folk in the village who still talk about the Italians who were sent to Soetfontein and what happened to them there.

They also still speak of Boetie Jan. He was always held in high regard as a good farmer, an upright citizen and a God-fearing man.

My mother, however, regarded him as an oaf and was heard to say, more than once, that she could never understand what my aunt saw in him.

Both my mother and my aunt were refined women who read widely and on the occasions that we travelled from Cape Town to visit Soetfontein, they would get together and converse happily about the latest novels they had read. My aunt had started the village library and my mother was helping her to stock it. This irritated Boetie Jan who regarded any form of leisure reading as a means to avoid work.

I recall a painful dinner episode when my mother, in her feisty way, tongue-lashed Boetie Jan for his anti-literature stance. Whereupon my uncle reached for the family Bible and, slamming his fist on it, thundered: 'This is the only book worth reading and it is the only one I read!'

I was 11 years old at the time and, like everyone else at the table, overawed by the scene. But my mother retorted: 'Bugger you, Jan!' and, seizing me by the hand, said: 'Let's get the hell out of here!' And she drove us home to Cape Town, 70 miles away, in our old Studebaker, even though it was raining heavily and the road in those days was a dirt-track best never attempted at night, even in good weather.

Whatever Boetie Jan's personal views were on literature, he had the good sense, or the oversight, to leave the education of his children in the hands of his wife, with the pleasing results that they became outstanding students and received degrees at the University of Stellenbosch. Boetie Jan attended their graduations suspiciously but not without pride.

Family squabbles sometimes take time to subside, so we didn't visit Soetfontein for some months after the dinner-time argument over books. The next occasion was when we went along with my Uncle Bill (my mother and Aunt Milly's brother) to introduce his fiancée, Veronica – a lovely, slender girl.

Boetie Jan greeted her with a gorilla-like embrace and then, sweeping her off her feet, sat her on his arm like a child and said: '*Yerra, Bill, sy's mooi maar 'n bietjie lig in die broek, nè!*' ('Gosh, Bill, she's pretty but a bit light in the pants, hey?')

I'll say this for Veronica, she proved a right sport. She took it all with a smile even though she paled somewhat and, as was later revealed, Boetie Jan had broken one of her ribs.

Sometimes I spent part of my school vacations at Soetfontein. (To this day I wonder why it was called Soetfontein ('Sweet Fountain') because its water was as brackish as most of the water in and around Mooreesburg.) The vacations were pleasant, and I enjoyed my cousins and adored my aunt, but it was only as I grew older that I came to terms with my uncle.

Boetie Jan's strange, brooding presence always cast a shadow throughout his home, even among his own children. They loved him but they also stood in awe, if not in fear, of him. He ruled by discipline. Everyone rose at 6 a.m. (you could have a lie-in until 7 a.m. on Sundays). Meals had to be served on time and all food eaten.

I once declined a rice-pudding dessert because I hate rice pudding. The rice pudding was placed in front of me every meal after that by order of my uncle, until I managed to slip it unseen to Skattie, the Labrador.

We had to go to bed at 8 p.m. and the lamps were extinguished at 8.30 (no electricity yet on Soetfontein in those days). We had to attend church on Sundays and sit stiffly in Sunday best and scratchy collars listening to droning sermons, and were ordered to bed on Sunday afternoons to rest for two hours after a gargantuan Sunday lunch.

Yet Boetie Jan was a kind man. It was just that his manifestations of kindness were physical rather than verbal. He would occasionally show me affection by ruffling my hair, nearly tearing my head off my shoulders in the act.

We once stood together in a wheat field watching a mechanical harvester at work. Suddenly he picked me up and threw me onto it, behind the driver, as it thundered past. I clung to the driver in terror as the thing bumped and roared along. As it passed him on the next cycle Boetie Jan leaned over and yanked me off it. 'Did you enjoy that, man? Good hey?' And he roared with laughter.

Years later, on one of my last visits to Soetfontein, he asked me what I was doing and I told him I was a journalist. As was to be expected, he smiled sardonically. But at least he didn't start thumping the Bible. Then he asked me which publication I was working for. '*Drum* magazine,' I replied.

'*Maar dis 'n Kaffer-blad!*' ('But that's a Kaffir newspaper!') he said in a tone of pained astonishment and shook his head in despair. He never mentioned my work again.

But a year later I dared to ask him a favour. I had begun to work for the London *Daily Mail* and they had sent out to South Africa one of their top feature writers, Henry Fairlie, who, many years later, was based in the United States as a prominent commentator on American affairs. Henry had asked me if he could meet a 'typical' Afrikaner family. I decided to take him to Moorreesburg and hoped for the best.

Boetie Jan agreed, reluctantly, when I put it to him. 'I suppose I will have to speak English,' he said.

'Just for a little while,' I assured him.

My aunt laid on a grand Sunday spread for us. There were now grandchildren in evidence and with the entire family seated there – my uncle, now grey-haired and grey-bearded, sitting at the head of the table, looking very patriarchal – it was just what Henry Fairlie was looking for, and I could see him taking it all in with relish.

Unfortunately, Henry was not a man who held his liquor well, and the sweet wine, my uncle's standard tipple for Sunday lunch, was going to his head fast. His questions about Afrikaner politics, Afrikaners and Afrikanerdom in general were becoming increasingly aggressive and beginning to verge on the offensive.

Boetie Jan, whose English was slow and deliberate, answered every question politely and patiently, seemingly quite tolerant. Nothing is more inviolate than the Afrikaner code of hospitality. Nevertheless I was feeling anxious.

Suddenly Fairlie threw at him what I suppose was his clincher question: 'It is often said that some of the best old Afrikaner families, such as yours, are of mixed race. Tell me, sir, is there coloured blood in your family?'

A great silence fell upon the table. From the older members of the family right down to the youngest sitting at the end, all eyes turned to look at the old man, who was suddenly still, as though he had been carved from granite.

What, I wondered miserably, was going to happen now? I remembered Mario the Italian, beaten near to death for his indiscretion. I remembered my Uncle Bill's fiancée, Veronica, who had suffered a broken rib through mere affection. What was now going to happen to Henry Fairlie? Would my uncle rise with a roar and drive his fist down on top of his head, smashing it right down between his shoulders? It would not be out of character.

But the old man simply said, 'Well, Mr Fairlie, if that is true, all I can say is I hope it's Zulu blood – nothing but the best.'

I must say, at that moment I loved him.

2

The beermaker of Soweto

When he got paid on Fridays Benny Mitshala would stuff his wages into a 35-millimetre film container and insert it into his rectum.

He had been doing this since the Spoke Men had beaten him up for hiding his money in his shoes. That was after they had thrashed him for hiding it in the lining of his jacket and before that for hiding it in the secret pocket his mother had sewn in an inside leg of his jeans.

The film-container method succeeded for several weeks. The first week, when he told them he had been fired and they could find no money on him, they gave him a hiding anyway, cursing him for having lost his job. The second week, they smacked him around a bit, but seemed to accept his story that he was returning from another fruitless week of searching for work.

After that they left him alone, assuming he was just another bit of the human flotsam of unemployed that drifted between Johannesburg and its gigantic black satellite city, Soweto, which was, in effect, a dormitory for the thousands of black workers who came to work in the white man's city.

So for more than a month Benny brought his wages home intact and the family's fragile economy enjoyed an uplift.

But soon after, there came a Friday when the Spoke Men were waiting for Benny Mitshala again. He recognised one of them on the platform of Soweto's Station Three as he alighted from the train. It was already dark and the man was standing under a lamp. He seemed to be looking straight at him as he spoke into a portable phone.

Benny began the long walk home from the station. Then he saw them move out of the shadows near Bali Naidoo's cash store. Apprehension filled his mind and drained into his heart and overflowed from there into his guts.

His wages were safely stored up his arse in the 35-millimetre film container, as usual, but what now? They had left him alone for weeks, so what now?

'Hullo, Benny,' said Lukas Ngwena, the hulking brute who always led the bunch working Station Three. 'What you got for us, Benny?'

'Nothing,' Benny mumbled. 'I still got no job.'

'You lie, Benny. Yesterday we phone this sports shop in Rissik Street – Van Zyl Brothers – and we say: You got a Benny Mitshala working there? And this white bitch, she say – ja, he our messenger, but staff not allowed to use the telephone – meaning black staff, of course. White bitch.'

Benny chilled as he realised he had been caught out. Lukas sensed his realisation and chuckled.

'Yeah, we been followin' you, man. Heh! Heh! Heh!'

'Heh! Heh! Heh!' echoed the other Spoke Men.

They stood around him in a circle, watching him, grinning at him. It suddenly dawned on Benny they had not assaulted him – or, at least, not yet.

'No Jokes, he wanna see you,' said Lukas.

Benny cringed in horror. No Jokes Tsholo was the leader of the Spoke Men. A summons from No Jokes could mean anything, but mostly something bad. It could be something very bad – in fact it could be the worst. It was well known that some people taken to see No Jokes had never been seen again.

'Come,' said Lukas. And seizing Benny by the ear, he led him to where a combi was parked. They pushed him into it and climbed in, sitting either side of him, behind him and in front of him.

They did not take a direct route to their headquarters. They drove for about 20 minutes, in an aimless but watchful sort of way, past the monotonous rows of matchbox-styled but otherwise featureless homes that made up most of Soweto. The houses were mostly either dimly lit or in total darkness, except for some, where shadowy groups of people stood about fires in front of the

20

houses. The atmosphere was smoky and the smell of wood smoke, coal smoke, paraffin and cooking was heavy in the air.

Eventually they arrived at their destination: the big house with the high wall around it, which was widely known to be the headquarters of the Spoke Men.

Heavy, steel-plated double gates opened and guards shone flashlights into the combi. Benny saw they were armed with AK-47 assault rifles. The driver parked in a parking area where more than a dozen vehicles already stood.

Benny was taken into a front room, which was part kitchen and part dining-room. A radio played soft background music. A coal stove gave off a smoky heat. There was a group of men and women seated around a table, eating. They were talking and laughing when he entered, but silence fell as they looked him over. Then someone made a remark and everyone burst out laughing. They resumed their conversations, ignoring him.

Lukas and three of his men herded Benny through to another, smaller room, sparsely furnished, where he was ordered to sit on a bench. Lukas and his men seated themselves on a large sofa and two chairs. Someone went out and came back with tins of Coca-Cola, which they sipped. Benny wasn't offered any. His mouth was dry and he wanted to ask for a drink but he was too scared to speak. He wanted to urinate, but he was too scared to ask. Lukas and his men sat staring at him, sipping their drinks, and no one said much. They all sat like that for more than an hour.

A door at the end of the room opened and a small, thin, bald man wearing rimless spectacles came out and stared at Benny. Lukas got up and spoke to him in a low tone. The man went back through the door, shutting it behind him. Ten minutes later he reappeared and said: 'Come.' Lukas and his boys all got up and followed him, shoving Benny ahead of them.

This was a much bigger room. The walls were bleak-white and bare. Maroon curtains that looked thick and heavy covered the two windows. The floor was of plain cement, once polished red, but now considerably faded. Plain wooden benches were grouped around the room, against the walls. A heavy-calibre shotgun stood in a corner. The room was lit by a cheap brass chandelier hanging from the centre of the ceiling.

But the most dominant item of furniture in the room was the chair. It was a massive ebony throne, carved in African style, with copper trimmings.

No Jokes Tsholo sat on this throne and he was fat. Had he worn a headman's headring and leopard skins he would, in that chair, have borne a striking resemblance to Lobengula, the great king of the Matabele, who was known to have been enormously fat.

But No Jokes wore merely a towelling dressing-gown, having just showered. His girth strained the garment to its limit. His bare feet were propped on a footstool and he held a porcelain mug in one hand and a cigar in the other. At his feet, beside the footstool, was an old-time, brown, earthenware, one-gallon jar with the words 'Castle Breweries, Cape Town' scripted on its side.

No Jokes was a Xhosa from the Transkei, but he was lighter-skinned than most members of his tribe. His eyes, however, were very black and very hard. He had a thin black moustache and the habit of touching the left-hand droop of it, very delicately, with the tip of his tongue. He did this quite frequently.

No Jokes drew on his cigar and expelled the smoke, through which he stared at Benny with his black, hard eyes. Benny stared back like a squirrel mesmerised by a snake.

'How old you, boy?' The voice was curiously high-pitched for so large a man.

Benny made two attempts at replying before the words came out. 'Sixteen,' he croaked.

No Jokes looked at Lukas. 'Teach him manners!'

Lukas smacked Benny's head. 'Say Nkosi!'

'Nkosi! Sixteen, Nkosi!' Benny gasped.

No Jokes nodded, satisfied. Then he said: 'You know boy – we bin thinking, we gonna kill you –'

Benny immediately wet himself.

'Jesus Christ!' shrieked No Jokes. 'He's pissin' on my floor! Get him outa here, quick! Bring him back clean. I don't want him stinkin' the place up!'

Benny was dragged off to a bathroom in the house where Lukas slapped him repeatedly in the face and around the head, while his men stripped him and pushed him under a shower.

While he waited for the boy to be brought back, No Jokes

puffed moodily at his cigar. The small bald-headed man, who was known as Doc, had found the scene funny, and was still chuckling.

But No Jokes didn't laugh. He never laughed and he never smiled. He was notoriously humourless. Not for nothing was he known as No Jokes. He was a big, moody man. He despised levity and was intolerant of anecdotes, especially of the light-hearted kind.

He had become leader of the Spoke Men through his dedicated, no-nonsense application to the serious business of murder.

For the Spoke Men were, primarily, assassins. They were a highly organised gang of killers who carried out executions in exchange for large sums of money. Their methods were unusual.

Their favoured form of execution was to drive a sharpened bicycle spoke into the armpit of a victim so expertly as to penetrate his heart. Thus a Spoke Men killing was usually mistaken for a heart attack – for the simple reason that the tiny puncture hidden in the hair of the armpit was rarely discovered.

Only occasionally, where a murder motive was suspected, did an alert police district surgeon, experienced in the affairs of Soweto, make a thorough examination and find the tell-tale puncture hole in the armpit, trademark of the Spoke Men.

That was not all. For a lesser fee, a victim could be merely punished – by the insertion of a bicycle spoke between vertebrae of the lower back, thus severing the spinal cord and rendering the victim a paraplegic for life. Or into the cartilage between the knee joint, to make him lame for life.

Required executions and paralysis punishments, carried out by élite Spoke Men, were well-paid but irregular business. For more regular income No Jokes and his management relied on prostitution, the protection business, armed robbery and plain mugging, carried out by a lower echelon of Spoke Men of the likes of Lukas and his men, who lacked the surgical skill to perform the top jobs but were permitted to brandish a spoke and revel in the title, so long as they knew how to use a firearm, wield a knife or handle other more mundane forms of thuggery.

There were many gangs in Soweto and the other townships around Johannesburg and Pretoria. But the Spoke Men were one of the three most notorious.

The other two were the Ama-Itali and the Blanket Men. The Ama-Itali confined themselves to the hijacking of vehicles and made so much money out of their chosen field that they had no need of other forms of crime. Their leaders dressed well, favouring natty Italian suits and Gucci shoes, which was why they were known as the Ama-ltali – The Italian People.

The Blanket Men specialised mainly in bank robberies and house robberies and confined their membership exclusively to people from the small mountain kingdom of Lesotho. Their leaders wore, on special occasions, usually in the cold months, the colourful blankets of their nation, like cloaks, over sombre business suits, adding for further effect dark glasses and black Homburg hats.

Of all the gangs the Spoke Men were undeniably the most sinister, the most vicious and the most feared.

Benny was brought back to No Jokes, barefoot and wearing only his shirt. No Jokes sought the left-hand droop of his moustache with the tip of his tongue, took another puff of a newly lit cigar and contemplated Benny through the smoke. The boy was shivering.

'As I was sayin' when you so rudely interrupted us by pissin' in your pants, we been thinkin' we gonna kill you because you not been honest with us. But then again I figure maybe you can make it up by being useful to us. Hey, Benny, what you say?'

'Yes, Nkosi.'

No Jokes studied the tip of his cigar. 'But before we get onto that, Benny, we gotta settle this matter of your dishonesty. Now, Lukas here, because he's stupid, he believed your bullshit about havin' no money for us on Fridays because you lost your job. So I told him to check it out, and now Lukas knows you lied to him and he's very angry, and I'm very angry. We all very angry, right Lukas?'

'Yeah,' said Lukas. He said it gruffly, with an American accent. Most Soweto gangsters spoke with American accents, aping the Mafia movies they watched on TV.

No Jokes went on: 'But because Lukas is stupid, he still don't know where you hidin' your wages. But I'm not stupid and I've been in this business longer than Lukas, so I know where your wages are. You usin' the Kodak method ain't you?'

24

Benny showed no comprehension.

No Jokes spoke quietly, menacing the boy with his hard, black stare: 'You got your money stuck up your arsehole, haven't you? In a little film tube, right?'

Benny nodded, miserably.

'Well, take it out. Here. Now.'

Benny squatted down and while No Jokes puffed on his cigar and the other men watched in fascination, he strained and probed until he got the little cylinder out. He stood up and held it out to Lukas, who shrank back in distaste.

'Take the money out and give it to Lukas,' said No Jokes, quietly. Benny unscrewed the cap of the container, extracted the tight wad of notes and handed it to Lukas, who took it between finger and thumb with a grimace of disgust.

'Jesus, don't you ever wipe your arse?' he whined.

'Shut up!' said No Jokes. He reached down and, picking up the gallon jar, replenished his mug from its contents. He drank from it, smacked his lips and said: 'You know this stuff, hey Benny?'

'Yes, Nkosi.'

No Jokes turned to Doc, seated on the bench in the corner near the shotgun. 'Benny's father makes this beer, Doc. He makes the best mealie beer in South Africa. How he gets this special taste, I don't know. You know how he gets it to taste like this, Benny?'

'No, Nkosi. It's his secret.'

'Well, I'm hooked on the stuff. One day he gonna tell me his secret, 'cos I'm not going to let him take it to the grave. He's a stubborn bastard, your pa. I've taught him one lesson for bein' stubborn. If I have to teach him another lesson to get this secret, I'll do it.'

He poured another slug from the jar into the mug, but got it only partly filled. 'Shit,' he said. 'It's empty.' He shook the empty jar at Benny and said: 'Boy, you gonna take this jug to your pa and tell him to deliver it back to me full, like usual.' He drained the mug and placed both jar and mug on the floor alongside his throne and stood up, grunting as his big body fought the force of gravity. He was not only fat. He was tall-fat, and he towered over the boy, scowling down at him.

'Listen, you little hyena. We got a job for you, so you come back here Monday to hear what you gotta do. OK?'

'Yes, Nkosi.'

'Good. Meantime, Doc here, he goin' to punish you for lyin' and pissin' on my floor. Doc, you teach this little shit a good lesson.' No Jokes strode out of the room.

Doc got up and walked over to the boy, his rimless spectacles gleaming in the light of the chandelier. He reached inside his jacket and Benny, glimpsing the butt of the pistol in the holster, recoiled in terror.

But the holster held not only a pistol. Doc drew out of it a bicycle spoke. One end of it had been fixed into a simple wooden handle. The other end had been sharpened to a gleaming pinpoint.

'Hold him,' said Doc. Lukas stepped behind Benny and pinioned his arms.

Swiftly and expertly Doc inserted the point of the spoke into Benny's left nostril. Benny flinched and gasped in pain and fright. 'If you keep still it hurts less,' said Doc, gently. Then he drove the spoke into the flesh until it protruded more than an inch outside the boy's nose. Benny screamed.

They heard the scream in the front room and conversation stopped for a second or two. One of the men leaned over and turned up the volume of the music. The guards outside heard the scream and someone said 'Aitsa!' and everyone laughed. The scream was heard in some of the nearby houses and residents knew with unease that someone had offended the Spoke Men.

Doc twisted the spoke and blood squirted down the boy's chin. 'Say you sorry,' he said. Benny screamed again, sobbed out an apology and went on yelling.

Doc twisted the spoke again. 'Promise you won't do it again?'

'I promise, Nkosi, I promise!' Benny shrieked. Doc withdrew the spoke with a jerk that wrenched another terrible howl from the teenager.

Doc wiped the spoke on Benny's shirt and returned it to his holster. He turned to Lukas. 'Take him home,' he said. And as they led the moaning, bleeding boy out of the room Doc picked up the empty liquor jar and tossed it into the arms of one of the men. 'And make sure his pa gets this. Tell him the boss wants a refill.'

Brightness Mitshala, Benny's father, brought the beer personally the following day. He cradled the brown Castle Breweries one-gallon jar on his lap as his wife, Sheena, pushed him along in his wheelchair. She had trundled him from their small cement-brick home more than two kilometres in the hot sun, through the dusty Soweto streets, to the Spoke Men headquarters. She was a heavy woman, still handsome, but heavy, and the wheelchair had grown old with use, so that its wheels squeaked in protest at the potholes in the dirt streets. Sheena was sweating and exhausted when they arrived at the headquarters.

The guards tried to take delivery of the beer, as they normally did. But Brightness refused. 'I wish to give it personally,' he said. 'This beer has been very specially made and I will not run the risk of you fuckwits dropping it or contaminating it with your filthy hands or trying to taste it with your foul mouths,' he said, uttering each insult unsmilingly and in tones of contempt.

They cursed him loudly but dared not touch him. This man was beermaker, by appointment, to No Jokes and no one was going to get in the way of that. Someone telephoned the house and a message came back to let Brightness through. Sheena wheeled him through the parking area. A jacketless flunkey, wearing dark glasses and a pistol in a shoulder holster strapped over a fashionable pink shirt, met them at the door and helped Sheena get Brightness up the steps, into the front room with its usual number of layabouts, and on into the anteroom. There they sat unattended for almost an hour.

Sheena rested on the bench where Benny had sat the day before while Brightness sat with the beer jar in his arms, staring stonily at the closed door leading to No Jokes's inner sanctum.

Brightness had been given his name at birth by parents hopeful about his future. In fact the future had turned out to be not so bright. He had slipped into a life of crime from teenage onwards and had become a member of the Spoke Men.

He now sat looking at the door behind which sat the man who had been his leader and who had ordered him to be paralysed from the waist downwards by having a bicycle spoke inserted between two vertebrae of his lower back, thus severing the spinal cord.

His punishment had been ordered after he had not only refused, at the last moment, to carry out an assignment, but also warned the victim, thus botching the entire contract.

Every meal a banquet, every night a honeymoon

She had been the wife of a foreign diplomat who had wanted her murdered so that he could marry his mistress. No Jokes had chosen Brightness to be the hit man because he had already proved to be efficient and an expert marksman. He had not yet come to learn that Brightness was a flawed assassin. While capable of killing ruthlessly in some situations, he faltered in others.

The plan was that Brightness, posing as a delivery man for a florist, would deliver a large bouquet to the diplomat's residence, thereby gaining access to the house. He would shoot the wife with a silenced pistol and steal items of value to make it seem as if the motive was robbery.

But Brightness had been taken aback when the victim herself had opened the door to him. He saw before him a lovely, fair-haired woman who greeted him charmingly. She spoke English with a slight Germanic accent. She had a child on her hip. She exclaimed in delight at the flowers – and the child gurgled and held out its arms to Brightness. Suddenly a great sadness descended on him at what he had to do. Instead of shooting her, he thrust the bouquet at her and said: 'Your life is in danger – you must run away!' And he ran back to the delivery van and said to its driver: 'Let's get outta here – quickly!'

The driver, who had happened to be Lukas, berated him all the way back to Soweto for not having finished the job. 'There she was – standing in front of you man, what the fuck?'

It had occurred to Brightness later that the smart thing to have done would have been to shoot Lukas and blame him for the failed mission. But he himself had been too depressed and con-fused by the situation to think clearly.

So Lukas had driven him back to headquarters where No Jokes had flown into a rage that was long remembered by all who wit-nessed it. Brightness had been mercilessly beaten. No Jokes him-self had led the assault and personally kicked Brightness into unconsciousness.

When he had revived he had been held down while Doc per-formed the operation that disabled him for life. No Jokes told him: 'Normally I woulda killed you. But I want you to be a livin' reminder to everyone about what happens when someone fucks with my orders!'

So Brightness learned to live in a wheelchair and eked out a living by moonshining, brewing a beer that grew steadily in popularity. No one worked out that all he did to give it a special taste was to throw in a mixture of nutmeg and cinnamon. He saw no reason to tell anyone, and it became his secret recipe.

One day, as Benny was wheeling his father along a Soweto street, a long black Mercedes-Benz stopped alongside them and a tinted back window was lowered. It was No Jokes.

'Hi Brightness,' he said, as though nothing ill had ever occurred between them. 'I been hearin' about this wonder beer you makin'. I reckon I'll have some.'

'I'm makin' no beer for you, man,' said Brightness, sullenly.

No Jokes grunted. 'We-ell, I'd reconsider that attitude if I were you, Brightness. Remember, you gotta family to look after.' He looked at Benny. 'Nice kid,' he said. The dark window rolled up, and he was gone.

The message was clear enough. Brightness commenced beer deliveries to No Jokes, who was heard to boast that Brightness made beer for him better than he made it for anyone else, in that it had a special spiciness about it – which was possibly true, because Brightness urinated in every jar he sent to No Jokes.

The jar that he now held to deliver personally was no exception. It contained the full special recipe for No Jokes, and a wintry smile lightened the solemn visage of Brightness for just an instant.

The door opened and Doc appeared. 'Hullo, Brightness. Come in,' he said tonelessly.

Sheena rose and wheeled Brightness into the next room until his wheelchair was positioned directly before the great black-and-copper throne in which No Jokes sat. He was wearing a white caftan, a beaded, red velvet cap and beaded, red velvet slippers to match.

No Jokes watched the approach of Brightness expressionlessly, except that he touched the left whisker of his moustache with the tip of his tongue.

Brightness turned his head slightly towards his wife. 'Leave us,' he said. She left the room.

Doc advanced and lifted the jar of beer from Brightness's lap and placed it on a low table at No Jokes's feet.

'Ahaa,' said No Jokes and lifted the jar onto his lap. Taking the wooden stopper by its brass handle, he worked it back and forth to loosen it from the wide mouth of the jar.

'You make great beer, Brightness, and I like your presentation. Where you get these old pots?'

'Old stock from the Castle Breweries. I picked them up from a sale.'

'And these fancy plugs?'

'I make them.'

'You clever guy, Brightness. Pity you so stupid in other ways.'

No Jokes got the jar open and sniffed its contents. He grunted in appreciation and, leaning over, he poured beer into the porcelain mug on the small table. He set the jar down, picked up the mug and drank from it. He smacked his lips and said: 'Good as ever, Brightness. You want some?'

'No thanks,' muttered Brightness.

No Jokes eyed him with his black, hard eyes over the rim of the mug as he took another pull. 'You wanna talk with me about somethin', Brightness?'

'Yes. You hurt my boy. You tortured him bad. They had to stitch his nose at the Baragwanath Hospital. His face's a mess.'

'So what? He needed a lesson. He told lies. You raised the kid bad. We had to give him some correction here that you yourself shoulda given him long time ago.'

Brightness tried to keep the tremor out of his voice. 'He's my son. You hurt him bad. And he tells me you want him work for you. I don't want him work for you. I told him he's not gonna work for you! I want him grow up straight and get a decent job ...'

No Jokes leaned forward, his eyes flat and hard. 'You messin' with me again, Brightness. You gotta short memory, man. You can't come here, give me orders! Look what happened to you last time you gave us trouble. You start fuck with us again, I tell Doc here put the spoke in your armpit this time! Got it?'

'I'm his father ...'

'No. I'm his father now. I've taught him better manners than you taught him. And he sure won't tell lies again. And he gonna work for me and I gonna make a soldier outa him – a better soldier than his pa was. Now get the hell outa here.' He turned to Doc. 'Tell the bitch outside get this pigshit outa here.'

30

Doc opened the door and said: 'Sheena, take your man home.'

As Sheena pushed him home in the midday heat, tortuously steering the wheelchair between the potholes, they said nothing to each other. Brightness stared stonily ahead.

When Monday came Benny presented himself at the Spoke Men headquarters. They made him wait three hours in the anteroom, as people came and went on gang business.

When he finally stood before the ebony throne, No Jokes introduced him to a lean and rangy man, wearing a natty brown suit and the pink shirt that the Spoke Men seemed to favour, along with a silvery tie and pointy brown shoes.

No Jokes was wearing a scarlet caftan, a beaded, blue velvet cap and beaded, blue velvet slippers to match. He said: 'This here's Barney Lotoli. He got somethin' to show you.'

Barney Lotoli took a hand-grenade from his pocket. 'You know what this is, boy?'

Benny ran his tongue over his dry lips and said: 'I think so. Is it a grenade?'

'Sure is. Now look. This here is the pin. You pull it out and five seconds later – boom! You got it? When you use it, you pull the pin out and you got five seconds to throw it, or get away from it. You understand?'

'I think so,' said Benny.

'Here, hold it,' said Barney. 'You feel the weight of it? Good. Touch the pin. Can you see how it will slide out? Good – No! Not now, you stupid brat!' Even No Jokes flinched back in his throne when it seemed Benny was about to pull the pin. Everyone wiped their brow or breathed out heavily.

'I understand it,' said Benny.

Barney took the hand-grenade back, wiped it carefully with a handkerchief and then handed it back to Benny on the handkerchief, taking care to keep his fingerprints off it.

No Jokes said: 'Now listen carefully, boy. This coming Friday night you go to Mama Cash's shebeen and you either leave this grenade under a table and pull the pin and get out quick, or you pull the pin and throw it from the door as you leave. Got it?'

Benny gaped. 'Mama Cash ...?'

No Jokes made an impatient gesture. 'Yeah – Mama Cash! The

old bitch won't pay her protection money. Now we gotta teach her she needs protection. That's gonna be your job!'

Benny was silent, miserably silent.

No Jokes said: 'Look kid. You gonna be one of us now. You gonna be a soldier. You gonna be a Junior Spoke Man. You do this job good and next week, you give up your job in Jo'burg and join us full time. How much you get paid in that Jo'burg job?'

'One hundred rands a week.'

'That's chickenshit. I'll pay you one thousand rands a week – and that's only a start. Now get going and hide that bomb carefully till you use it. And surely I don't have to tell you if you talk to anyone about your work for us, you will die, OK?'

Benny nodded vigorously, and left.

After he had gone, Barney Lotoli said: 'He's too young.'

No Jokes shrugged. 'If he fucks it up, too bad. No one can prove we gave him the bomb. What's strong for us is that he will get into the shebeen. Mama Cash loves him like a son. Heh! Heh! Heh!' He lifted the beer jar to pour a drink, but found it empty, and cursed. He turned to Doc. 'Tell one of the boys to take this jug along to Brightness and get me a refill.'

Benny walked home miserably. It was true that Mama Cash loved him – and he loved her. His whole family loved her. She had helped raise him after his father had been crippled by the Spoke Men. She lent them money in bad times and never hassled them if they were unable to pay her back on time. Everyone loved Mama Cash. She helped people and listened to their problems, and loaned – even gave – money where needed. And she ran a good shebeen. She was one of the great institutions of Soweto.

Now he was to bomb her shebeen – wreck her business so that she could be blackmailed. The grenade may kill Mama Cash herself. Benny shuddered and began to weep as he walked home. This was truly a heavy thing.

He was silent during dinner. Brightness, who knew he had been due to see No Jokes that day, watched him carefully.

After the boy went to bed Brightness said to Sheena: 'They have given him a job to do and he is clearly distressed. I knew this would happen. I am sure they have given him a weapon. We must try to find it.'

32

Benny took a long time to go to sleep, but finally slept. They searched his room, quietly, going through all his possessions. It was a small home and there were not many hiding-places. It was Sheena who eventually found the hand-grenade, hidden in one of the Nikes that Benny kept for Sunday wear.

When he awoke in the dark early hours of the morning, to dress by candlelight and go to work, he found his father, his mother and his father's brother, Uncle 'Wheels' Mitshala, seated by his bedside.

'Where did you get this?' His father held out the hand-grenade. Benny was silent.

'Look,' said Brightness, 'you know you can trust me.' Benny remained silent.

'Listen now, listen very carefully, because you have now reached a crossroads in your young life. You must tell me what they want you to do with this because if you do it you will enter a desert from where you will be unable to return.'

'They told me they would kill me if I spoke of it.'

'They will kill you anyway, one way or another. Those who work for the Spoke Men do not live long. Either they will kill you themselves, or another gang will kill you, or the police will kill you, or you will rot to death in a prison. Look what they did to me, and I am lucky. I am only half-dead.'

Benny was silent again, but this time only for a short while. Then he told them of the plan to bomb Mama Cash's shebeen.

'OK, that's enough,' said Brightness. 'Now I will tell you what we will do. Your mother will pack clothes for you in a bag and Uncle Wheels here will take it in his taxi. You will go to work today as usual, but Uncle Wheels will pick you up when you leave work and drive you through the night to Mozambique, where he will cross the border at a secret place, and you will stay with friends in Maputo until you hear that it is safe to return.'

'What will you do with the bomb?'

'I will return it to No Jokes.'

'He will kill you.'

Brightness smiled. 'No, he will be very angry, but he will not kill me. I am his beermaker, and that means a lot to him.'

After Uncle Wheels and Benny departed, Brightness and Sheena sat in the kitchen and tried to comfort each other. They knew that, in a way, they had lost their son. It was highly unlikely that Benny would be able to return home safely. The Spoke Men had long memories. But at least he now had a reasonable chance of remaining alive and, hopefully, avoiding a life of serious crime.

About mid-morning there came a knock at the door. Sheena opened it and Lukas pushed past her rudely. He slammed the empty beer jar on the kitchen table. 'You don't make this stuff fast enough,' he told Brightness. 'Boss wants a refill and says he wants it quick. Gimme it now. I'll take it back with me.'

'It'll take an hour to prepare the way No Jokes likes it,' said Brightness, quietly. 'Anyway, I got to see him, so I'll deliver it my-self.'

'Brightness,' said Lukas self-importantly, 'if you want some use-ful advice don't come whining about your son again. Last time you left No Jokes mighty upset, and when he's upset everyone suffers, man. So don't come with all that crap again.'

Brightness did not reply, and Lukas departed, muttering.

An hour later Sheena set off on the tedious journey to the Spoke Men headquarters, pushing the squeaking wheelchair along the dusty road in front of her. Brightness sat with the refilled beer jar on his lap, staring moodily ahead.

The usual pleasantries were exchanged on arrival at the big steel-plated gates:

'Fuck me if it isn't Michael Schumacher in his Ferrari again,' sneered the guard who opened the gate.

'Shut up apeshit and tell your boss his beer has arrived. Personal delivery. And I wanna talk to him.'

The message was relayed to the house and the guard delivered the reply with a smirk: 'No Jokes says he don't wanna talk shit with you – just gimme the beer, man, and piss off.'

Brightness was still for a moment and then shrugged and handed over the jar. The gate slammed shut and Sheena began the long trek back home. Brightness sat slumped in the wheelchair, his eyes closed as he tried to ignore the irritating squeak of the wheels. I gotta oil this damn thing, he thought.

No Jokes received the beer jar with a grunt of satisfaction. 'Now we got something to celebrate with,' he said, as he began to ease the stopper from the jug. Doc and Barney were seated around him, preening themselves.

No Jokes was wearing a royal blue caftan, a beaded, gold velvet cap and beaded, gold velvet slippers to match. He had been reading the daily newspaper *The Sowetan*, now becoming creased on his lap under the weight of the jar as it rocked back and forth with his efforts to open it.

The newspaper carried a front-page report of the death of a prominent taxi-organisation executive, engaged in a taxi war over ranks and routes, who had died in his sleep, reportedly of a heart attack. The tiny puncture hole amidst the hair of his armpit had apparently not been discovered.

'Nice job, Doc,' said No Jokes. 'Who operated?'

'I did,' replied Doc. 'But Barney and the boys had to hold him down tight. He fought like a crazy baboon. He even bit one of the boys.'

'Yeah, well,' said No Jokes. 'Everybody gets a bonus. We gettin' good bucks on this one. I sure like it when a good plan comes together.'

He finally managed to unplug the wide neck of the jar, but was puzzled by a clinking sound of metal. He stared at the steel object dangling from underneath the wooden stopper.

'What the fuck's this?' asked No Jokes.

It took him three seconds to figure out that it was the pin of a hand-grenade, and another two seconds to realise what it meant.

With a wild yell of terror he tried to fling the jar of beer off his lap, but it was too late.

3

Hennie's bad day

A terrible thing happened to Hennie Vermaak, manager of the Springbok Bottlestore, Sonderwater Street, and people still speak of it to this day.

Let me begin by explaining that Hennie was a great lover of tradition. His life had been built upon the traditions of his people and the orderliness that flowed from it. It made him feel secure and confident. By his standards he was a God-fearing man who attended church regularly, lived a respectable life, raised his children in accordance with Christian principles and worked hard. He had few weaknesses, of which, perhaps, the worst was that sometimes he stayed too long in the bar of the Federal Hotel in Johannesburg, drinking with his friends instead of getting home in time for dinner. But if that is the worst sin of which a man could be accused, he still had a sporting chance of making it through the Pearly Gates. Anyway that's how Hennie Vermaak saw it.

Part of the problem was that there was such a lot to talk about in the bar of the Fed those days. The political situation was going from bad to worse. The strong leaders – such as Hendrik Verwoerd, Johannes Strydom and John Vorster – who had promised that South Africa would always be ruled by whites, were dead. Even Pieter Botha, who had seemed strong in the beginning, had begun to waver and make concessions. 'Adapt or die,' he had warned his astounded followers. Then he became ill and was bundled out of power.

And then came the sell-out, Frederik Willem de Klerk, who released Nelson Mandela from prison and handed the nation over

36

to a black government. For this he shared a Nobel Peace Prize with Nelson Mandela. But in the Fed bar anyone mentioning the name of De Klerk risked having a bottle broken over his head.

Hennie Vermaak was a liquor-store manager. He ran a good store in which the old traditions and orderliness were preserved as long as possible. There were two entrances and a partition that divided the counter space into two. Whites came in on the one side to buy their liquor and blacks came in on the other side.

That was how it had always been in Hennie's experience. Separate arrangements for whites and blacks. Separate schools, separate churches, separate railway coaches, separate toilets, separate areas to reside in, separate counters at the railway stations and post offices and other government offices – and, of course, separate entrances to liquor stores. That was traditional and it was orderly.

But it was all changing. One day Hennie's boss walked in and told him that the apartheid signs and arrangements in his store had to be removed. Whites and blacks would henceforth be served as equals.

For Hennie it was a personal shock, as these changes were for many other whites. He obeyed the instructions, as he later told his friends in the Fed bar, *met lang tande* ('with long teeth'). In other words he conceded with bad grace and he served the black customers, who now stood shoulder to shoulder with whites at the counter, sullenly.

Like many other whites who felt deeply about these changes, he joined the Afrikaner Weerstandsbeweging – the Afrikaner Resistance Movement – popularly known as the AWB. Great comfort was derived from the speeches of the AWB leader, Eugene Terreblanche. His oratory, delivered in a deep, rich voice, rolled on and on, recalling past glories in Afrikaner history, quoting from the Bible and promising a revival of the fortunes of the Afrikaners.

Hennie Vermaak, wearing his khaki AWB uniform with the swastika-like insignia on the shoulders and on the cap, felt a tingling excitement running up and down his spine as he listened to the magnificent voice of Terreblanche, rolling on and on, as he thumped the podium with his huge fist and spittle flecked his beard.

It was the speeches of Terreblanche and the camaraderie at the

Fed bar, where the shortcomings of the new, inexperienced black government were greeted frequently with shouts of derisive laughter, that kept Hennie's spirits up in those troubled times and enabled him to maintain at least an apartheid attitude in his liquor store even though he could not have the trappings.

Then this terrible thing happened. A well-dressed black man came into the store one morning just after opening time and requested a six-pack of beer. Hennie was just about to serve him when a white customer entered and asked for a bottle of brandy. Naturally Hennie turned and served the white man first.

Whereupon the black man said: 'Excuse me, I was here before him, and I am in a hurry. Please serve me first.'

Hennie and the white customer, one of his regulars, stared at each other in amazement. What a bloody cheek! Hennie turned to the black man and said: 'Listen, Kaffir. I decide who to serve first. So wait your turn, hey!' Whereupon, to the astonishment of both white men, the black man walked out.

Hennie wrapped the bottle of brandy for the white customer and they shook their heads in despair as they lamented how things were deteriorating throughout the country and how cheeky the Kaffirs were becoming. The white man paid his bill and left.

The next day, shortly after opening time, a group of five blacks walked into the store. A gut instinct told Hennie this was trouble. He was the kind of person to whom blacks in numbers usually meant trouble. Perhaps it was an ancestral twinge, related to the bygone days when the covered wagons would wheel hastily into laagers to withstand the onslaught of black hordes. Anyhow, he wasn't wrong. It was, indeed, trouble.

Two of the blacks closed the door of the shop and locked it with the inside bolt. With exaggerated casualness they advanced to the counter.

Hennie noticed a difference about these men. They exuded an air of arrogance and self-confidence. Very cheeky Kaffirs, in fact.

They were also extremely well-dressed and, even in his growing anxiety, the fleeting thought crossed Hennie's mind that in another time and in another place he and his friends would have soundly thrashed any black man who'd had the insolence to dress this well. They all wore expensive suits that were obviously tailored, with jackets fractionally shorter than the norm, neat shirts with button-down collars, bright, fashionable ties and Gucci shoes of the latest design.

The man who seemed to be the leader of the group and who was surveying Hennie with an expression of mild amusement wore a pearl-grey Homburg hat and grey suede gloves to match and he carried an ebony, silver-topped cane.

Hennie sensed he was in the presence of criminals – the closing and locking of the doors indicated that – and he now expected to be robbed.

His visitors were in fact the élite Soweto gangsters known as the Ama-Itali – The Italian People – thus named because of the smart Italian-designed suits, the Versace ties and the Gucci shoes they usually wore. The Ama-Itali specialised in the hijacking of vehicles and cash heists, and were very wealthy. It turned out, however, they had not come to rob Hennie.

'Good morning,' said the leader of the group, politely. Hennie tried to return the greeting but his rapidly drying tongue had become glued to his palate.

The leader indicated one of the group with a wave of his ebony cane. 'I am sure you recognise my friend here. He came to buy beer from your shop yesterday.'

Hennie stared blankly at the man thus introduced. Like many South African whites he had difficulty telling one black man from another. It was one of the problems often discussed in the Fed bar. 'They all look the same to me,' someone would lament into his beer. However this was clearly not the time to make such an admission, so Hennie simply nodded.

'My friend tells me you insulted him by refusing to serve him properly and by calling him a Kaffir,' said the man with the ebony cane. 'We thought we would come along with him this morning and help persuade you to apologise to him.'

Hennie realised, as he later told horrified listeners in the Fed bar, that he was *diep in die kak* – in deep shit. So he apologised. 'I'm sorry, hey,' he said to the man he had offended.

'Well OK, I think we can let bygones be bygones,' said the leader, pleasantly. 'However I'd like you to do something for us. Do you have any Chivas Regal?'

'Hey?' said Hennie.

'Chivas Regal whisky,' said the leader, a trifle impatiently. 'You know? Chivas Regal whisky?'

'Ja,' said Hennie recovering some of his composure. 'Sure. That's good stuff. I got a case of it for Mr Donaldson, one of my best clients.'

'Well I'm sure Mr Donaldson won't mind if you get another case for him. I want the one you have. Please go and get it.'

Eager to get rid of these visitors Hennie hastened to the back of the shop where the precious case of Chivas Regal, Mr Donaldson's regular three-monthly order, was carefully stored, aloof from the more mundane liquors that made up the bulk of Hennie's stock. He carried it to the front where he placed it on the counter. He was already making a mental calculation of how much this theft would cost. Never mind, it could be claimed from insurance. In the meantime it was important to get rid of these thieves.

To his astonishment the leader of the group asked: 'How much will that be?'

'Hey?' said Hennie, open-mouthed.

'I asked you how much it will cost,' said the leader, coldly, tapping the case with his silver-topped ebony cane. 'I wish to pay for this whisky.'

Jesus Christ, Hennie thought to himself. This fancy-talking bloody Kaffir in his fancy suit isn't going to steal Mr Donaldson's whisky, he's going to pay for it!

'One thousand, three hundred and fifty rands,' he said. The leader nodded to one of his henchman. The man took a mind-boggling wad of cash out of his pocket, peeled off the required amount and placed it on the counter.

Hennie watched, impressed. Yerra, he thought. I should have added fifty bucks for myself. That would have been smart – and it would have put one over these black bastards.

'Give him fifty for a tip,' said the leader. The henchman peeled off a fifty-rand note and added it to the pile on the counter.

Hennie swallowed hard. 'Thank you,' he said. 'Will that be all?' He stopped himself, just in time, from adding 'sir'.

'No,' said the leader, pleasantly. 'Bring the whisky outside.' Two of his men unbolted the doors and opened them.

What the hell. Hennie picked up the case and waddled out into the sunshine.

A beautiful silver-grey Mercedes-Benz 600, the latest model, was parked directly outside the store. The five blacks gathered around it and one of them unlocked it with a remote-control key. Hennie stared at the car, wordlessly, waiting for someone to open the boot. Nothing surprised him anymore.

'Put the case down on the ground,' said the leader. Hennie transferred his stare from the car to the leader. What the hell now? But he did as he was told.

The leader said: 'You will open the case, open all the bottles and wash my car with the whisky.'

Hennie stared at him. He almost said: Are you mad? But he stopped himself in time. 'I haven't got a wash rag,' he mumbled, lamely.

'You don't need a wash rag. You will use your shirt.' Hennie's eyes narrowed as the old instincts stirred within him. They were, after all, now outside in broad daylight, and it was a crowded street. 'You're crazy, man. I'm not going to do that. Anyway it's a new shirt.'

'All the better to wash the car with,' said the leader. 'Go on, do it.'

Hennie stood his ground, shaking his head, and then turned to go back into his store.

In a flash the blacks were around him. They moved like lions heading off a prey. The leader stood in front of him, and suddenly the attitude of friendly casualness was gone. His eyes were flat and cold like the eyes of a snake, and the silver-topped head of his ebony cane was against Hennie's chest. Even the timbre of his voice changed. The words now came out clipped and hard, and with a more familiar accent. 'You do what I say, man, otherwise we shoot you sommer stone dead and leave your fat carcass here to rot in the sun!'

In later deliberations over this matter in the Fed bar, Japie Arendse, who always had a big mouth in such matters, said: 'Hell, I would have told him to bugger off. What could they have done? There were people around you.'

That, indeed, had been Hennie's first reaction. But at that

moment, as he tried to explain to the boys in the Fed, a sort of video ran through his head. The images on it were of things that had been happening lately in Johannesburg and other major South African cities: images of people dragged out of vehicles in broad daylight by hijackers and shot dead if they resisted. Of people shot dead in bank and house robberies. Of people shot dead for no apparent reason at all.

Slowly he bent down and ripped opened the case of Chivas Regal and opened the bottles one by one. He then unbuttoned his shirt, took it off and saturated it with whisky. With lips tightly compressed and keeping his eyes focused on what he was doing, he commenced to wash the car.

An interested crowd gathered, intrigued by the unusual sight of a pudgy white man, stripped to the waist, washing a Mercedes-Benz under the critical gaze of five smartly dressed black men. Some folk watched in sheer puzzlement. Others smirked and nudged each other.

After four bottles of Chivas Regal had been used up, the leader said: 'I think the buttons on your shirt may be scratching the duco on my car. Please use your trousers instead.'

Hennie spun round and glared at the man. The leader turned his head slightly towards one of his men, who eased his jacket aside to reveal a glimpse of the pistol holstered beneath his armpit. Silently Hennie removed his lightweight summer trousers, revealing that he wore pale blue brief underpants and, rolling the trousers into a tight wad, he wet them with whisky and continued to wash the car.

The crowd had grown larger. The sight of a white man in his underwear using his trousers to wash, with expensive whisky, a large Mercedes-Benz apparently owned by blacks, was a sight never before seen in Johannesburg – or, for that matter, in South Africa. Possibly it had never – ever – happened anywhere before. People came out of nearby shops to watch. Others hung out of office windows. The crowd on the sidewalk grew larger, spilling into the street, causing a traffic jam. People began to get out of their cars to watch.

Hennie wasn't a pretty sight. He was middle-aged, portly and out of condition. His customary garb was short-sleeved, open-necked safari suits, so that, in his present state of undress, he was suntanned from the top of his semi-bald head down to a V on his chest and from his elbows down to his hands. All the rest was podgy, pallid white.

The crowd's reaction to the general scene was overall astonishment but thereafter somewhat mixed. Feelings among white observers ranged from bewilderment to disgust – even anger. Some blacks watched silently, while others tittered or burst out laughing. Jeers and catcalls began to be heard.

The leader stepped up to Hennie and said: 'You've forgotten the windows, man. For that we need a soft cloth, so take off your underpants and use those.'

Hennie howled with rage and humiliation. 'If I take off my underpants I'll be kaalgat – people will see my arse – I'm not going to wash your bleddy car kaalgat!'

At which the leader made a swift motion with his cane, his chief henchman immediately drew his pistol and, stepping forward, placed the muzzle against Hennie's head.

The leader said: 'You can be bare-arsed, or you can be dead. Make your choice.'

Hennie hung his head as he slowly removed his underpants and soaked them with the contents of the last bottle of Chivas Regal. Puce-faced with mortification he began to wash the windows of the car.

The sudden brandishing of the firearm scattered the crowd. Some fled in various directions. Others stepped back. But all who remained fell silent as they watched Hennie Vermaak at work, now totally naked except for a pair of brown shoes and grey socks.

The leader declared himself satisfied with the work. 'That's enough,' he said. Walking up to Hennie he placed the tip of his silver-topped ebony cane beneath the white man's testicles. 'I leave you with a warning, my friend. The next time you insult one of my friends, I will cut these off.'

The five black men got into the Mercedes-Benz and drove away. The crowd began to disperse. Hennie began to pick up his clothes, moving dully, as though he had been stunned by a heavy blow to the head.

Suddenly there was a blare of a siren and a police car raced up, summoned, no doubt, by a concerned observer. A sergeant and a constable leaped out of it, appalled by the sight of Hennie.

'Sies man!' shouted the sergeant. 'Sies! What are you doing all kaalgat in public?' Taking off his cap, he held it over Hennie's private parts as they hustled him towards their car.

'Leave me!' said Hennie. 'I want to go into my store!'

'Leave you be buggered!' shouted the sergeant. 'You are under arrest and you will be charged with indecent exposure!'

4

Advice on addressing a witchdoctor

Never tell a witchdoctor to fuck off. That's one of the most important guidelines in Africa for a trouble-free life. I'm not saying it's impossible to escape the consequences. I'm only saying it's better to play it safe because, even if for no other reason, you never know what could happen.

I do not regard myself as a superstitious person. On the other hand I have lived in Africa most of my life and I have seen and heard of some strange things that have drained me of any arrogance or derision I might otherwise have entertained about this darker corner of African society and culture.

I know my friend Gift Khumalo shares this caution with me. He was raised in a Christian mission school and emerged from it fairly well disciplined in terms of such things as witchcraft. But Gift is, after all, an African and even more sensitive than I am to what he calls the 'old traditional hang-ups'.

And, he says, if there was ever a reason against his total abandonment of superstitious belief it was the case of Eyes Matuba.

Gift told me the story of Eyes Matuba in Mama Cash's shebeen on a cold winter's night. It was a good night to be in Mama Cash's place. The wind outside was bitter and it howled like a dog. Inside the shebeen there was only warmth, light from candles and oil-lamps, laughter and talk, along with the friendly smells of wood smoke, lamp oil, sweat and the delicious mealie cobs frying on the wood stove in the centre of the room, which Mama Cash served with butter, salt and pepper.

It was a Saturday night, which also meant it was a good time to be inside Mama Cash's place rather than outside it, because it was situated in one of the rougher areas of Soweto, marked on police operational maps as Section 7, in which muggers, buggers, thieves and murderers were active at weekends.

But inside Mama Cash's place it was always safe. The unwritten law laid down by Mama Cash was that anyone who crossed her threshold left all bad habits outside. She did not employ bouncers. She dealt with all problems personally. And, as she was – in the words of Gift Khumalo – 'built like a brick shit-house', and wielded a knobkerrie the size and weight of a baseball bat, her customers tended to avoid irritating her. So you could always count on having a safe and peaceful drink and a mealie on the cob at Mama Cash's place.

We ordered two beers and Gift began the story of Eyes Matuba: 'It all began with this little whore called Pinkie,' he said.

Pinkie, Gift said, operated in an underground strip joint in Johannesburg's Hillbrow district. Her work was highly illegal. Firstly the place itself was illegal because it served unlicensed liquor and was a place of prostitution. Secondly her work was illegal because she was a prostitute. Thirdly her very presence in Hillbrow at the time these events occurred was illegal because it was at the height of the apartheid years when the racist laws forbade work or residence by blacks in white Johannesburg without a permit – and Pinkie did not have a permit.

What she did have, however, was far more valuable than a work permit. It was, in the words of Gift: 'A face like a picture and a body like a dream.' Men desired Pinkie more than most women were desired by men. And for such women work was available without permits in Hillbrow no matter what their race, colour or religion, even at the height of the apartheid regime.

The place where Pinkie worked was called 'The T-Bone', which implied that you could get a good steak there, which was true, but it was just about the only thing available that was legal.

The police, especially the vice squad, were well aware of The T-Bone and what went on there, but took no action to close it down for two reasons. One was that its clientele was a cross-section of humanity related to various branches of crime in Johannesburg. So it was useful for police undercover work. The other reason was that certain members of the police force were themselves clients of the establishment's less legal services and enjoyed what it had to offer – and they got it all for free.

One such client was a sergeant in the vice squad, Hannes van Deventer. He was a tall, fair-haired young Afrikaner who developed a passion for Pinkie and had frequent sessions with her. Thus another of the iron laws of apartheid was broken because sex across the colour line was strictly forbidden. Sergeant Van Deventer could have had any of the white girls in the establishment, but he wanted only Pinkie.

Then the unexpected happened. Hannes and Pinkie fell in love. The situation immediately became fraught with danger, especially as the couple became increasingly indiscreet. They would meet in public places at times when both were off duty and would hold hands, drawing immediate shocked attention to themselves in a country not yet ready for such a sight.

One day Hannes took Pinkie into a fairly scruffy but otherwise conservative Hillbrow coffee-shop for a cup of coffee. When the owner, also an Afrikaner but one of more traditional attitude, asked Pinkie to leave, Hannes hit him. Police were called to the scene and Hannes was arrested by his own colleagues.

He was called to the office of his commanding officer, a Captain Loftus van der Merwe, who told him: 'Sergeant, you are behaving like a fool. You have been charged with assault. And because of your behaviour with this black woman you are under investigation in terms of the Immorality Act. I have to tell you that you are now suspended from duty until these matters have been concluded one way or another. Hand me your firearm and leave these premises until further notice.'

Hannes van Deventer drew his service revolver from its holster, placed it on the captain's desk and walked out of his office without a word. Rebellious and angry, he resigned from the police force.

Rejected by his scandalised family, Hannes went to live with Pinkie in the small, modest, cement-brick house she shared with her family in Soweto. Thus he broke yet another apartheid law, for whites and blacks were forbidden to live together and were not even permitted to reside in each other's areas. But this law, like other apartheid enactments that ruled against a natural way of life, was also sometimes contravened with impunity where neighbours raised no objection.

The assault charge was eventually dropped because the sheriff's office failed to find Hannes's new address. The police came to know where Hannes lived but did nothing, nor did they pursue the investigation under the *Immorality Act*. They simply did not wish to become tainted by the scandal of a brother officer having sunk to such low levels of behaviour and preferred to leave the matter to drift into obscurity rather than see it emerge in court with all the attendant publicity.

'You know,' said Gift, as he ordered two more beers, 'from that time on Hannes and Pinkie could have had some kind of a life. Her family accepted Hannes, although they didn't really like the situation. But, in the beginning, he gave them no trouble. He got a job as a taxi-driver and he was bringing in money for the family. The neighbours were polite to him. You see, they had no hang-ups about him – a white man – living among them. I know because I was one of those neighbours. Hannes used to talk to me, and I got to know him quite well. He seemed an OK guy.'

But in fact Hannes's new life did not rest well with him. As the first flush of his passion for Pinkie faded he became disturbed and unhappy.

The ostracism by his family and friends left him stricken. He was no longer welcome at his parents' home, where his father had forbidden that his name even be mentioned in his presence. He began to regret the loss of his career in the police force, where his future had seemed bright and where he had enjoyed such close friendships.

Gift explained: 'Between the loss of his family and his old friends, and his new life where he experienced polite acceptance but no real friendship outside of his love affair with Pinkie, Hannes felt lost. He felt he had no one to turn to, except one day when he was giving me a lift in his taxi to the train station and he spoke to me about his problems. It all just came pouring out. I didn't know what to say to the guy. All I could think of saying was: "Give it time, man, give it time."'

Gift shook his head and took a long swig of beer to fortify himself for the next part of the story. He put his empty glass down, sighed and said: 'So then Pinkie gets pregnant.'

He replenished our glasses and continued: 'You'd a thought Hannes woulda been happy. But oh no, it just seemed to make things worse. I reckon it was the old Boer struggling to get out of that white boy. He didn't see his seed growing in Pinkie as new life being created. Maybe a son to make him proud. Or a daughter to delight his heart. I reckon he just saw a little bastard Kaffir on the way and when word got back to his white Boer family and friends they would hold their noses and puke and write him off as dead.

'Well what happens next is that Hannes starts to drink. And shit, does that guy drink! First it's straightforward brandy and Coke, but then he starts buying skokiaan from a low-class shebeen – you know, the stuff that eats away your brain and sends scorpions running around inside your skull. He gets drunk on skokiaan almost every night and fights with Pinkie.

'Next thing, one night, Hannes hits Pinkie. Slaps her around something real bad. Pinkie's little brother, Chisa, only eight years old, gets real upset and rushes at Hannes and kicks him on the shin, screaming, "Leave my sister alone!" whereupon Hannes smacks his head and he goes off yelling. So Pinkie's old man, Jake Matuba, who's usually a fairly quiet ou but who's now had enough of all this shit, goes out in the backyard where they chop their wood and comes back with the axe. And he says to Hannes: "Now you listen white man. You hit my daughter or my son again and I'll chop your fuckin' head off." That gives Hannes quite a skrik and sobers him up quick, and he goes to bed quietly.

'But now there's trouble in that house, real bad trouble. And the whole neighbourhood knows it, cos like you know our houses are close together and we hear all the hitting and the screaming and the yelling, and the mamas are talking and the whole bad story is doing the rounds in Soweto on the mama circuit.

'So Pinkie then does what a lot of girls in her situation would do. She goes to see a sangoma – in your language, a witchdoctor.

'This sangoma lives two streets away. He has the usual signs painted on the wall of his house and a kudu horn nailed to his door. He's a highly regarded sangoma. A dried-up little guy, very old, very wise, with twinkly bright eyes – but the eyelids and the skin around them are so old that he has trouble keepin' his eyes open, so he props them open with matchsticks – so he looks kinda weird. He wears the usual kinda fur hat that sangomas wear and always wears a threadbare old army military overcoat, even on the hottest days, and limps along leaning on a bloekomboom staff with strange carvings on it.

'Well, the sangoma throws the bones for Pinkie, looks at them for a long time and tells her: "You have unusual problems, my child. Go home and I will come to you, later. I will bring you a muti that I will prepare for you and your man to drink and it will help you both."

'So Pinkie, feeling more hopeful, goes home and waits for the sangoma to bring the muti.'

At this point Gift told me that the next part of the story was going to blow my mind and that we both needed sustenance to fortify ourselves – him for the pain of telling it and me for the shock of hearing it. So I ordered two more beers and two steaming plates of mealie on the cob, buttered and spiced as only Mama Cash knew how.

Mama Cash brought it to our table herself. Her mighty tits brushed my shoulder as she plonked it all before us. In deference to her and in my haste to get back to the story, I tipped her far too much. Her great moon-face split in a wide grin and she honoured me with a shout of 'Yebo!' and a friendly slap on the back. It knocked me breathless for nearly a full minute.

We lashed the mealies with butter, salt and pepper and Mama Cash's own special herbs, which make all the difference, and Gift showed me how to tilt the cob on its end, strip the mealies off it with the edge of a knife and then eat them with a fork. 'We suck the rest of the cob later when it's cooled down a bit,' he said. 'That way you don't burn your lips to hell.'

The shebeen was filling up and Gift edged his chair around slightly to face me more fully for better privacy. He ate a forkful of mealies and took a sip of beer. Then he took a deep breath and said: 'Now listen to me. I'm not strong either way on this sangoma stuff. I was raised in a Christian church school, and I graduated at Rhodes University with a journalism degree, and I'm a newspaperman like you, and I consider myself pretty well a man of the world, right? But my mother, she still sleeps on a bed raised on bricks to give it extra height because of the tokoloshe. You know about the tokoloshe?'

I told Gift that I had indeed heard about the tokoloshe. But he told me about it all the same: 'The tokoloshe, in African folklore, is this tiny little guy about 12 inches high, a sort of little devil thing but with a huge dick, bigger than he is, and he runs around at night looking for women's beds to get into for a good time. I'm not joking when I tell you that most African women, whether they admit it or not, are more terrified of the tokoloshe getting into their bed and fucking them than an elephant is of a mouse running up its trunk. So a wise girl puts bricks under the bed base to raise it – or at least goes to sleep with her fingers crossed.

'White folk tend to regard all sangomas as witchdoctors. But for us blacks there are two kinds of sangomas: the one kind will sell you stuff that will cure you and stuff that will do nothing for you and will deal in nothing more harmful than love potions, which sometimes work and sometimes don't. The other kind is the bad kind. They are the guys who smell out enemies, cast evil spells and need body parts – especially of young children – to concoct their muti. We regard the first kind as medicine men and the second kind as ... yes, as witchdoctors, just like you say. And I tell you straight, one of the problems in dealing with these people is that you are never quite certain which kind he is. They all start off by throwing the bones and you have to sit there with ice in your guts sending shivers up your spine wondering if the thing in front of you is kind of ... well, can I put it this way? Is he just a wolf or can he become a werewolf?

'Personally I've never consulted a sangoma and that's the God-honest truth. But I can't say I never will. How can I say I never will when even the president of this goddamn country and most of his cabinet talk to sangomas? And who was it who said: "There are more things in heaven and earth, Horatio, than are met with in your philosophy"?'

'It was Hamlet,' I said.

'That's right. Shakespeare. Hamlet.' Gift took a gulp of his beer, and worked his shoulders as if they were stiff. Then he said: 'But let's get on with this story:

'The sangoma goes to the house that evening with a little bottle of the muti, the medicine he made to help Hannes and Pinkie in their troubles. He must have heard the row going on because

Hannes had arrived home drunk again and was swearin' at Pinkie. Maybe the sangoma hesitated. Who knows? But anyway, he knocks at the door. It's opened by Hannes, who stares at what to him, an ignorant white Boer, must have been a strange sight: a little old man in an ancient, threadbare military greatcoat and a fur hat, carrying a staff, and eyes propped open with matchsticks. To Hannes he musta looked like something outta Halloween.

'"What the fuck are you supposed to be?" shouts Hannes.

'The old man, he replies with dignity: "I am the sangoma who brings muti for you and your woman," he says. "To help you in your trouble." And he holds out a little black bottle with a wooden stopper in it.

'But Hannes does not take the muti. Instead he strikes it from the hand of the sangoma so that it smashes on the ground, and its contents, a thick brown liquid, oozes onto the ground.

'And Hannes shouts: "Fuck off, you stupid old Kaffir! Get the hell outa here!" And he slams the door shut. From Pinkie comes a long, sobbing scream of terror. Her family is shocked and shit-scared. The neighbours who are watching from nearby doors and windows shrink back into their houses. No one has ever heard a sangoma spoken to like that before. No black man would ever speak to a sangoma like that. Only a stupid white man would do such a thing.

'Next morning Pinkie and her grandma go to the sangoma to apologise for Hannes's behaviour and ask his forgiveness. But the sangoma won't see them. He wants nothing more to do with them. He won't even open his door. Now, that's bad news. They go home terrified and uncertain, not knowing whether he is just pissed off with them, which would be bad enough, or what kind of sangoma he is in the final resort or, most especially, whether he has cast a spell on them, which is what they fear most of all. Only time will tell and their pain will be that they have to wait to find out.

'Well, they don't have to wait long. That very night, Hannes, driving home in his taxi, drunk, goes through a red light, gets hit by a truck and is killed. Six months later, Pinkie gives birth to his son and the child is healthy other than it has no arms and no legs. One month later, Pinkie commits suicide by drinking a bottle of caustic soda.'

Gift picked up a mealie cob and chewed and sucked at it in silence.

I said: 'That's a terrible story. What happened to the child?'

'Well, I'll tell you, because the story goes on. But you gotta get us some more beer cos we're going to need it.'

I ordered two more beers and Gift continued: 'In the old days such a child would not be allowed to live. Very few African tribes accept deformity at birth. Even these days such a child would, discreetly, be done away with, and no one would question that it simply died at birth. But here was a child involved in what was now widely regarded as a sangoma's curse and no one wanted anything to with it at all – except Pinkie's grandmother, old Malala, who undertook to look after it after her granddaughter died. The child bore the Matuba family name, but Pinkie's old man, Jake Matuba, wouldn't have it in the house, so the woodshed in the backyard was converted into a room and that was where Malala raised the boy for the next 20 years.

'Now, I don't have to tell you about the problems and the detail involved in caring for someone who has no arms and legs from birth. You only have to think it out. Because the kid had no limbs he was light and he grew up small anyway. Malala dressed him every day of his life and she took care of all his needs.

'Even when he was coming on to be a young man she carried him in her arms to and from the outside toilet in the yard.

'As he grew older the boy developed an undersized torso but a regular-sized head, and his head became a matter of discussion among those who saw him. It was a damn good-looking head, he had. A fine face, which was not surprising seeing how good-looking his parents had been. His hair was dark like his mother's had been and, being a half-caste, he was light skinned.

'But it was his eyes that stunned everyone. He had inherited his father's deep-blue eyes. And they were compelling eyes. I need hardly tell you that blue eyes attract a lot of attention in a black township, anyway. But it was more than that. Maybe it was because he had no limbs that a lot of the intensity of his life went into his eyes. They were disturbing eyes that seemed to see right through you. Weird eyes, in a way, because of how blue they were and because of how he looked at you, without blinking. Well, I can't even remember what his given name was. All I know is that he came to be called Eyes Matuba, and that was the only name he was ever known by.

'There was another thing. He had this deep voice, like it came from a hole in the ground. Not unpleasant, but maybe a little creepy and very deep. What with the good looks and the voice, girls who saw him said he was an attractive guy and what a pity it was he had no arms and legs.'

The time had come to pass on some of the beer we had drunk and we went outside to the toilet, which was lit by a kerosene lamp. We peed in the slanted horse trough that Mama Cash had installed for the purpose. 'You can't take a crap in here,' said Gift. 'Mama Cash has no facilities for removing shit. She says if you need to take a crap you gotta hold it or leave.'

I said: 'It must mean some loss of business.'

Gift shrugged: 'She seems to do OK on a pissing-only basis. Most of what she sells is beer anyway.'

There were two men lurking just beyond the circle of light given out by the kerosene lamp. One of them spoke to Gift in Xhosa. I caught the word umlungu – 'white man' – so I supposed it referred to me. Gift answered tersely in the same language and the men went out. When we finished and went outside they were nowhere in sight. I was glad, anyway, to get back into the warmth and safety of the shebeen where Mama Cash upheld the law with her knobkerrie. We ordered more beer and Gift went on with his tale:

'The other thing about that boy's head was that it contained a remarkable brain. He never went to school. It was, of course, just impossible. But his grandmother taught him to talk. She bought him comic books to amuse him. Then she managed to scrape together enough money to buy a small TV set. From those things Eyes built up a vocabulary and a hungry, inquiring mind.

'He learned from the TV what books were, and demanded to learn to read. She taught him the little she knew and from that time on became a sort of literary packhorse to meet his demands, transporting books – any kind of books – from wherever she could find them: from dustbins, from rubbish heaps, from places where books were given away to the poor, from wherever. And she pleaded with her family and the few friends she had to donate books, which some of them did.

'Eyes would read the books, propped in a chair in front of the kitchen table, turning the pages with his tongue. He wanted more and more books. He was now demanding books from libraries, which was almost impossible for people in Soweto to get in those days – but old Malala did manage to get him books from the United States Information Service library in Johannesburg and from the Methodist Mission in Soweto and from charity organisations and so on.

'One does not know where such a life of reading would have led in the end. All we do know is that one night Eyes's uncle, Chisa, the little boy who had defended his sister against Hannes by kicking him on the shin, crammed into his grandmother's tiny room with three members of his gang.

'Because that is what Chisa had become – a gangster. For this reason his father would not have him and his friends in the house. So they used to meet in the room in the yard where Malala and Eyes lived. There they used to spice up the coffee Malala made for them with shots of skokiaan from their hip flasks, and discuss their plans.

'Old Malala would get into bed and pull the blankets over her head so that she could not hear what was being said, and Eyes would be picked up by Chisa and placed against the door like a doorstop, with a chair propped under the door handle for good measure to discourage intruders.

'On this particular night Chisa and his men had important business to discuss. They were planning their first bank robbery. They had obtained firearms – two pistols and a sawn-off shotgun – and they had decided to rob the Standard Bank branch in the Carlton Centre.'

Gift sighed and sipped his beer. 'Chisa was always ambitious,' he said. 'Not much brain power, but ambitious.

'They're involved in a discussion about how to conceal their guns, how to wear masks, the getaway plans and so forth, when a deep voice comes from the door. "It won't work," Eyes tells them.

'Chisa is irritated. "Shut up, Eyes!" he says.

'But his friend, Chops Mlope, says: "Why won't it work, Eyes?"

'Chisa says: "OK, Eyes. How would you do it?"

'Eyes says: "I would go in with no weapons. I would choose the most likely looking lady teller and pin a deposit slip to an envelope and slip it in the deposit tray under the bulletproof glass. She opens the envelope and finds a cigarette box weighted with sand or whatever and with bits of wire sticking out of it and a note saying: 'THIS CONTAINS A BOMB WHICH WILL BLOW YOUR PRETTY FACE TO PIECES IF I PRESS THE BUTTON ON THE REMOTE CONTROL I AM HOLDING. JUST SAY NOTHING AND PUT ALL YOUR PAPER CASH INTO NORMAL CANVAS BAGS AND PASS THEM THROUGH TO ME. IT IS IMPORTANT FOR YOU TO REMEMBER I CAN DETONATE THE EXPLOSIVES FROM OUTSIDE THE BANK SO DON'T DO OR SAY ANYTHING FOR FIVE MINUTES AFTER I LEAVE.' The teller looks up in shock and horror and sees me holding an ordinary pocket calculator with my finger on one of its buttons. She will do exactly as she is told, I promise you. And if she bleats I say I know nothing about the fake bomb and the note. It must have been handed to her by the guy in front of me who just went out. No guns. No fuss. Her word against mine. Minimum risk. I may be arrested but I reckon no court would convict me."

'There is a long silence after Eyes finishes speaking. Then Chisa says: "Jesus, Eyes, where you get all this from? You never even seen a bank in your life!"

'Eyes says: "Every day and every hour of my life I read books and I read newspapers and I watch TV. I don't need to go in a bank to know how it works."

'Well, they carry out Eyes's plan and it works. You probably remember that Carlton Centre bank robbery when no one was ever caught. That was done by the Matuba Gang.'

Gift took time off to suck at what was left of his mealie cobs and smacked his lips in appreciation. Life in the Mama Cash shebeen was now going like a train and it was very cosy. We decided to order more mealies and another round of beer.

Gift said: 'Well, that was the beginning of the rise to prominence of the Matuba Gang, and a very strange set-up it was. Chisa Matuba was the up-front leader, the action man. But it was his nephew, Eyes Matuba, an armless, legless torso with a fine head and a big brain, who was the effective leader, the real leader who

56

planned the strategy of every operation and established their policies and codes of conduct.

'The Matuba Gang went from success to success, from strength to strength. They robbed banks, hijacked vehicles, robbed department stores and jewellery shops. Every operation was fast and slick, showing immaculate planning, remarkable sophistication and a lot of creative thinking. In every case it bore the mark of the planning of Eyes Matuba.

'The gang members became awed by Eyes Matuba. They virtually worshipped him. His terrible deformities, his brilliance, his compelling eyes and deep voice, their dependence on him for their success and income, recollections of the witchdoctor's curse that had clouded his birth and the death of his parents – all of this created about Eyes an aura and a mystique that grew steadily in proportion to the repeated successes of the Matuba Gang.

'His fame – or his notoriety, if you like – became widespread. It was tinged with superstition and stories that he was a wizard blighted while in the womb of his mother by a witchdoctor's curse that had deprived him of his limbs at birth while, at the same time, giving him supernatural powers.

'These tales earned for the Matuba Gang deep respect and fear among those who knew of them, and rival gangs – who used to scoff at their puny efforts at crime when led solely by Chisa – now treated them with caution.

'Meanwhile the gang had grown wealthy and large as a result of the successful operations planned by Eyes. Much of the money was spent on the usual things – big cars, bonuses, clothes, women and more guns. The gang now owned several AK-47s, bought on the black market, and had even got hold of hand-grenades. It was big time now, man, really big time.

'They had also taken over a big house in the Dube area of Soweto and built a high wall around it and made it their headquarters. Eyes was given his own room with his own TV and shelves for books, and old Malala was moved into an adjoining room to keep on caring for certain of his needs. A gang member called Barney Motisi, a big guy, was appointed with the special task of looking after him as a sort of combination bodyguard, batman and babysitter.

'There was a long room in the house called the Ops Room and this was where the gang held its meetings. No meeting was held without Eyes being present. Barney would carry him in and plant him in a high chair at the head of the table, suitably cushioned and propped. Eyes had taken a liking to smoking cigars, feeling that it befitted his status as a gang chief. When he wanted to smoke Barney had the job of sticking a cigar in Eyes's mouth and lighting it and then removing it when necessary to knock off the ash. He also had to pat Eyes on the back if the cigar made him cough.

'Eyes had now voiced a long-cherished but heretofore never-achievable desire for women, and Barney's duties included bringing him whores, two at a time, because Eyes's disabilities were such that it took one whore to help him with the other whore. I guess I have to leave the details of that to your imagination.'

Gift paused and lit a cigarette. 'I reckon you could say Eyes was now living a more interesting life than he might ever have hoped for. His handicaps apart, life was good.

'But as you know, it is when life is at its best that things tend to go wrong. And so often it is a result of greed.

'The gang was holding a meeting in the Ops Room one day and Eyes was in his high chair and Barney had just stuck a cigar in the corner of his mouth and lit it, and everyone was set for a discussion of the gang's finances.

'Chops Mlope, officiating as treasurer, reported that there was a substantial surplus in the bank and the question before the meeting was what to do with it.

'Everyone looked at Eyes, anticipating that it would be his wisdom that would prevail on this.

'Eyes was confident with his answer. His recently begun sexual exploits had stimulated his creativity, opening up his mind to new avenues of profit that could be explored with by-products of pleasure. "We'll put the money into a whore-house," he said, speaking from the corner of his mouth opposite the cigar. "And we'll operate whores on the streets. There's big bucks in prostitution." And he puffed on his cigar.

'Everyone present smacked the table with the flats of their hands – a Matuba Gang demonstration of assent. That's it – whores – good ole Eyes had the right answer as usual!

'But in fact Eyes had made his first mistake – and it was a serious one. As you know there are three main gangs in Soweto: they are the Ama-Itali, who wear Italian suits and Gucci shoes and whose business is the hijacking of vehicles. There are the Blanket Boys, whose main work is bank robberies and burglaries. And then we have the Spoke Men, who specialise in murder by contract and vice. Uppermost in their vice operations, providing the most lucrative and regular income, is prostitution.

'Now the Ama-Itali and the Blanket Boys paid little attention to the Matuba Gang's intrusion into hijacking and bank robberies, taking the view that this was a wide field and there was enough in this for everyone. But prostitution was a different matter. It was a tightly organised business, operating in specific areas of Johannesburg, and the obtainable stock for the trade – good whores – was limited in number. The Spoke Men had cornered the prostitution market and had always guarded it as their very own domain. They had no intention of letting any rivals in on it. And such was their reputation for swift and ruthless action that no rival gang had up to now dared intrude on a Spoke Men preserve.

'So it was that when the Matuba Gang opened a whorehouse in Hillbrow and had the further audacity to recruit for it prostitutes already being operated by the Spoke Men, the latter gang held an urgent meeting.

'Fastman Fafi was the leader of the Spoke Men. He had taken over from No Jokes Tsholo who, you might recall, had been taken out in a revenge killing, an explosion that had also wiped out several of his lieutenants. The Spoke Men were in a bit of a mess after that but Fastman, who had come up from the ranks, had managed to get the gang back on its feet and back in business. So he wasn't going to let no upstart outfit like the Matuba Gang muscle in on this revival of the Spoke Men fortunes.

'Fastman figured that in the normal course of events there would be little trouble in discouraging the Matubas. Chisa Matuba could be picked up and given personal experience of the Spoke Men's notorious methods – the insertion of a sharpened bicycle spoke between the vertebrae of his spine that would leave him crippled for life. Or, if necessary, fatal punishment by the insertion of a spoke into the brain from behind the ear – or into the heart from the armpit. Or maybe even a warning would be enough. The sheer horror of the Spoke Men's methods was often enough of a deterrent. And, unlike his predecessor, No Jokes, Fastman didn't like killing unnecessarily. Eventually it led to trouble with the cops ...'

I interrupted him. The talk of bicycle-spoke surgery was making me squeamish. 'Have another beer,' I offered.

'OK,' said Gift, 'gimme another beer!'

It was a relief to get up and walk to the counter and collect the refreshment myself.

Gift took a long pull at the new cold beer and continued his story:

'The one thing that worried Fastman was Eyes Matuba. You see, if Fastman had one weakness it was that he was superstitious, and he didn't want no trouble with the supernatural, if you get my point. Everyone knew that Eyes had become the force behind the recent successes of the Matuba Gang and everyone had heard the story of what his father had said to the witchdoctor and what had happened to his father and his mother, Pinkie, after that. Even those who had never seen Eyes knew he had no arms and legs and that the Matubas carried him around in a rucksack like a talisman, or a mascot, or a fuckin' lucky charm, or whatever.

'The point was, you see, on the one hand the witchdoctor's curse had killed his ma and pa and had also left Eyes with no arms and legs. But on the other hand here he was leading this gang and makin' it famous, and him just a little stompie with no arms and legs, like you could use him for a doorstop. So, shit man, what was he? Cursed by a witchdoctor or part of a witchdoctor's magic? He looked creepy and the situation was creepy. Creepy stuff, man. Creepy stuff. Can you blame Fastman for hesitatin'? Nobody in his right mind wants to mess with a witchdoctor or his spells. Nobody man, nobody!'

Gift looked into his beer. I was silent. It was interesting that his careful and well-spoken English was slipping into township jargon and that he had drifted away somewhat from his earlier, more sophisticated pronouncements on sangomas.

'So Fastman decides to handle this business carefully,' said Gift. 'He decides to call a meeting with the Matuba Gang. He suggests that eight top men of each gang meet on a certain night and that the venue be an old warehouse in Braamfontein owned by a spray-works firm that pays protection to the Spoke Men and does them favours, including letting them use the premises upstairs.

'So it's upstairs that they meet. The Matubas had agreed to the meeting, though you can bet your arse it was Eyes who'd made the decision.

'It's a shitty night, man. It's pissing with rain like you know how in the summer months it really pisses down in Joburg?

'But they all meet there, eight chosen top men from each side as agreed, about ten o'clock that night. The Spoke Men had arranged two trestle tables, put together, for everyone to sit around. They'd even put a kettle on to boil for tea, and had brought a cheesecake from Woolworths. Real hospitality, man, real hospitality.

'Right from the start Fastman's freaked out. The Matubas come in carrying a big golf-bag. The Spoke Men jump up and feel for their pistols because they think it contains an AK-47.

'Instead, the Matubas lift Eyes out of the golf bag and put him on the table. Just like that. Plonk. Like a ten-kilo bag of salt.

'Now maybe the Matubas were relying on psychology, or maybe they weren't. First acquaintance with Eyes for anyone is always disturbing, but in those circumstances it's electric, man, just electric! They'd dressed him in black – black shirt and black jeans that flopped because he had no legs – and a red bow-tie, and on his head's a pirate hat – the sort you can buy in a fancy-dress shop or a kiddies' store – with a skull and crossbones on it.

'Fastman Fafi flinches back in his chair and sweat breaks out on his forehead.

' "Good evening, Mr Fafi," says this apparition in his deep creepy voice like it's coming from a grave.

'Fastman's eyes are bulging and his mouth is dry. He croaks a greeting in reply.

'Eyes says: "Are we ready to talk business?" Right on cue Barney Motisi sticks a Havana in Eyes's mouth and lights it with a flourish. They were being real cheeky, those Matubas.

'Fastman is about to answer when all hell breaks loose. There's noise of a fight out in the street. Chops Mlope looks out of the window and sees that Spoke Men – guys who were not included in the arrangements – have dragged their two drivers, Joe Makulu and Buks Hlongwe, out of their cars and have them pinioned up against the wall of a building across the road.

'Now no one knows to this day the real reason why the Spoke Men guards got heavy with the Matuba drivers. It appears to have been a serious and very stupid misunderstanding on someone's part. But understandably the Matubas thought the worst.

'Chops yells: "Shit – it's a trap! We been set up!" And he pulls a gun and shoots Fastman in the head – stone dead, man, stone dead. And everyone pulls guns and there's one helluva gunfight all round the room, with guys keeling over and dying like fuckin' flies.

'Now the Matubas always had a prepared plan to protect Eyes – their most precious asset – in any dangerous situation. Not even the president of the United States could have expected more dedicated protection from his own bodyguards. And this plan now went into operation.

'Barney Motisi grabs Eyes off the table and heads for the door with his head down, battering everybody outta his way. Chops Mlope covers him, walking backwards all the way, shooting at every Spoke Man in sight. They make it out of the room and down the stairs, outside and into the street, where they run like madmen through the rain that has now become a major cloudburst.

'The Spoke Men guards, who've heard the shooting upstairs, see them running and open fire. Barney gets hit in the side and stumbles.

'Chops sees this and yells: "Pass! Pass, man, pass!" like a desperate centre three-quarter in a rugby game, and Barney, now falling, manages to throw Eyes his way.

'Chops catches Eyes and tucking him under his arm like a rugby ball runs like a wing three-quarter, ducking and weaving his way through the rainstorm and hail of bullets. But he gets hit in the knee and goes down with a splash, sprawling in the gutter run-off, which has now become a torrent. He loses his grip on Eyes, who bounces once, bounces twice, and is swept along the gutter by the torrent and down into a storm-water drain that has lost its cover and that the Johannesburg municipality, maintaining its standards of inefficiency, has not yet got round to replacing. Eyes goes down the drain, disappears from sight, never ever to be seen again.'

The abrupt ending to the story took me by surprise. 'What?' I said.

'I said Eyes goes down the drain. Disappears. Gone.'

'You mean gone like dead?'

'Yep. Dead for sure. No one ever found where his body ended up. Maybe in some sewer. Or the Vaal River. Wherever. Barney and Chops, both wounded, fussed around the drain, sobbing and moaning in the rain, while the Spoke Men pissed themselves laughing and then shot them both dead.'

'Jesus!' I said.

'Yeah,' said Gift. We swallowed the last of our beers.

I gave the matter some thought, and said: 'So what your story says is that, going right back to the start, the old witchdoctor's curse wiped out Hannes and Pinkie, produced Eyes to the world hideously deformed, gave him a short life and a window of fame – and then wiped him out too.'

'That's right,' said Gift. 'And the moral of the story is: never tell a witchdoctor to fuck off.'

5

A ride with the Pope

I was not happy to be travelling with the Pope. It had nothing to do with religion. It had only to do with fear.

Here we were in an ageing Boeing 720, seemingly about to crash, and by all appearances it was going to be a messy demise in dense fog and high mountains.

There were a couple of cardinals on board along with various other high dignitaries of the Roman Catholic church, a large number of officials of the Vatican and, if I recall correctly, 103 media representatives, which included journalists, photographers and TV camera crews.

The aircraft was lurching and weaving and we all knew we were in trouble. I believe that I knew better than anyone else – other than the pilot, perhaps – that we were in trouble because I was nearest to the glistening, craggy mountain peak that had just emerged from the mist and had flashed by a mere ten metres or so from the port wing.

I don't react well to crises on aircraft and it remains a wonder to me why the armrests on my seat failed to disintegrate beneath the grip of my whitened knuckles. And if I had tightened my seat belt any further I would have broken a rib.

Cardinals and bishops were honking into paper bags, as were even some of my most travelled colleagues about me, and the Zimbabwean air hostesses, under-trained and panic-stricken, were screaming and slipping in the vomit as it streamed across the floor.

At this point we were making the second attempt to land at Maseru airport in Lesotho and, as he had done in the first attempt,

64

our pilot made a split-second decision at the last moment not to do so. He gunned the engines, overshot the runway and climbed steeply. People moaned and puked again, someone fainted and I felt as though a bag of cement had been placed on my head. This time, thank God, we kept going up, away from the fog, away from the mountains, until we burst through the clouds into blessed sunshine.

I'll say this for His Holiness: he knows how to handle an impending plane crash. Very, very cool. He sat calmly through it all, reading a little book. I suppose it's all part of being a Pope. Sort of comes with the territory.

The press were, as usual, disgraceful. There were loud shouts of 'Fucking hell!' and 'What's the bastard doing?' and 'Ooohhh shit, you've done it all over my cameras!' There were sundry other curses – and prayers – in various languages. Someone sang a hymn. Someone behind me was weeping.

His Holiness must have heard all this. But he just went on reading his little book. What a Pope!

I recall that my own reaction was one of pure fear. It was the worst experience on an aircraft that I had ever had. But I can also remember that even in the midst of my terror came the cynical thought that here I was on the scene of potentially one of the biggest stories of all time – the first Pope ever to die in an air crash – and I probably wasn't going to live to write it. On the other hand, if this was the time to go, I was in good company, and I wasn't ruling out the possibility that being a member of the papal entourage was probably the best chance I would ever have of slipping through the Pearly Gates.

Soon, however, we revived with the realisation that we had all been spared – possibly because of the calibre of the prayers being prayed by men who knew their job.

But we were now faced with a political crisis, and it was interesting to note that it seemed to cause the papal group more concern than the deathly crisis it had just escaped.

Our pilot informed us that, due to the serious weather conditions that had just prevented us from landing at Maseru and insufficient fuel to get us back to Gaborone in Botswana from where we had come, we would have to land at Johannesburg airport.

Land at Johannesburg? In apartheid South Africa? Horrors! Without any doubt this was the work of the devil! There were flurries of anxiety as the Vatican clergy on board conferred in agitated groups.

Up to this point Pope Jean-Paul's visit to Southern Africa had gone well. We had taken off from Rome in the high spirits that always seem to mark the commencement of a tour by a world leader accompanied by a press entourage – quite different from the mix of ragged nerves, exhaustion, indigestion, gastric disorders, boredom and hangovers with which such a tour often ends.

In the first-class section of the Alitalia Boeing provided for the main part of the tour was the austere group comprising His Holiness, three cardinals, various archbishops and lesser church dignitaries and officials of the Vatican.

In the rear section were the journalists, comprising the highly respected Vatican press corps representing mainly the Italian media, writers of different nationalities representing important church publications in various languages, some eminent newspaper and magazine columnists, and the usual rat pack of news correspondents, photographers, television correspondents and cameramen. This section of the plane was in lighter mood and some were already shouting for liquor.

But (wisely), before being allowed to drink, we enjoyed the privilege of meeting the Pope. His Holiness, supported by two members of his staff, came up the aisle and blessed us.

He then stood among us, frail, stooped, dignified and carefully held by his attendants to protect him against aircraft sway and air turbulence. He chatted informally and answered several questions, inclining his head gravely on a couple of occasions to have a question repeated, indicating a slight deafness. But he replied faultlessly to every question in the language in which it was put to him.

Everyone tried to be near him. People crowded and climbed on top of each other to get to him in the narrow confines of the aircraft. Photographers lay in the luggage racks to photograph him. Finally he became tired and was assisted back to the front of the plane.

The African tour had begun officially in Zimbabwe where, in the course of a three-day visit, His Holiness had met with the government and addressed thousands of worshippers in Harare and Bulawayo. Then on to Botswana where he had spoken to the faithful in Gaborone. All the occasions had been hugely successful. Roman Catholics in Africa – especially black followers – are passionate worshippers and wherever he went the Pope was met by cheering crowds, ululating women and flowers strewn before him.

On every arrival where he had stepped from his aircraft, His Holiness had knelt and kissed the ground. For most Africans this was a touching – even an awesome – tribute. No black had ever before seen a white man – far less the Pope – kiss the soil of Africa. It was PR of the most Divine kind and it was an act that went a long way to making a grand success of this tour.

Thus it was in good heart that we had departed from Gaborone in the early morning for Maseru on the Lesotho leg of the tour. Because some of the African runways to be used were too short for the Pope's Alitalia long-range jetliner, Zimbabwe had provided a shorter-range jet for the shorter flights within Africa. It was in this aircraft that we now sat, shaken from our ordeal of trying to land at Maseru and facing the awful prospect of landing at Johannesburg.

It was a grotesque turn of events for the papal tour, which had been devised in large part to give the black-ruled states of southern Africa comfort and support in their unfortunate circumstances of being dependent on and dominated by the ogre of the region, the apartheid government of South Africa.

Now, snatched from the jaws of death, His Holiness and all with him were to be delivered into the very maw of the racist Boers. Truly has it been said that the Lord works in strange ways – even, as we were now witnessing, with his most highly appointed disciples. So bizarre was the situation that we were touched by its humour. But no one dared laugh too loudly.

It was the Vatican press corps that, under the urgency of the crisis, first shook off the nauseous effects of our near-crash and recovered their news sense. The doyen of the corps, a pallid man with large spectacles, on hearing the pilot's announcement of our new destination, put aside his sick bag, unbuckled his seat-belt, and made his way, groggily and still sweating, to the papal compartment up front.

He returned after several minutes of consultation with the Vatican press spokesman to make an important announcement. Standing before us and wagging his finger from side to side in negative motion he said: 'No kissing. His Holiness will NOT kiss the ground when he lands in South Africa.'

With that established, we leaned back to await our fate.

The scene now switches to Pretoria where South African Foreign Minister Pik Botha had just heard that the Pope would be arriving at Johannesburg airport, unexpectedly, within the next hour.

There is not a government in the world that would not have been startled at this news. After all, a papal visit is something that is usually arranged a year in advance.

It was said later, in government circles, that South Africa's president, Pieter Botha (no relation to Pik) waved his hands helplessly in the air when told what was happening, telephoned his foreign minister and said: 'Ag, Pik, you must handle this.'

In fact the emergency could not have been dumped on a man more suited to it. Pik first established that the information was not a prank. He then hurled himself into action.

Pik Botha is one of those remarkable men who revels in crises and confrontations, and his political adversaries treated him with caution. A big, black-haired, chain-smoking man with a bristly moustache and a rumbling voice, he once stood in his living room with a glass of whisky in his hand and an arm around my shoulders and indicated the monstrous head of a buffalo mounted on the wall, glaring down at us. 'That bastard nearly got me,' said the Foreign Minister. 'I had to shoot him twice – once through the heart, the second time through the brain. When he fell his nose was a metre from my foot. You have to be cool and quick in situations like that.'

It was with such coolness and swiftness that Pik Botha now dealt with the unheralded onrush of Pope Jean-Paul the Second.

He summoned his official vehicle and a motorcycle escort and barked out orders over the car phone as he raced to the airport with a cluster of officials in his wake. In the 30 minutes that it took him to get from Pretoria to Johannesburg airport, he set into motion the arrangements for the remarkable demonstration of immaculate organisation that followed.

Aides who drove with him said later that as he got to grips with it, the irony of the situation seemed to appeal to Pik, who was of course well aware that South Africa had been avoided in the papal tour as a pariah state. Nevertheless here was an opportunity, however brief, to display the utmost welcome, hospitality and courteous assistance to the leader of 800 million Christians. Only good could come of it.

When we landed at Johannesburg airport His Holiness was met by a purring Pik Botha and a busy team of civil servants. Cameramen and photographers spilled from the aircraft to record this unexpected moment in history – and to be on hand in case the Pope changed his mind and, in a spirit of forgiveness, kissed the ground. But there was none of that. As the man on the plane had said: kissing of this defiled portion of earth was definitely out.

The Pope rested in the VIP lounge at the airport, attended by the Minister and his team of high officials, and the papal party and the press corps were served liquid refreshment and quite a delicious lunch.

Meanwhile a convoy of vehicles had been assembled and 90 minutes after we had landed, His Holiness, ensconced in a presidential bulletproof Mercedes-Benz and followed by buses containing his entourage and the press corps, was travelling at a fast clip to Lesotho.

The convoy was led by a motorcycle escort, an armoured car, a troop carrier, carloads of police and security officers, two ambulances and backup vehicles and buses in case of breakdowns. It was accompanied overhead by helicopters and spotter planes.

Telephone and radio alerts sent ahead had arranged that every crossroad in the country areas and cities, towns and villages en route to the Lesotho border was manned by local police, who would hold up traffic to ensure safe and unbroken passage.

The convoy travelled at a steady 120 kilometres an hour and did not need to stop or slow down at any stage. Residents of small towns and villages stared curiously as the column of vehicles rushed through. A customer emerging from a bar in one small town lost his hat in the rush of wind as we whirled by and his reaction reached us as a faint cry: *'Wie's julle?'* ('Who are you?').

We crossed the border into Lesotho in the early evening. The road journey had taken four hours. It had been a slick, praiseworthy operation. The only disturbing factor was that as we entered Maseru, capital of Lesotho, we heard shots. Aboard the press bus we sat up, squawking, like a flock of startled geese. Oh shit, what now?

At this point the scene shifts back to Pretoria. Foreign Minister Botha, returning to his office, may well have been congratulating himself on a job well done. But his troubles were far from over. A call from the Defence Department informed him that a rebellion, seemingly timed to coincide with the papal visit, had broken out in Lesotho and anti-government insurgents had seized hostages at a local school.

Still reeling from the horror of nearly having the Pope's plane crash on arrival in its country by air, the Lesotho government was now panic-stricken at the outbreak of warfare on his arrival by road. Could the South African government please do one more favour and come and put down the rebellion?

Yes, of course, was the answer – and even as we were on our way to the small mountain kingdom by road, South African airforce helicopters flew in a SWAT force of troops and police to clobber the revolt ahead of the Pope's arrival.

The shots we heard as our convoy drove in was the mopping up of what had been quite an exciting shoot-out. The revolutionaries had been, variously, shot, arrested and dispersed and the hostages rescued.

Of course we were not to know that so, abandoning the Pope, we, the members of the press, leaped into taxis or whatever other vehicles we could lay our hands on and rushed to the fighting. But the South Africans had promised the Lesothians to deal with the problem as expeditiously and discreetly as possible, so we were chased off the scene almost as ruthlessly as the rebels had been dealt with. Nevertheless we worked hard at the story and it was near dawn before we had wrapped it up and filed it.

For the ageing Pontiff it had been a trying day. First he had nearly crashed, then he had suffered the irritation of having had to land in South Africa and be entertained and processed by Foreign Minister Botha – and just when he thought he had rid himself of the apartheid miasma, his ill-fated visit to Lesotho had

had to be rescued by the South African army. But he treated the latest event as he had treated the first: he ignored it.

My newspaper, the *Daily Mail*, had by now become thoroughly aroused by the Pope's tour. It had not been intended that way. I had been sent to cover the event as a mere precaution. For a popular Fleet Street paper, a routine papal tour without unusual event was of no significant interest. But ever present in the minds of nervous editors was the fact that this peripatetic Pope, this lover of world travel so unlike his more sedentary predecessors, was nevertheless a frail old man not in the best of health, who had already suffered one assassination attempt. So in a news sense I was in attendance only as a babysitter, with a very clear brief from my editors: if nothing unusual happens, don't bother us. But if something does happen, you'll be in the right place at the right time. (Of course had we crashed in Lesotho it would all have been a waste of money.)

I also had a mild personal reason for going on this trip, although I confess to it with some shyness. I had often been told that I bore a striking facial resemblance to the Pope, and I was therefore quite interested in seeing him at close quarters. My interest was heightened when I checked in on the flight and a member of the Vatican clergy sidled up to me and whispered: 'Do you know that you have a remarkable resemblance to His Holiness?' And on one occasion I saw a member of the papal staff nudge a colleague and point me out.

A couple of times, when our coverage brought me close to the pontiff, I found myself leaning forward a little to assess the likeness. Not easy, as he stooped a lot and tended to tilt his head downwards. But on one occasion it seemed as though he was looking directly at me and I drew back, startled. Could he be checking the likeness out too? Had someone told him? Good heavens! On the other hand, the Pope probably checked everyone out.

The tour ended back in Harare where we were due, the following morning, to return to Rome on the papal flight. It was that last evening in Harare that we had our final rumpus.

What happened was that one of the Vatican journalists scooped his colleagues. The news leaked by a member of the Vatican staff to that particular correspondent was that the Pope would visit Mauritius the following year. To some of us that did not seem to be world-shattering information. But in Vatican press circles it appeared to be dynamic news, and there followed a terrible uproar on the part of the other Vatican reporters, who felt that a statement that should have come to all of them collectively as a press announcement had been casually mentioned to only one of them.

I was sending a wrap-up feature article to the *Daily Mail* on the week's events. I was trying to meet my deadline and was filing it page by page through the hotel telex system.

I came down into the lobby with the first page just as the big row erupted. I had never seen an Italian journalist scooped before – far less the entire Vatican press corps, and the scene that followed was awesome.

The lobby was filled with wildly gesticulating Vatican correspondents screaming at each other and in particular at the chief Vatican press spokesman whom they had pinned in a corner. I battled my way through this dangerously milling crowd, gave page one to the hotel telex operator and fought my way back to get upstairs and write page two.

When I came downstairs with page two, the scene had become more frenetic. The sense of betrayal and outrage had obviously intensified. Once again I ran the gauntlet of threshing arms and shrill expletives. The press spokesman appeared to have escaped, but by now they all seemed to be in altercation with each other.

They argued stylishly. A man would flick another on his lapel and follow through the gesture with an upward swing of his open hand. His opponent would then flick him back the same way. In between there was much chest-prodding and quivering of forefingers under unyielding noses, accompanied by bared teeth and faces only centimetres apart. In the mêlée one would accidentally catch someone else nearby with the glancing blow of an expressive gesture or inadvertently tread on his foot. These two would then turn on each other and become new adversaries, and a separate round of lapel-flicking, chest-prodding and finger-wagging would begin. In these ways the conflict continued to mutate.

When I came downstairs with page three, there were fewer in

the mêlée, but two aggressors had finally come to blows. Immediately all the others pulled them apart and enjoined in admonishing them and reminding them that they were Vatican correspondents on a papal tour.

When I came down with page four, there was still a small group tenaciously involved in lapel-flicking, arm-waving verbal conflict, the others having retired, exhausted, to the bar. The hotel management, possibly in an attempt to help disperse them, had switched off the lights in the lobby except for a row of footlights, which cast the shadows of the combatants, huge and gesticulating, on the wall behind them.

That was my last recollection of the Pope's tour of southern Africa: big black shadows on a white wall, leaping about and waving their arms to the sound of obscenities.

6

Every meal a banquet, every night a honeymoon

Ryk van Dalen was mildly startled by the touch of the hand on his shoulder. He had swivelled his chair towards the window and was watching the rain. He had been calculating that, at the age of 52, it would be another eight years before he could take early retirement. These thoughts and the rain filled him with gloom.

He turned slowly to face David Woodley, the foreign editor. He had known it would be Woodley. The man was always creeping up on people and touching them on the shoulder and whispering in their ear, like an usher in church, instead of using the intercom phone – or bellowing across the news room in the good old-fashioned way.

But Ryk managed a patient smile. 'Hullo David.'

'Ryk, can you come to lunch?'

Van Dalen hesitated. A luncheon invitation from Woodley was unusual because they had little liking for each other. This could be something unpleasant wrapped up in a luncheon. Or a conspiracy. Woodley loved Fleet Street gossip and office conspiracies. Ryk no longer cared for them. But he had no objection to a free lunch. And this was, when all was said and done, the foreign editor. So he nodded.

'Good man,' said Woodley. 'See you downstairs. Transport's waiting.' He scuttled away.

Transport's waiting, thought Ryk as he drew on his raincoat. So it wasn't going to be a pub-across-the-road kind of lunch. Somewhere special. He wondered why.

He grew more wary when he saw the transport. It was the

74

editor's Jaguar in the dark racing-green colour he favoured and the chauffeur was holding the door open for them.

'Thank you, Rawlings,' said Woodley, pompously making the most of the rare moment. 'Carlton Club, please.' Rawlings – who had already received his instructions – touched the peak of his cap with an expression of controlled contempt. No one liked Woodley much.

Van Dalen now withdrew into silence, leaving Woodley to do most of the talking. But inwardly he was assessing the signs. Lunch at the Carlton Club, presumably with the editor as host (because Van Dalen knew Woodley was not a member), could only mean they wanted something. The venue suggested it was important. Had it been anything mundane, such as a major story, or even his dismissal, it would have been discussed in the office.

As if reading his thoughts Woodley said: 'Something very important has come up, Ryk. Best if the editor tells you himself. Very hush-hush.' He indicated with a slight inclination of his head in the direction of Rawlings that no more should be said.

The Jaguar crawled along St James and set them down outside the fairly nondescript entrance of the Carlton Club. They entered the foyer past the plaque commemorating the bombing of the premises by the IRA and were led by a porter up the magnificent staircase under the life-size portraits of past Tory premiers and icons of the aristocracy.

Ryk van Dalen was not a club man in the generally accepted sense, nor was he a supporter of the Conservative Party (of which the Carlton Club was a citadel), but he had to admit its art collection was impressive.

On the second floor they were taken not into the long, chandeliered lounge or the dining room, now filling with members and luncheon guests, but through a discreet door and down a short flight of back stairs into a small room reserved for private functions.

John Resnick, editor of the *Daily Courier*, and the newspaper's managing director, Gordon McCrae, were already seated at a table set for four. They rose and Resnick said: 'Thank you for joining us, Ryk. You know Gordon – yes of course you do. Sorry for the suddenness of all this but everything is having to be done in a hurry.'

He turned to a waiter who had entered the room. 'Please take the orders now, George and bring everything quickly, there's a good man.' He turned to his guests and said: 'I've ordered the house wine if it's OK with you chaps. It's good and it's fast. No time for sniffing and tasting and cork-popping. OK?' Everyone murmured assent.

Ryk now knew he had been called in on something highly unusual. The extraordinary hospitality meant he wasn't going to be fired. It could not mean promotion either because he was too disliked for that. It was something special and it was important – important enough for them to put aside the past troubles for which he knew he had not been forgiven. Important enough for McCrae to be present, which also meant it extended outside the editorial department.

The waiter took their orders and left. Resnick waited until the door was closed and wasted no more time.

'I've called this meeting at this place because I didn't want to take the risk of having it in the office – not even in my own office. So if anything about it leaks out it can only be from someone in this room.'

Ryk nodded, his eyes on the table in front of him.

'OK,' said Resnick. 'Now listen. It's about young Stephen Walmer. He's disappeared.'

Ryk looked thoughtfully first at the editor, then at the foreign editor. 'So that's why we haven't seen his byline for a while.'

'Not for almost two weeks,' said Woodley.

'What was the last message you had from him?' asked Ryk.

Resnick gestured at Woodley. 'Show him,' he said.

Woodley took a sheet of telex paper out of his pocket and passed it to Van Dalen. It bore the usual communication codes and began with the words 'PROWOODLEY'. The message said: 'EVERY MEAL A BANQUET, EVERY NIGHT A HONEYMOON.' It was signed 'WALMER'.

Van Dalen gave a slight nod and smiled. But when he looked up no one else was smiling. They were all watching him intently. Resnick, heavy-set, black-haired, jowly and bulgy-eyed. McCrae, balding, with blue eyes cold behind his typical accountant's rimless spectacles. Woodley, ferret-like, prematurely grey and sweating

76

slightly, which was understandable. He had just lost the Honourable Stephen Walmer, his chief foreign correspondent who was also the only son of the proprietor of his newspaper. If this ended badly he would be held responsible and fired. Those were Fleet Street rules. For every mistake there had to be a sacrifice.

'What does it mean, Ryk?' asked the editor.

'Well, I suppose you could say he's eating well and getting laid.'

Resnick and Woodley remained expressionless. McCrae raised his eyebrows and looked sideways with an expression of mild distaste.

'No, Ryk,' said Woodley. 'Your first reaction was as though you knew the message had a special meaning. This is a serious matter and we are looking for clues. Please be helpful.'

For a moment Ryk stared at Woodley in surprise. Then he remembered the man had little field experience. He was one of the new breed of foreign editors who had achieved his positions more through expertise in handling foreign-desk budgets and pleasing management by saving costs than through experience in the field. Woodley was a management functionary wearing a journalist's badge.

He tossed the telex on the table. 'You're reading too much into it. That's old-time foreign-hack language. It simply relates to the other side of foreign reporting. In between the risks and the stress and getting his arse shot off your average foreign hack lives it up in five-star hotels on his expense account and gets laid wherever he can find it. What Walmer's telling you in that message is that he's doing exactly that and you are not to interrupt him.'

Woodley flushed and shot a quick look at McCrae who pursed his lips. Resnick looked irritated and also looked at McCrae. This was not a good discussion to have in the presence of the man who sanctioned the editorial budgets.

'Yes, well, you'd know all about this sort of thing, wouldn't you?' snapped Woodley. The air went hot with tension for an instant as his words touched the nerve of the past event for which they were intended. Van Dalen went pale, but said nothing.

'Now cut it out you two,' ordered Resnick. 'David, shut up! Ryk, do you have any ideas?'

Ryk picked up the telex again and studied it. 'Was this sent in reply to something?'

Woodley became defensive. 'All I did was to chide him. He missed the story about the assassination attempt on Mobutu. All the opposition scooped us. We had to pick up the pieces from a drunken stringer and from agencies. All my message to Walmer said was: 'WHY YOU UNFILE MOBUTU? ARE YOU ALIVE AND WELL AND STILL IN AFRICA?'

'Yes ... well,' said Ryk. 'Anyone else you would have fired. But your problem with Walmer is that he's a snotty little brat who hopped from Eton to Oxford to the news room in three hops and demanded to be an instant foreign correspondent and got his way and after one year you appointed him chief foreign correspondent and what you now have is a case of insubordination and of course you can't fire him because he's The Old Man's boy who might soon become your editor.'

Ryk caught Resnick's baleful eye and added hastily: 'That is after you become editor-in-chief, of course, John.'

He glanced at the telex again. 'Incidentally, while he may well still be in Africa, I see this telex was sent from Lusaka in Zambia, so it appears he might not have been in Zaire when the attempt was made on Mobutu's life. Was he supposed to have been in Zaire, David?'

Woodley nodded, glumly.

'Well, there you are then,' said Ryk. 'He's obviously out of control, even to the extent where he feels he can send you cheeky messages. And piss the company's money up against the wall.' He glanced at McCrae who again looked away. He threw the telex back on the table. 'It's probably girl trouble, and when he's finished screwing or needs more money he'll surface. And I think you should then order him home or get his father to deal with him personally if you can't.'

There was a silence. Then Resnick said: 'Ryk, Stephen was last traced to the Ridgeway Hotel in Lusaka, from where that telex was sent. According to the Zambian police and the British High Commission in Lusaka his possessions are still there, but he is not.'

'I see,' said Ryk, after a moment's silence. 'That doesn't sound good.'

There was a discreet knock on the door and lunch was brought in. There was total silence as it was served.

After the waiters had left Resnick said: 'Ryk, we would like you to go and look for Stephen Walmer and bring him home, if he's alive. Or find out what happened to him. Gordon and I were with Lord Walmer this morning and he is naturally deeply upset. He has asked us to convey his request for assistance to you personally. As you know, he is very unwell at present, and this is affecting him badly. The Zambian police and the High Commission seem to have got nowhere. We don't want this to leak out at present. The opposition papers will make a meal out of it. Lord Walmer is particularly anxious to avoid a scandal. He wants no publicity under any circumstances.'

Nothing like owning a newspaper if you want to kill a good story, Van Dalen thought to himself. But he said nothing. The time for jokes was past. Stephen Walmer might be dead. Or in dire peril.

'What do you say, Ryk?' Resnick asked anxiously.

'Can I have a moment to think?'

Minutes passed as they ate silently. Resnick was visibly irritated at having to wait for a response. Woodley looked up anxiously every few seconds.

McCrae cleared his throat and said: 'If it's a question of money, say so. I'm here to deal with anything like that.'

Ryk shook his head – but the remark flashed a sudden thought into his mind. Another minute passed as he swiftly considered it. Then he laid his knife and fork to rest, wiped his lips with a serviette, leaned back and gazed levelly at these colleagues with whom he had shared little liking for several years. They looked back at him with a similar lack of affection, but awaiting his reply with anxiety.

'Look,' he said, 'of course I will do whatever I can to help. But I am going to ask for a deal and, yes, I suppose it does involve money, although it would mean more to me than that. You gentlemen know I am no longer happy on this newspaper and I'm sure you will agree our relationship is no longer what it was.'

No one denied what he said. They merely watched him.

'So I propose that bringing Stephen Walmer home, if I can find him, is the last assignment or work of any kind I do for this newspaper. I want an agreement, in writing, before I go, that I can have immediate early retirement on full pension.'

Resnick and Woodley both looked at McCrae who shook his head. 'It would be creating a precedent ...'

Resnick went red in the face. 'For God's sake, Gordon! This isn't the time to be a bloody civil servant!'

McCrae sighed. 'Alright. I'll discuss it with His Lordship. Yes, I suppose it can be done in these special circumstances on condition it remains a totally confidential agreement.'

Van Dalen pushed back his chair abruptly and stood up. 'I'd like to leave now. If I can get your agreement to my proposal in writing this afternoon I'll fly out tonight.'

Resnick responded with the same speed, learned and honed at editorial desks. He took a card from his card case and scribbled a note to his driver. 'Right. Give this to Rawlings. He'll take you wherever you want to go this afternoon – and drive you to the airport. We'll go back to the office in Gordon's car.'

'There's a flight to Lusaka tonight,' said Woodley. 'I have already booked you a seat on it.'

Van Dalen sneered inwardly. They had clearly assumed from the start that he would go. 'Please switch that to a Johannesburg flight,' he said.

'Johannesburg?'

'Yes. The search begins in Lusaka but the trail will begin in Johannesburg.'

Woodley look mystified at this curious remark but merely nodded. Resnick began to thank Van Dalen and wish him good luck. But Van Dalen left without another word. There was a brief silence after his departure.

'Odd fellow,' said McCrae.

'Yes, well, he's a South African,' said Resnick, as if by way of explanation.

'Seems bitter.'

'Yes, he doesn't like us. We had to take him off the foreign beat and transfer him to the features desk after that Cairo scandal he involved us in.'

'What Cairo scandal?'

'You don't remember the Cairo affair?' asked Woodley, surprised.

McCrae sighed. 'I have to look after two national newspapers and 16 provincial papers and a television station for this company,

David. I don't have the time to follow the exploits of your particular menagerie, except to know that they cost us rather a lot of money.'

Resnick intervened swiftly. 'Van Dalen had an affair with the British ambassador's wife in Cairo – just as the poor sod was about to get his knighthood. Broke up their marriage. Broke up his own marriage. Upset the Foreign Office. Upset Lord Walmer who was a personal friend of the ambassador's, upset me, upset David here ... upset everybody in fact. We had to ground him. Can't have a foreign correspondent who goes round screwing the wives of ambassadors. It upsets the diplomatic circuit and queers our pitch with the Foreign Office.'

'He should have been fired!'

'Can't fire him. He knows too many of our secrets. He could have gone of his own accord, but for some reason he's hung on – until now.'

Woodley chipped in: 'Keeping him on has had its advantages. He was a brilliant reporter. Amazing knowledge of Africa. Having him on the features desk as a foreign-affairs feature writer means we can still tap into his knowledge and experience – and keep him away from recruitment by the opposition. It's paid off pretty well, and he's ideal for the job in hand.'

'I'm still glad he's going,' said Resnick. 'He makes problems and he's an insolent bastard. So I'm sorry I shouted at you earlier, Gordon, but the chance of getting young Walmer back *and* getting rid of Van Dalen is too good to miss. So let's order some excellent port and drink to that.'

Back in the office Ryk van Dalen cleared his desk and spent 45 minutes on several telephone calls, locally and to Johannesburg. Then, while waiting for an air ticket and traveller's cheques to be brought to him by the foreign-desk secretary, he stood with his hands in his pockets, watching the rain.

The features department was a long row of desks in a corner of the huge hangar-like *Daily Courier* editorial floor and Van Dalen had managed to obtain the desk nearest the window. A strategically placed filing cabinet gave him a certain degree of privacy. He completed the privacy now by standing with his back to the editorial floor with its medley of noise.

He stood motionless and stooped – a thin man, slightly above

81

average in height and grey-haired. His face was interesting in that it bore signs of wear. The eyes were pouchy and the nose was slightly bent, hinting that it had been broken and reset at some past time. It seemed related to a faint scar that travelled from its vicinity to just below the corner of his left eye. The scar enhanced Van Dalen's reputation as a veteran foreign and war correspondent although in fact he had acquired it in an unseemly barroom brawl in his student days after a rugby match.

His thoughts were now on the luncheon meeting. He imagined they were probably drinking a toast to his request for severance and having the inevitable gossip over the Cairo debacle. Well, sod them. He was equally glad to be leaving the newspaper, where he had once starred as its most outstanding award-winning foreign correspondent, but where he now merely drifted along under a cloud. Curious lot the Brits. Fair in so many ways, yet break certain rules and they would never forget or forgive.

His thoughts then focused on the Cairo affair. He wondered what had become of her. Her husband had weathered the storm. He had got his knighthood, although it possibly wasn't the one he had hoped for. And he was now ambassador to Rome. Not too bad. But Veronica had dropped out of sight and broken off all contact, although he had been willing to keep it going. 'We have to end it,' her last message had said. 'I've got too many pieces to pick up.' But she had not rejoined her husband and Ryk had never heard from her again – and he himself had had fences to mend. The memories of all that had been lost in the most disastrous affair of his life left him filled with sadness.

He was glad when his travel documents reached his desk and he was able to go. He slipped out, bidding no one farewell, and Woodley remained behind the closed door of his office. A sealed letter signed by Gordon McCrae confirming his requested terms of severance had accompanied his travel documents and there was no more reason to stay.

The man from the South African National Intelligence Service met Ryk van Dalen when he arrived in Johannesburg. He was standing beside airline officials at the bottom of the disembarkation steps and touched Van Dalen on the sleeve as he drew level. He showed his ID. 'This way please, sir.'

He led the way to a black Mercedes-Benz with dark, tinted windows that had drawn up discreetly on the far side of the aircraft and opened a rear door. Marius Retief, a big sandy-haired man, was seated behind the wheel. He greeted Van Dalen in Afrikaans. 'Welcome home, Ryk. Good to see you again. Give your passport and baggage tickets to Frans here. He will clear you and everything will be sent to your hotel.' Van Dalen got into the car and they shook hands.

'Where are we going?' asked Ryk.

'Safe house. The Doctor would like to welcome you back personally.'

Ryk smiled briefly. 'Any news on my enquiry?'

'Yes. The good news is that we've traced your man.'

Ryk sighed with relief.

'But the bad news is that he's got himself tangled up in a messy situation.'

'Like what?'

'Like that he's joined up with a so-called liberation group operating from Uganda whose aim is to overthrow Mobutu's regime in Zaire.'

'Bloody hell ... where's he now?'

'Literally up a creek, a tributary off the Congo River just north of Kisangani. This rebel outfit's got a base there.'

Ryk was thoughtful. 'You can't say he's joined them. He might be with them to get a story. Nothing wrong with that, except it sounds dangerous.'

'*Ja-nee*,' said Marius, responding with the traditional old Afrikaner affirmative-negative that can mean any one of many things. 'Anyway, the Doctor asked us to go flat out for you on this one, so someone is coming along with everything we've got so far.'

'Thank you, man. You guys are stars.'

'It's alright, man.'

The safe house was in a leafy suburb at the end of a cul-de-sac behind the sort of eight-foot-high wall that surrounded most of the big houses in Johannesburg. Marius pressed a button on his keyring and an electronic gate opened. They drove in. They were watched from the road by two men sitting in a white Toyota Corolla. Marius ignored them but as they swept through the gate

Ryk saw the man in the passenger seat speaking into a radio hand-set. Marius drove into a double garage and its door swung down behind them. They entered the house through a door that connected the garage to the kitchen and Marius led the way to the lounge where coffee cups and biscuits had been set out.

Within minutes there was the sound of another car arriving, the garage door opening and shutting and seconds later the Director-General of the NIS entered, followed by a thickset, bespectacled young man whose blonde hair was thinning prematurely.

The Doctor, as the chief of the NIS was popularly referred to in the Service, had one serious career problem. He was an astonishingly good-looking man who had the appearance of a movie star. He was tall, dark-haired and elegant, a man of obvious refinement whose attractiveness had a brooding quality. Women tended to look at him in a thoughtful sort of way. The lecture rooms at the university where he used to teach philosophy and history were usually filled predominantly with female students who came to gape at him rather than to harvest his wisdom. None of this was desirable in the position he now held, where ordinariness of appearance and a low profile would have been preferable. As if conscious of his problem the Doctor worked hard at achieving nonentity. He was hardly ever seen in public, avoided social events, was rarely photographed, never interviewed and seemed a fleeting background shadow even at the official working sessions that he was obliged to attend.

His appointment as chief of Intelligence at the age of 28 had staggered the nation, even though he was the holder of a double doctorate and clearly possessed an outstanding intellect. Whatever was thought of it the appointment showed brilliant perception. In the years that followed he had transformed the NIS from a crude but reasonably competent service to one of the world's top six secret services. The other major services worked hard at seeking to integrate with the South African NIS's unique and highly developed African network but the Doctor dealt with them as he saw fit. He co-operated to a limited degree with the Americans, whom he distrusted. He worked fully with the British, whom he respected, avoided the French and worked closely with Israel's

Mossad whose abilities he admired and whose interests in some instances South Africa shared.

This was the man who now shook Van Dalen's hand with his customary directness of gaze and quickness in getting to the point. 'Welcome back, Ryk. I hear the heir apparent of your newspaper has gone walkabout and you have to find him?'

'Greetings, Doctor. Yes, we have a problem, and I'm grateful to you for your help.'

'Ja-nee ... well from what I hear your task is not going to be easy. I've brought Jan Rademeyer from our Central Africa desk to fill you in on what we've got for you. Let's sit down and talk while Marius plays mother and fixes the coffee.'

Marius Retief hastened to the kitchen as the others seated themselves. Rademeyer unzipped the slim briefcase he was carrying and took out some sheets of typed paper. He looked at Van Dalen and cleared his throat.

'Your man appears to have joined the *Armée Libération du Congo*, a recently formed rebel organisation, backed by Uganda, whose main headquarters are in Kampala. Its aim is to overthrow the Mobutu regime in Zaire. Stephen Walmer is at present at one of the advance camps near Buta, north of Kisangani.'

'You cannot say he has joined them,' said Ryk. 'He's obviously onto a story.'

'Possibly,' replied Rademeyer. 'Except that he actively took part in an attack on a village in that region a few days ago. That does not seem like the behaviour of an observer.'

Van Dalen frowned. 'Can I ask where you are getting this information from?'

Rademeyer glanced at the Doctor who said: 'No Ryk, you can't.'

'Can I show him the photograph?' asked Rademeyer. His chief nodded, and Rademeyer drew a five-by-eight black-and-white print from the briefcase and passed it to Van Dalen. Ryk stared at it for several seconds, then drew a hand wearily across his brow and said: 'Christ!'

The photograph showed a small group of armed men in combat fatigues. They were looking down at a bloodstained corpse in shorts and a T-shirt lying at their feet. One of them must have cracked a joke because they were all laughing. All the men in the photo were black except one. He was the Honourable Stephen Walmer and, like the others, he was in full combat gear and carrying an AK-47 assault rifle. Appallingly, he was standing with his right foot on the corpse.

The Doctor asked: 'How much could I get for that photo if I offered it to one of your opposition newspapers?'

Van Dalen, his hand still covering his brow as he continued to stare at the picture, said: 'Please Doctor, don't make jokes.' The NIS chief smiled thinly.

'How the hell did this happen?' muttered Van Dalen.

'It seems to have come about through a romantic liaison,' said Rademeyer.

'Just as I thought,' said Van Dalen. 'There's a bloody woman involved!'

'Not a woman, a man,' said Rademeyer.

'What?'

'Yes, it seems Walmer is having an affair with a young Ugandan ex-army officer called Wani Korobi who is assisting the rebels. That's him standing next to Walmer in the picture. The one with his hand on Walmer's shoulder. We gather they met in Lusaka where Korobi was recruiting expatriate Zaireans.'

Van Dalen examined the photo closely. The Ugandan was indeed young. Possibly in his early 20s. Slim, good-looking.

'I never knew Stephen was a homosexual,' he said.

'Bisexual it seems,' said Rademeyer. 'According to our information he has a huge appetite for men and women – and lots of parties. Every meal a banquet, every night a honeymoon.'

'Where did you get that from?' enquired Van Dalen sharply.

'Get what from?'

'That banquet-honeymoon stuff.'

Rademeyer shrugged. 'I gather it was a phrase he often used, according to one of our informants.'

The Doctor stood up. He patted Van Dalen gently on the shoulder. 'Don't get upset, Ryk. I think you are going to need all your cool on this assignment. What are you going to do now?'

'Obviously I have to get to Zaire quickly. But I will go to Lusaka first.'

The Doctor nodded at Rademeyer who handed Van Dalen a folded slip of paper. 'When you get to Zaire,' the Doctor said, 'feel free to contact that name at that telephone number in Kinshasa. We'll tell him you may ask him for help. Good luck.'

Van Dalen stood up. 'This has been of tremendous assistance. I don't know how to thank you.'

The Doctor inclined his head at the others. They understood and left the room immediately.

'Just thank us in the usual way, Ryk. We have been swapping information for a long time, you and I. Just let us know anything you come across that you think we might like to know.' They shook hands and the Doctor turned to leave, then paused.

'By the way, I hear you might be leaving your newspaper?'

'Yes, for sure.'

'My offer to you is still open. We would like you to work for us.'

'You know I can't do that, Doctor, but thank you anyway.'

The Doctor sighed. 'I know, I know. You like us but you don't like what we stand for. Well, time will tell who's right. Meantime, remember we like you.' He walked quietly from the room.

Marius returned and they waited until all the sounds of the departure of the others had faded. Then they left. As they drove out of the security gate Van Dalen noticed that the white Toyota was no longer there.

He wasted little time in Lusaka. He checked into the Ridgeway Hotel where Walmer's personal effects were still in his room and the *Daily Courier* was still paying for the accommodation, leaving the impression that Walmer would soon return. Only the High Commission and the Zambian police knew of the newspaper's worry. Van Dalen requested and was given access to the room by the hotel manager after producing identification and convincing him that he was a colleague from the same newspaper.

'There's something wrong, isn't there?' asked the manager as he unlocked the room. 'The police and someone from the High Commission have been here asking questions.'

'Nothing at all,' lied Ryk. 'He's away on a long assignment. Caused a mild fright because he forgot to tell us where he went, that's all. We know where he is now.'

The manager grunted. 'Well, frankly we don't miss him. Arrogant bugger. Lots of parties, lots of women. Lots of other strange visitors at odd hours. Strained our staff a bit.' Ryk made no reply.

After he had gone Ryk searched the room. There was a suitcase and a fair quantity of clothing, enough to all but fill the suitcase. There were various toiletry items scattered about the bathroom. Ryk noted the absence of a razor. He also noted the absence of hand baggage. Walmer had departed travelling light.

He then commenced a methodical search of the room section by section. As he slid open each drawer he ran his fingers about underneath the drawer above it. It was not until he came to the drawers in the wardrobe that he found the envelope stuck to the bottom of one of them with camera tape. So much for the Zambian police.

He opened the envelope and found it contained a British passport. On paging through it swiftly he saw that it contained mainly stamps recording entries into and exits from Israel. He understood immediately. Like some British foreign correspondents Walmer was permitted to carry two passports: one for use when visiting Israel and the other for general use, including Arab countries, where indications of visits to Israel could cause problems for the passport holder.

He was about to tape the passport back where he had found it, but after a moment's thought slipped it into his pocket.

Ryk let himself out of Walmer's room, returned the key to the reception desk and went out onto the inner patio next to the pool where baby crocodiles used to be kept until one bit a guest. As it was late afternoon and as it was the Ridgeway Hotel he ordered, for old times' sake, one of the gloriously leafy, highly fruitified and aggressively colonial Pimms Cup Number Ones for which the place used to be famous, and found that it was still good. As he sipped it he tried to work out what had got into Stephen Walmer.

Clearly he had not intended to go away for long, had intended to return to Lusaka, and had gone somewhere where the Israeli-tainted passport could have proved an embarrassment. All this tallied with where South African Intelligence said he now was. Only his motives were still in doubt. Van Dalen still clung to the hope that Walmer was after the story, which was a good one. But his apparent involvement with the action and the killing was disturbing. And that disgusting photograph! My God, thought Van Dalen, his father would freak out ...

He suddenly remembered that Lord Walmer was an ailing father anxiously awaiting news of his son. He downed the rest of his drink, went to the reception desk and composed a brief telex message for the *Courier*: 'PROWOODLEY: TARGET TRACED ZAIRESIDE SEEMS UNHARMED HOPING REACH HIM WITHIN FEW DAYS WHEN WILL RECONTACT VAN DALEN.'

He asked the reception desk to send it on the hotel telex. He knew Woodley would, as soon as he received the message, try to telephone him to discuss it and extract details so that he could appear as involved as possible in the finding of Walmer. Screw him, thought Van Dalen. That's all the good news they need at present. He resolved to avoid all telephone calls until he felt better prepared to talk to London.

He had also resolved to avoid all contact with the Zambian police and the British High Commission, seeing that he now knew where Walmer was and was eager to get on his way.

But as he breakfasted on the veranda the following morning an hour before leaving for the airport, a shadow fell across the table. 'Good morning, Ryk, mind if I join you for a cup of coffee?'

Van Dalen looked up, groaned inwardly, and motioned to a chair. 'Hullo, Jeremy.' He signalled to a waiter to bring another cup.

Jeremy Willoughby, First Secretary at the British High Commission in Lusaka, sank languidly into the chair opposite Van Dalen. He was a tall, foppish man with lank brown hair, wearing a fashionably crumpled linen suit and a pale-yellow waistcoat adorned with a gold watch chain. An Old Harrovian tie matched a handkerchief of a similar dark hue in the breast pocket of his jacket. As an added affectation he wore a pince-nez on a thin gold chain. It sat uncomfortably on the high bridge of his beak-like nose and gave him the appearance of an Edwardian headmaster. He was much given to removing the pince-nez and polishing the lenses, taking the gold watch from his waistcoat pocket and consulting it, and flicking unseen specks of dust from his trousers. He did all three things now as he waited for his coffee.

'Not nice you coming into our parish and not coming to say *jambo* to His Excellency,' said Willoughby as he watched his coffee being poured. His previous posting had been in Kenya where he had picked up the colonial habit of throwing bits of Swahili into conversation.

'I didn't think His Excellency would want to see me,' Van Dalen replied.

'Also true,' murmured Willoughby, stirring his coffee. 'Anyhow, I hear you've found your lost property.'

Van Dalen was silent. Willoughby had got the news either from the hotel telex staff via the police or his own contacts or from the Foreign Office, which would have got it from Resnick or Woodley. He decided it didn't matter.

Reading his mind, Willoughby said: 'It would have been nice if you'd told us, if only to save us further workload. We've had to drop everything and jump around like rabbits looking for this fellow, just because of who he is.'

'Sorry about that, Jeremy. But isn't looking for missing British nationals part of your job?'

'Doesn't usually involve my section, old boy, unless it's the offspring of Fleet Street potentates and others of that ilk. Care to tell us where you found him?'

'Can't, Jeremy. He's on a special assignment.'

'Odd that he didn't tell his editor and you had to come looking for him. All this has given us a lot of *taabu*, you know. H.E. is very upset.'

'I'm sorry. And I'm sure a message of appreciation will arrive in due course from the appropriate sources.'

'One hopes so. Always a worry, you know, when one of your kind pitches up. Usually trouble. Young Walmer's a case in point. Lacks manners. H.E. invited him to dinner – he sent apologies but we know he went to a sleazy nightclub instead. H.E. furious. Kept strange company, too, your man …'

'You realise of course journalists sometimes keep strange company to get information.'

'Grant you that, but this lad's a bit of a wild one, isn't he? Likes beating up the town and got the reputation of being a kind of sexual loose cannon. And it's a small town, I might add. Things get around. I wonder if his father knows what he gets up to. Between you and me H.E. found it necessary to send a confidential memo to the F.O. on all this.'

Van Dalen contemplated Willoughby in distaste. Diplomats

were not usually this garrulous or indiscreet. Was the man trying to get a deliberate message across to him?

Willoughby continued his rambling lament: 'And then the fellow disappears into thin air. Lots of sudden frantic panic. Lots of P.T., with the F.O. on our back and H.E. *very* displeased. All unnecessary, as we now discover ... but in the meantime *you* pitch up and I can tell you that doesn't please H.E. either, given your past history ...'

Van Dalen concluded that Willoughby might be sick. He also reminded himself that this was his last assignment and he had no further reasons to be polite to diplomats. He pushed back his chair and stood up. 'Tell H.E. to get stuffed. I've got a plane to catch,' he said, and walked away. A plaintive bleat came from Willoughby. 'Steady on, old chap ...' but Van Dalen quickened his pace, until he was out of earshot.

He arrived in Kinshasa, capital of Zaire, and succumbed to the well-remembered feeling of depression that always descended upon him when he arrived in what used to be called the Congo and would regain that name officially under the next despot, one Laurent Kabila.

The air-conditioning in the airport, as usual, was not functioning and the humidity and heat enveloped him stickily. Even the excuse for the malfunction had not changed from bygone days: 'We are awaiting parts for the system from Brussels, monsieur.'

He surrendered his passport to immigration for holding at the airport in exchange for the usual receipt without qualms, knowing it would be safe because it was valuable to them. On his exit they would appear to have lost it but would find it with exclamations of relief on production of 100 US dollars.

He checked into the Hotel Memling, recognising the well-remembered smell – like that of a sweaty gymnasium. But at least here the air-conditioning was functioning.

He went down to the bar and was delighted by the sight of John Ridley of the *Daily Telegraph*, acknowledged queen of the Africa Press Corps, perched on a bar stool, moodily contemplating a cognac. They greeted each other with mutual pleasure.

'John! You're sitting on the same bar stool you were on last time I saw you four years ago! Have you never moved off it?'

'Quite untrue, dear boy. I've been covering the far-flung outposts of the old empire on which the sun has set – mainly Zimbabwe, Kenya and so forth. Just back here to cover the aftermath of the assassination attempt on Mobutu. Frightfully boring. Thought they would merely execute the perpetrators. But now it appears they are going to have some sort of charade called a trial.'

He had courteously dismounted from his bar stool to shake hands. A small man, and slightly drunk, he now had difficulty getting back on it. 'They make the bar stools too high in this bloody country,' he complained. 'You need a fucking Sherpa to get you up on them!'

Van Dalen helped him to mount. 'Thank you, dear boy ... always so kind.' He fumbled for something in his pocket. 'Got a message from my desk today. Something about your man, young Walmer, reported missing, believed eaten or whatever happens to one on this God-forsaken continent. Is it true he is in some sort of trouble?'

Van Dalen lied again. 'No John, he's on a special assignment somewhere, that's all.'

'I see. Well, I'll send a reply reassuring my inquisitive masters. I suppose the words "special assignment" mean he is soon to come hurtling out of the jungle to scoop us cruelly.'

'I suppose so. Have you met him?'

'Yes, indeed. We met briefly in Nairobi. Most attractive young fellow. Quickened my pulse, I must confess. But I had to give him wise counsel on his African adventures.'

'What African adventures?'

'Sexual African adventures. He runs through women like a child runs through hay. Men too, when he feels he needs a change, I suspect.'

'Well, you would know, John.'

'Of course, old boy. But in his case I think it's merely a restless libido. He simply has to dip his winkie into flesh wherever he finds it. Trouble is he had been putting it in places where I would not even place the tip of my umbrella. He raved about the beauty and the availability of the women of Ethiopia, from where he had just arrived. I had to warn him – my dear boy, beware of Ethiopian whores, they can give you the dreaded purple syphilis!'

92

Van Dalen burst out laughing. 'What did he say to that?'

'He said I was not to worry because he always used a condom. So I had to tell him – my dear boy, the purple syphilis can corrode its way through a Wellington boot!'

Van Dalen spluttered into his beer and raised his head laughing. 'Jesus, that's one I haven't heard before. How did he take it?'

'Well, he looked thoughtful for a moment. Then he dismissed it with bravado and said: "Oh well, every meal a banquet, every night a honeymoon – and to hell with the consequences!" To which we raised our glasses, as is always done.'

Van Dalen sighed. 'Yes, it certainly didn't take him long to pick up all the old hack jargon – and some of the bad habits that go with it.' He looked at his wristwatch. 'John I have to meet someone. Can I buy you another cognac before I go?' Ridley shook his head. 'Bless you, no, dear boy. I'm going to bed early with a good book. See you anon.'

Ryk selected a taxi from the ratshit bunch at the hotel entrance. The Memling was no longer the best hotel in town, nor was its taxi rank. The other taxi drivers made despairing gestures at him for choosing what they considered to be the worst taxi in the rank, while the driver of the battered old Peugeot he had chosen swore at them in French and Swahili.

Van Dalen gave the address of the Papillon Rouge restaurant and made it clear he knew the route to avoid the driver transversing the city three times to get there to increase his fare. They arrived within minutes. He could have walked the distance, but no white man in his right mind walks in Kinshasa after dark. He paid the driver one third of what he demanded, which was generous. Nevertheless he entered the restaurant with the man's curses ringing in his ears.

James Murray of the British Embassy was already seated, waiting for him. 'Hullo, Ryk,' said Murray, rising and shaking Van Dalen's hand warmly.

He was about the same age as Van Dalen, but younger and fitter-looking, his dark hair touched only faintly with grey at the temples. Like Van Dalen he was wearing a lightweight jacket, open-necked shirt and casual trousers. Informal dinner wear in a hot African country.

The two men sat down, smiling broadly at each other. They

were long-time friends whose paths had crossed in various parts of the world, and they had built up a relationship based on mutual liking, respect and trust. Murray now held the title of Assistant Head of Chancery in the embassy in Kinshasa. But as some suspected and a few, like Van Dalen, knew, the title was a cover for his real work.

They gave their orders to a waiter. Murray glanced casually around him to assess the proximity of other diners, then leaned forward, speaking quietly. 'I know why you're here, Ryk.' His Scottish accent was slight and, unlike most Britons, he pronounced Van Dalen's first name correctly – as 'rake' and not 'rike' or 'rick'.

'I'm glad you do, Jim. I might have to plead for some help from you.'

'Well, if, as I assume, it concerns your colleague Walmer, I have to ask you if you have the latest news on him?'

Ryk was cautious. 'He's on a special assignment in eastern Zaire. But we're a bit worried because he's gone out on a loose rein and he may have become a bit too involved in the story.'

Murray shook his head. 'No, Ryk, it's much worse than that.'

Van Dalen grew tense. Did Murray know about the photograph?

Murray said: 'Let me fill you in on recent events. Two weeks ago rebels backed by Uganda and led, we are informed, by an officer seconded from the Ugandan army overran a village north of Kisangani loyal to Mobutu and killed a lot of people.'

Bloody hell. That's when the photograph was probably taken, thought Van Dalen anxiously. Was it possible that Murray's lot had a copy of it – or had evidence related to it?

But Murray made no further reference to the event and continued: 'A week ago Zairean troops engaged the rebel group and killed a number of them before the rest retreated. They also killed the Ugandan officer who has been identified as Captain Wani Korobi, listed in fairly up-to-date Ugandan military records as a captain in their regular army. Appropriate diplomatic shit is now hitting the fan on that one.'

Watching Van Dalen carefully Murray went on: 'In that engagement a white man in rebel uniform was seen taking an active part in the fighting.'

Van Dalen realised that he was beginning to sweat slightly, even though the air-conditioning in the restaurant was well turned up. But he held Murray's gaze and said nothing.

They were interrupted by the arrival of the first course and Murray kept quiet until the waiter had departed. Then he said: 'Our latest information came in this afternoon and this I do not think you will like. The rebel group very cheekily counter-attacked the Zairean unit at dawn today and this time they were led by the white man. Unfortunately for them the Zaireans had been reinforced by the arrival of a unit of mercenaries and the rebels were virtually wiped out. The good news is the white man survived, and has been taken prisoner, although I understand he is wounded. I say good news because he turns out to be your colleague and heir apparent, the Honourable Stephen Walmer, and he is alive. But it remains bad news in that he shouldn't be there and he certainly should not have been doing what he did. In short, your man didn't simply go walkabout. He went rogue elephant.'

Van Dalen suddenly lost his appetite. He pushed away his plate.

'Jim, can you get me up there? I've got to get there.'

Murray shook his head. 'Sorry, old boy. No can do. Our shares are too low in the local regime at present, and journalists, especially, aren't allowed anywhere near Kisangani. Mobutu doesn't want it known that there are mercenaries in action there. All commercial flights and charters have been cancelled. Only military aircraft are flying there and you can't get on one without a *laissez-passer* signed by the president himself. It's that bad. No room for us to manoeuvre or fiddle for you, I'm afraid.'

Ryk signalled the waiter to bring the bill. 'I've got to go,' he said. 'Somehow I have to find a way of getting there fast.'

'I'm sorry,' Murray repeated.

'It's OK.'

There was a silence as they waited for the bill. Then Murray said, casually: 'By the way, I was in Nairobi last week. Bumped into Veronica at an otherwise boring cocktail party.'

For Ryk, unprepared for the information, the words came as a blow to the sternum, followed by an aching emptiness. He also felt resentment until he remembered that James Murray, based in

Cairo at the time of his problem there, had given friendship and support when most others had run for cover.

'Oh yes,' he murmured. Then added helplessly: 'How was she?'

Murray watched him. 'She was alone. Told me she was staying on her brother's farm near Naivasha. Living a quiet life, I gather. Seems to have become reclusive ... rather like you.'

The bill came. Ryk paid it and left, leaving James Murray to finish the meal and enjoy a cognac on his own.

There were no taxis outside. Impatient, Ryk decided to walk back to the Hotel Memling, his mind churning with the now momentous problem of Stephen Walmer. He also found his thoughts distracted by the news of Veronica.

As he neared the hotel two men stepped from the shadows and one flourished a doubtful-looking ID card. 'A moment, monsieur. We are from the *Sûreté Nationale*. You are please to accompany us to police headquarters.'

'Fuck off!' replied Van Dalen, distractedly, continuing on his way.

Nonplussed, the would-be muggers stared after him. '*Comment, monsieur?*' said the one who had addressed him. '*Vous êtes impoli, non?*'

When he reached his hotel room he turned up the contact number given him in Johannesburg. Alongside the number were the words 'Marc Benatar. Dealer in African curios and art'.

He dialled the number. The response was not immediate and when it came the voice was sleepy: '*Oui?*'

'I understand you deal in African art,' said Van Dalen.

'Not at this time of night, monsieur.' The accent was unmistakably Congo-Belge.

'Unfortunately, monsieur, it is urgent. I very much need to discuss business with you. You were recommended to me by our Doctor in Johannesburg.'

'Ah ... our Doctor. Where are you?'

'The Hotel Memling.'

'Meet me in the bar downstairs in half an hour.'

It was a small dark-haired man, wearing khaki slacks and a crumpled blue shirt, who arrived. Like most Belgian colonials he had the curious habit of wearing dark glasses at night. He studied the occupants of the bar for a brief moment and walked straight over to Van Dalen. 'You are the one who telephoned me, yes? OK, I'll have a beer. Being awakened this time of night makes me thirsty.'

Van Dalen ordered and they took their drinks to a quiet corner table.

Benatar listened, without interruption, to Van Dalen's urgent need to get to Kisangani and, to Ryk's surprise, replied: 'It will not be a problem to get you there. But you know it is not safe there at present, OK? Wait while I make a phone call.'

He went to one of the telephone booths in the foyer and returned within 20 minutes.

'All right. Now listen carefully. Go to the Intercontinental Hotel immediately. Speak to the dwarf behind the porter's desk. He is on duty now – no, do not smile. A dwarf is a dwarf and this is a sensitive dwarf. If you smile at him he will not help you. Ask him for the room number of the Portuguese pilots. Then go to that room. They are expecting you. They will arrange your flight. They will expect payment in hard currency. Take at least 1 000 dollars – and another 100 for the dwarf.'

'And for you?'

'For me, nothing. My business is with the Doctor. I received instructions to help you if needed.'

Van Dalen hesitated, then gave way to his unease. 'I didn't expect all this to be so easy ...'

The mouth below the dark glasses became a thin smile. 'It is because you came well recommended. But, my friend, getting there will be the only easy part. You will not, of course, reveal your true identity. If they discover you are a journalist they will, at worst, kill you, at best, lock you up for a long time.'

Van Dalen was silent.

Benatar leaned forward, studying him. 'My friend, you do, I hope, have a plan and people to see. Otherwise you are embarking on a foolishness.'

'I'm having to take this one step at a time. I will make my enquiries when I get there.'

Benatar grew suddenly agitated. '*Non, monsieur!* Allow me to advise you further, for my sake as well as your own. You cannot arrive there ahead of planning. Apart from what might happen to you, I do not wish to have my name beaten out of you.'

He looked about him, assessing who might be within earshot rather as James Murray had done. He was now speaking in a whisper: 'Look, avoid having any dealings with the Zaireans. The serious business there is being attended to by South African mercenaries at present. Get to them as quickly as you can. Carry no professional identification. Tell anyone who questions you that you have to report to ...' – he glanced quickly about him again – '... to Colonel Rolf Steiner. Let them think you are one of them.'

Van Dalen's eyes widened. 'My God – Steiner! Is it the same Steiner who was with Mike Hoare's outfit in Katanga?'

'Yes, yes. If you know him, already it will help.'

'Not if he remembers what I wrote about him,' said Van Dalen uneasily.

Benatar made an impatient gesture. 'That you must deal with between you and him.'

The journalist in Van Dalen surfaced. 'Who's really providing these mercenaries? Pretoria? CIA?'

'I do not wish to discuss such things,' replied Benatar coldly. 'You had better go now. The men you are going to see are flyers who begin their work early and need their sleep.'

The Intercontinental was a 20-minute ride away. It was now the leading hotel in Kinshasa, with a busy lobby that had become one of Africa's crossroads. It teemed day and night with arms dealers, gunrunners, illicit diamond dealers, mining contractors, seekers of government concessions, politicians, diplomats, journalists, pimps marketing their whores, gorilla hunters and various other interesting people. For this reason and because of the nature of his mission Van Dalen had avoided the Intercontinental, and he now hoped he would not run into other foreign correspondents or anyone else who might know him.

The dwarf, with large, soulful eyes behind the porter's desk, was wearing a red uniform with gold trimmings, a pillbox cap and gold epaulettes designed for a normal-sized tunic, and they did not look well on him. He was overworked but responded readily to Van Dalen's question and the 100-dollar bill. '*Chambre deux cent douze, monsieur,*' he said, pocketing the money swiftly.

Contrary to Benatar's concern about their sleep the Portuguese pilots, sharing suite 212, were entertaining two attractive African girls who looked not much more than 15 years old and were already drunk. The senior of the two men drew Van Dalen into a bedroom to get away from the noise and said cheerfully: 'What do you have for me, my friend?'

Van Dalen produced five 100-dollar signed traveller's cheques. The pilot raised an eyebrow and did not lower it until another five 100-dollar cheques were produced.

Then he said: 'Go to the airport at 05:00 hours but do not enter by the main entrance. Follow the ring road until you come to a gate on the far side of the runways, where you will find a C130 being loaded with drums of fuel. Enter the aircraft. No one will stop you. Go behind the cargo where you will find a row of seats. Sit there and wait. No one will disturb you. After take-off come into the cockpit and join us for a coffee.'

That had been two days ago. The five a.m. rendezvous at the airport and the four-hour flight to Kisangani on the lumbering C130 cargo plane had gone smoothly. But his arrival at Kisangani had not.

He was arrested within minutes of landing. A Zairean army captain in charge of a squad waiting to unload the cargo of fuel approached him suspiciously. '*Laissez-passer, monsieur?*'

He produced the only identity he possessed – the receipt he had been given for his British passport at Kinshasa airport – and said: 'I have to report directly to Major Steiner.'

The officer glanced at the receipt with contempt. '*Anglais,*' he sneered. Then, with the confidence of a man who likes to arrive at simple solutions he added: 'You are a spy. You are under arrest.'

There followed the usual disorder of being arrested by the Zairean army. He was flung into the back of a truck with unnecessary force.

He caught a glimpse of the Portuguese pilots who now ignored him and walked hurriedly away.

He was taken to an office in the airport's passenger arrivals and departures complex – now swarming with Zairean troops – where the shoulder-bag containing a change of clothing and other personal possessions was taken from him and searched. He was stripped of his wristwatch, money, gold signet ring and shoes. He was then beaten up.

The Zairean captain stood over Van Dalen as he lay on the floor and screamed: '*Cochon Anglais! Pourquoi êtes-vous ici?*' He was holding two British passports – Van Dalen's and Stephen Walmer's – taken from an inner pocket of the bag.

'I have come to report to Colonel Steiner.'

'Who is this Colonel Steiner?'

'He is the commander of the mercenary force here.'

The captain kicked Van Dalen and screamed: 'Liar! There are no mercenaries in Zaire!'

At this moment the door to the office was flung open and two white men entered. They wore camouflage fatigues and green berets. One, a blond, bearded giant, carried an Uzzi sub-machine gun and the other, lean and sallow-faced, wore a pistol in a holster on his hip. Van Dalen, from where he lay on the floor with one hand defending his face and the other clasped protectively over his groin, recognised the wild-goose insignia on their shoulders. They were mercenaries.

The captain, further enraged at the interruption – and the contradiction of what he had just said – screamed at the intruders: 'You enter my premises unannounced – get out!'

The lean mercenary, who wore a lieutenant's rank, said in badly accented French: '*Mon Capitaine, c'est très urgent. Venez avec moi s'il vous plaît.*' He made a curious gesture, a dipping motion with his left thumb, while his right hand rested on his pistol butt. The captain seemed to understand whatever the signal meant, for he quietened and followed him out of the room. The other mercenary, holding the Uzzi, remained standing in the doorway, his eyes on Van Dalen and the group of Zairean soldiers about him. No one moved.

Several minutes went by. Then the Zairean captain, accompanied by the mercenary officer, returned and ordered his men out of the room. He pointed at Van Dalen and said, angrily: '*Voilà – écartez l'ordure!*' ('There – remove the garbage!')

The mercenaries helped Van Dalen to his feet and walked him down a corridor to another far larger office where four white men – all wearing the wild-goose badge on their camouflage fatigue jackets – were seated at an assortment of desks and tables. Camp-beds were arranged along one wall and four AK-47 assault rifles were stacked in a corner. The office was dirty and unpleasantly fetid. Empty beer cans, Coca-Cola bottles, unwashed eating utensils and cigarette butts were littered about it.

A door to an inner office opened briefly and Van Dalen heard the crackle and squawk of radio communication. An officer came out and stood in front of Van Dalen. 'He's a mess,' he said in Afrikaans. 'Get him some coffee, clean him up and call the medic.'

Two hours later Van Dalen sat washed and repaired in front of the same officer who introduced himself as Captain Brink. A cut lip and a gash above his eye had been stitched, a badly loosened tooth had been removed and a broken rib had been strapped up. He had been made hideous with dabs of crimson Mercurochrome on minor cuts and scratches on his face and hands.

Brink looked him over with satisfaction. 'Sergeant Koos has patched you up nicely. He always wanted to be a doctor.'

Van Dalen began a cautious tale about confidential arrangements that had been made for him to see Colonel Steiner, but how he had been abandoned to the Zairean military by the treacherous Portuguese pilots.

But Brink interrupted him. 'Don't knock the Portuguese pilots, Van Dalen. It was they who tipped us off about your arrest. They probably saved your life. And look, cut out the bullshit. We know about you and why you are here. I've been in touch with Colonel Steiner on the radio and he says you can go to him at Buta. He has got your friend there. I have arranged river transport for you with two boatmen to guide you. The Zaireans control the choppers at this airport, I'm afraid, and there's no ways they are going to fly you anywhere.'

He motioned at Van Dalen's shoulder-bag on a nearby chair. 'There are your things. I understand there was also a wristwatch and some money. How much was it?'

'A few thousand Zairean francs, some rands ... and 800 US dollars ... and there was the signet ring.'

'Well, the money, the ring and the watch are missing. I'm sorry, man. Fortunes of war, you might say.' He avoided Van Dalen's gaze and looked out the window. 'I can lend you some bucks if you like, and you can repay me in a London bank account.'

Then he got up and terminated the discussion. 'I suggest you stay here with us tonight and get some rest. Don't go into the town. We can't protect you there.'

Now Van Dalen was on a small craft puttering up the Maiko River, a tributary of the great Congo. He had accepted Brink's offer of a loan and of a boat. He wondered who had stolen his money: the Zaireans or the mercenaries. He also wondered about Brink.

There were, broadly speaking, three kinds of soldiers of fortune, which was, of course, what mercenary troops really were. There were the raw recruits, often criminals who, to varying extents, revealed gaps in military training and discipline. There were ex-soldiers from other armies, many of whom displayed professionalism and sometimes remarkable courage quite out of proportion to their rewards. These were in the main old troopers still committed to military traditions and combat. It was of this kind that the greatest mercenary army of all time, the French Foreign Legion, largely consisted. Finally there were the mysterious ones who held key positions of command and who were sometimes a clue as to who was involved at the top, who was doing the hiring or paying the money.

In the case of the Foreign Legion there was no subterfuge. It was owned by France and under the command of French officers above NCO rank.

But in Africa the operation of mercenary forces had always been varied and murky.

The legendary Colonel Michael ('Mad Mike') Hoare, who had led the first mercenary force in the Congo, had been hired by powerful mining interests to back up the attempted secession of the copper-rich province of Katanga. Later, when Moise Tshombe had replaced the assassinated Patrice Lumumba as president of the Congo, his regime had been bolstered by a mercenary force hired by America's CIA.

Since then various African governments have used mercenary troops to help them stay in power or have been overthrown or fought by mercenaries paid by rebel forces or outside interests – in countries such as Nigeria, the Sudan, Angola, Sierra Leone, the Seychelles and Comoros.

Mercenaries were now again active in Zaire – the former Congo –

and had clearly been hired by Mobutu to help his regular army stave off the rebellion in the east, backed by Uganda. Steiner was an old hand. He had fought under 'Mad Mike' Hoare. He was South-African born of German parents. In the old days his un-complimentary nickname had been 'The Prussian Pig'. Recollection of the nickname now came back to roost uneasily in Van Dalen's mind, for he had used it in the article he had written about the man – whom he was now about to meet again.

There were indications that, as was so often the case, South Africans made up the bulk of the mercenary unit. Which made Van Dalen wonder, again, about Brink. He was clearly an Afri-kaner, but he spoke English with faultless grammar and a very slight accent, indicating careful upbringing and good education. When he spoke Afrikaans it was with the precise, somewhat plummy accents of a northern Transvaler. Although young (he could not be older than 30) there was an efficiency and easiness of command about him that hinted at professional military train-ing. Was he a seconded South African regular army officer? He had said: 'We know about you and why you are here.' Van Dalen recalled Benatar's apparent link with the mercenaries. Did all this mean that the Doctor and the NIS were also involved?

These were Van Dalen's thoughts as the boat, a mere 18-footer with a canvas canopy for sun protection, muttered up the river. The Zairean, with his hand on the tiller of the outboard engine, kept his eyes steadfastly on the river ahead while his companion, seated in the bow, scanned the banks nervously. They wore khaki shirts and shorts and straw hats. Both were taciturn and uncom-municative and had probably been ordered to speak to him as little as possible.

Van Dalen was in a severe state of depression over his predicament. The searing pain in his side left little doubt that at least one rib was broken and the other injuries he had sustained in the beating were throbbing. He had always detested the Congo Basin with its oppres-sive heat, its humidity and its problems as numerous as its disease-laden mosquitoes and its odious reptiles. Although he was restricted to virtually no movement in the small craft he was sweat-sodden and the perspiration burned as it seeped into the cuts on his body.

But greater than his discomfort was the knowledge that his

mission, difficult from the beginning, had now become thoroughly unpleasant and hazardous.

He watched in distaste as a water snake, disturbed at their approach, slid from a partially submerged tree root and disappeared beneath the surface of the water.

They had passed from the Lualaba River, which eventually expanded through a maze of marshlands and minor rivers to become the Congo itself, and were creeping up the Ulindi tributary. The riverside growth on either bank was thick and oppressive with dank reed, fern and a riotous broad-leafed tendril that seemed to dominate everywhere. The trees grew high enough in places to blot out the sunlight and leave part of the river in shade. The waterway seemed to be narrowing, the banks came closer and the smell of rotting vegetation grew suffocating.

There seemed to be a sense of arrival among the two-man crew. Both were scanning the left-hand bank. The steersman had slowed the engine and the bow watcher was standing upright.

Suddenly the water in front of him erupted in a line of spray that drenched everyone in the boat. Simultaneously came the ear-lashing sound of automatic-rifle fire from close by. The boat rocked violently as first the lookout and then the helmsman dived overboard and swam for the opposite shore.

Van Dalen tried to follow but the pain in his side paralysed him and he cried out with the agony of it as he sank below the gunwale to obtain what protection he could.

In his haste to abandon ship the helmsman had flung the tiller away from him and with the rudder locked to starboard the boat was now slowly gyrating in the middle of the river.

Even in his agony and fright Van Dalen was astonished to hear laughter. He raised his head and saw two white men in camouflage and green berets on the riverbank. One of them was swiftly replacing the expended magazine in the AK-47 he had just fired while the other, also armed, was slapping his thigh as he laughed uproariously.

The two crewmen were swimming furiously for the opposite bank. Both reached it and scrambled into the foliage, disappearing from sight.

The taller of the two soldiers, the one who had fired, beckoned to Van Dalen. 'Come! Come on, man, drive your boat here!' he bellowed in the heavily accented English of a South African more accustomed to speaking Afrikaans.

Van Dalen moved painfully towards the tiller and managed to grasp it and turn it. He zigzagged the craft uncertainly towards the men until it beached, its stern swinging slowly downstream.

'Come on, man, get out!' said the taller man.

The shorter man noted Van Dalen's slow movements. '*Yerra*, Lieutenant,' he said in Afrikaans, 'I think he's hurt. You didn't shoot him did you?'

'Don't talk *kak*, Corporal. Help him out of the boat!' With experienced forethought both men glanced at the shallows immediately before them in case anything hostile lurked there and then waded as briefly as possible into the water. While the shorter man helped Van Dalen ashore the other found the painter and secured the craft to a nearby tree.

They examined Van Dalen with interest as he gasped to control his pain. 'Jesus,' said the taller man, noting the layers of Mercurochrome. 'You're a picture book.'

The wild-goose insignia on the shoulders of their camouflage jackets confirmed the men as mercenaries. Van Dalen had regained his breath and his shock gave way to uncontrolled fury. He addressed the taller mercenary in Afrikaans, a more colourful language for abuse than English. 'You fucking bastard! Your mother was a whore who should have strangled you at birth when she saw you were a baboon. You could have killed those two men. They could have been taken by crocodiles ...'

Van Dalen found himself in darkness as he struggled to focus his mind. The darkness became a greyness and he grew aware that his head was hurting. The greyness lightened until he was back in the heat of the Congo sun and saw the trees above him. He realised he was lying on his back. Water was being splashed on him – on his face, on his neck, on his chest. It was tepid and hot, it smelled unpleasant and tasted foul.

He turned his head and saw the shorter mercenary sitting on his haunches, smoking a cigarette.

'What happened? Did I faint?' he murmured, holding up a hand against the glare of the sun and the wetness.

'No. The lieutenant hit you,' replied the corporal, studying the tip of his cigarette in embarrassment. 'He didn't like what you said about his mother.'

Van Dalen looked upwards through his spread fingers and saw that the taller mercenary was standing over him and urinating on him.

'Come,' said the lieutenant, buttoning up his fly. 'Pick him up and get him to the Jeep. We're wasting time.'

The ride to the base was fast and the road was rough. The corporal drove and the lieutenant sat beside him in front. Van Dalen lay on the back seat as ignored and odorous as a sack of garbage. He was tortured by the bucking and slewing of the jeep and his breathing came in gasps of agony through clenched teeth.

They reached the base camp in the late afternoon. It was an abandoned mission station. Mercenaries were billeted in the church, a school, some outbuildings and several surrounding dugouts. The jeep pulled up outside what had been the mission residence.

Van Dalen climbed out of the jeep. The corporal tried to assist him but Van Dalen shook off his hand.

Colonel Rolf Steiner was standing on the veranda, his hands on his hips. He was a short, torpedo-shaped man with a bronze, totally bald head and an old-fashioned waxed moustache. He wore faded camouflage fatigues and carried a holstered pistol on his hip. His eyes were black and button-like. He stared at Van Dalen and wrinkled his nose in disgust. '*Mein Gott,* Van Dalen, but you look terrible. You go and have a wash and a rest and tonight you must come and have dinner with me and we talk of old times, *ja?*'

Van Dalen ignored the invitation. 'Where is my colleague, Stephen Walmer?' he said, coldly.

'All in good time,' replied Steiner. To the lieutenant he said: 'Take him away. He smells bad.'

Van Dalen was billeted in a lean-to behind the school building, which contained only a camp bed and a mosquito net. A makeshift bathroom at the end of the building contained a perforated bucket into which ran hot and cold water from petrol drums positioned on high brick-built platforms outside. The hot-water drum had a wood fire burning under it. Van Dalen, grateful for the familiar old colonial-African invention, was able to cleanse himself of the filth of the day's events. He touched, tenderly, the new bruise under his left eye, which had all but closed.

He put on the one change of clean clothing he had brought with him and washed what he had taken off. He went back to his small quarters. No guard had been placed over him, which figured. Where could he run to? And in any event he was here at his own request, for his own purpose. He lay down on the camp bed to rest and fell asleep instantly.

He was awakened two hours later by the corporal who said: 'Oom, it's time for dinner with the colonel.' Van Dalen sighed at the courtesy title. Young Afrikaners, out of respect, called older men 'Uncle' once they discerned a certain age. It did little to raise his morale.

Steiner greeted him by lamplight and candlelight. But surprisingly there was ice with the whisky. 'The good fathers left behind their paraffin fridge, and my men got it working,' he explained. 'Praise the Lord.'

Dinner was served by a young army cook, a Belgian, assisted by another mercenary, an Australian. It came on tin plates and it was nothing great – barbecued meat, pumpkin and rice.

'Only a short step above field rations I'm afraid, Van Dalen. Fortunes of war, *ja?*' his host apologised. Van Dalen murmured that it was fine.

'But look what I have,' said Steiner, triumphantly. 'A Côte-de-Provence 1972, a wine of no great significance, but adequate for this occasion. Also left behind here by the good fathers, bless them. We found it in the cellar beneath the church with the sacramental wine. Or maybe this is the sacramental wine, I do not know. I am not a Catholic.'

Sliced pawpaw was presented as desert, followed by coffee.

'Alas, we have no cognac or liqueur,' Steiner apologised, 'but I can offer you pawpaw juice made interesting with alcohol from our medical stores, *ja?*' Van Dalen declined. But he accepted the offer of a raw-flavoured Brazilian cheroot, and they moved, at Steiner's suggestion, from the table to two imitation-leather easy chairs.

'So now,' said Steiner, with a relish that indicated he had been savouring this moment, 'we meet again. Me, "The Prussian Pig", and you, the journalist who gave me that name.'

'I used it, but I didn't give it to you,' said Van Dalen.

Steiner sipped his whisky and regarded him stonily over the rim of his glass. 'Maybe,' he said. 'But it was a shit article, and I will never forgive you. You wrote that I was a murderer who killed for pleasure and that I was mad. When I read it I swore that if I ever met you again I would indeed kill you.'

'What I wrote about was your reputation. I didn't make the accusations.'

Steiner continued to regard him stonily. 'Whatever.'

Van Dalen shifted uneasily. The switch in tone had become sinister. Steiner was undoubtedly unstable. And he had just threatened to kill him. He was about to point this out in justification of the article, but thought better of it.

As if reading his mind Steiner said: 'But I don't want to kill you, my friend, because I need you.'

'Oh yes?'

'*Ja*. We come now to the matter of your colleague, this Stephen Walmer. His father is an English lord who owns a newspaper. Therefore he must be very rich. I will release this prisoner but only on payment of one million dollars.'

Van Dalen felt a weariness descending on him. He wondered why he had not anticipated this.

'You see, Van Dalen, I am getting too old to go on fighting for Kaffirs in their silly wars. I wish to retire. One million dollars will enable this to be my last campaign. But it must be a private arrangement only for you and me to know of, *hein*? His father will agree to this offer, *ja*?'

Van Dalen was silent for a moment. He saw no other way out of the predicament. He said: 'Yes I believe he will. But as a matter of interest, what if he will not?'

Steiner tipped ash from his cheroot onto the floor. 'Then, of course, we come to the end of the road. I will be obliged to kill you both – to get rid of the problem. No one will ever know how or why you died. You will simply disappear.'

'So my article about you was not all that inaccurate.'

Steiner took the sarcasm in his stride. 'I never denied it. I just didn't like it. Such publicity only makes problems. But I do not need to discuss your rubbish articles or your opinions. I require only an answer.' The black eyes were hard as pebbles.

Van Dalen took a deep breath. 'There must be conditions.'

'What are they?'

'One half of the money can be paid now but the rest can only be paid after we leave Zaire safely. Also, I want fast and safe transport out of here. That rules out river transport. Thirdly, I must see Walmer. Furthermore I need to talk to someone in Kinshasa.'

Steiner was silent for almost a full minute before replying. 'I agree to the money arrangement. Because I know that you know if the deal is not honoured completely I will find you and I will kill you. I have no means for you to talk to anyone in Kinshasa. The telephone line from here is down. The transport is difficult. The enemy has Stinger missiles, which makes flying from this base risky at present, but I will make a plan. We'll get you to Kisangani and on a flight from there to Kinshasa, *ja*?'

'What about Walmer? How badly wounded is he – and when can I see him?'

'The wound is not life-threatening … but it is unfortunate … a genital wound. He has lost his penis.'

Van Dalen sank his head between his hands. After a few moments he muttered: 'Every meal a banquet, every night early to bed.'

'What was that?' enquired Steiner.

'Nothing. Just a private thought … but listen, Colonel, he must still need medical attention.'

'We have a field hospital and a competent surgeon here. Initial surgery has been performed successfully and infection has been controlled. But *ja*, he should go to a hospital. The sooner you get him there the better. But that is now up to you – and your people – is it not?'

'Give me something to write on. Give me the bank and account number.'

Steiner reached to a side-table and handed him a pad and pencil. 'Just write the message. The bank and account number will be advised separately to the addressee in a more confidential manner. Kindly stress confidentiality in these arrangements. Otherwise, Van Dalen, it will not go well.'

Van Dalen set out the usual foreign-desk codes but addressed the message to Lord Walmer. He wrote: 'HAVE LOCATED STEPHEN WHO IS PRISONER IN REMOTE REGION STOP HE

WOUNDED AND NEEDS IMMEDIATE MEDICAL ATTENTION STOP CAPTORS DEMANDING ONE MILLION US DOLLARS RANSOM HALF NOW BALANCE ON RELEASE STOP SUGGEST IMMEDIATE COMPLIANCE AND TOTAL CONFIDENTIALITY WILL PRODUCE BEST RESULTS STOP STAND BY FOR SEPARATE ADVISORY ON PAYMENT ARRANGEMENTS.'

He handed the pad back to Steiner who read the message and grunted his satisfaction. '*Ja*. I have the means to get this message to your people within hours. We should have their reply before midday tomorrow, unless they are stupid. Now come with me to see your friend.'

Steiner drove him in a jeep to one of the low buildings behind the mission school. It had been converted into a rudimentary field hospital. A soldier seated in a chair by the door leaped to his feet and saluted. Several men lay on camp beds under mosquito netting. A single storm lantern provided a dim light. Steiner took him to a small room at the end of the makeshift ward, raised the mosquito net over a bed and switched on his flashlight.

Van Dalen recognised the features of Stephen Walmer, looking somewhat wasted. He was on a drip and he was asleep. Van Dalen touched his forehead. It was moist but there was no indication of fever.

A bespectacled young man joined them and said: 'He has been sedated, Colonel. I would rather he was not disturbed now. Come through to the office.'

They went through to another part of the building where a corner had been boarded off and shelved to form a combined pharmacy and office. 'This is Captain Steytler, our doctor,' said Steiner. 'Captain, this is Ryk van Dalen. He may wish to evacuate Stephen Walmer.'

'He needs to get to a hospital, but only by airlift.'

'I would prefer him to go by road, at least as far as Kisangani,' said Steiner.

'Certainly not. The roads in this country are hell. This patient is on a catheter and he has wounds that might open during a rough ride.'

'Wounds? I thought he had only one wound,' said Van Dalen, looking at Steiner, who looked blank.

'Two wounds,' said the captain, curtly. 'The bullet passed through the frontal upper thigh, narrowly missing the femoral artery. That's one wound. It then took off his penis. That's two wounds. We have repaired him as best we can but the surgery will need revision. He must go to hospital as soon as possible. Not by road. By air.'

Van Dalen was impressed by the captain who seemed efficient and clearly had little regard for Steiner. The combination of his name, his apparent nationality, his medical knowledge and his air of command suggested they were in the presence of a South African doctor who may have had previous military experience.

Steiner turned and left without another word. Van Dalen thanked the captain and followed him. 'We cannot commit an aircraft,' snarled Steiner angrily as he drove Van Dalen to his quarters. 'These swine have already shot down two of our helicopters. You will have to take him by river. I don't care what the doctor says.'

He was permitted to visit Stephen Walmer again the following morning. He picked his way through the eight other patients and approached the bed in the room at the end. Walmer, wearing a grimy T-shirt and lying under a single sheet, was on his back, face turned to the wall.

But he turned his head slowly when Van Dalen sat down on the flimsy camp chair beside the bed. Walmer stared at his visitor uncomprehendingly at first, then sighed and closed his eyes. 'Jesus, Ryk, you look like hell. What happened to your face?'

'You don't look so good either, Stephen. I've come to take you home.'

Walmer smiled slightly without opening his eyes. 'Not so sure I want to go, old boy ... I suppose you've heard I'll be leaving an important part of me behind in Africa?'

'Yes. I'm sorry. Honestly Stephen, I wish you hadn't got mixed up in all this. These African wars are shit and they lead nowhere.'

'Don't lecture me, old boy. I know I've been unprofessional. But it would be a waste of time trying to get you to understand. You're just an old Boer hack working for my old man's ratshit rag.' He tried to shift his position on the narrow cot and winced.

'Can I get you anything, Stephen?'

'You can give me a cigarette. Pack's on the floor under the bed.'

Van Dalen lit the cigarette and passed it to Walmer. He drew on it and let the smoke ebb out.

'You know, Ryk, I've always been one of your admirers, even when you blotted your copybook, so to speak. But don't start telling me how I should not have become involved in this caper. Have you ever realised the extent of the suffering in this country? Have you ever really appreciated the absolute evil of the man who is responsible for it? Well, I met someone who opened my eyes to it and helped me do something about it and I found it a lot better than just observing it. I'll miss him now that he's gone ... so much the cost of it all.'

Van Dalen suddenly realised Stephen Walmer was weeping. He averted his gaze in sympathy and embarrassment.

Walmer wiped his eyes and blew his nose unashamedly on the bed sheet. 'Oh well, what the hell.' He gave a short bark of a laugh. 'And Jesus, how they'll laugh at El Vino's when they hear Stephen Walmer has lost his dick. Don't know how I'll manage without my dick. You got any ideas on this, Ryk? Do they provide artificial ones, like when you lose a leg?'

Van Dalen remained silent.

Walmer handed him the half-smoked cigarette. 'Here, take this and get out. I want to sleep now.'

He was met outside the medical station by the corporal who seemed to have been delegated to his needs. 'Does Oom want breakfast?' he asked in Afrikaans, respectfully using the customary third-person form of address.

'Stop calling me that!' snapped Van Dalen. 'Yes I do want breakfast.' He was guided to a tent under nearby trees where several men, their weapons placed carefully to hand, sat eating. They were taciturn, almost hostile, and had clearly been given instructions not to talk to him. But Van Dalen, listening to their muted conversation between themselves, recognised South African, Belgian and German accents.

He had hardly finished the warmed bully beef and fried bread, which comprised breakfast, when the corporal reappeared. 'Oom, the colonel wants to see Oom,' he said.

He was shown into Steiner's quarters. The Colonel entered swiftly from an inner sanctum that emitted the crackle of short-wave radio noise when the door opened. 'There's good news and bad news,' growled Steiner. 'The good news is that your people have made the first deposit. The bad news is that the river option is now more risky than air travel. So we are sending you and Walmer out by helicopter. Departure 04:30 hours tomorrow morning. That's the safest time.'

'Listen,' said Van Dalen. 'I am not here to write a story, so maybe we can be a little relaxed with each other. Maybe Mobutu is your paymaster but I have a fairly good idea who else may be involved. That leads me to hope you might have channels to get an urgent message to someone I know in Kinshasa who will pass it on at my request to a friend in the British embassy.'

Steiner paused for only a moment. Then, without speaking, he picked up a pad from the desk and passed it to Van Dalen who sat down and wrote a message to James Murray. He addressed it to Benatar at his telephone number in Kinshasa with a request that it be passed on urgently and discreetly. He prayed silently that he was causing no gross violation of security for either person and that, if so, he would be forgiven. But it was highly possible that Murray and Benatar knew each other anyway. Steiner read the message, nodded and went into the radio room.

The departure in the murk of the following dawn went smoothly. Stretcher-bearers eased Stephen Walmer into the back of a combi and Captain Steytler and a medic climbed in beside him. Van Dalen sat in front beside the driver. Accompanied by two vehicles carrying a heavily armed escort, including Colonel Steiner, they drove gently for two kilometres to a heavily sandbagged position under trees where men, working by flashlight, were removing a camouflage net from above a helicopter. It was wheeled into a clearing.

While Walmer was transferred to the chopper Steiner made his farewell. 'Remember, Van Dalen. As soon as he is out of Zaire you complete our transaction, *ja?*'

'*Ja,*' said Van Dalen. Steiner walked away without another word.

The chopper whined and coughed, its rotors turning slowly, then spinning faster. It took off, racing low over the trees. 'Only way is to catch Charlie sleeping,' said the pilot in an American accent.

The terminology for the enemy was familiar. 'You ex-Vietnam?' asked Van Dalen. The pilot did not reply and there was no further discussion.

They landed at Kisangani an hour later in emerging daylight. A full platoon of heavily armed mercenaries surrounded the helicopter and Van Dalen sensed tension as Captain Brink approached, ducking under the whirling rotors, and pointed at a nearby worn-looking Beechcraft, the identification markings of which had been painted out.

'We must get him on that plane quickly and you'll be taking off immediately,' he shouted.

The mercenaries were watching a contingent of Zairean troops, also heavily armed, positioned alongside three trucks about 100 metres distant. The Zaireans were watching them and Van Dalen recognised the feisty captain who had assaulted him on his arrival four days ago speaking into a field radio.

Walmer was transferred to the Beechcraft within minutes and they were airborne ten minutes later. There was a pilot and a co-pilot at the controls, and seats had been removed to accommodate the stretcher. Van Dalen looked back as the plane cleared the airport perimeter. The Zaireans had not moved from their positions and the Zairean captain was now standing with his hands on his hips, watching their departure.

'What the hell was all that about?' Van Dalen shouted to the pilot. He shrugged and spoke to the co-pilot who removed a set of earphones and unfastened his seat belt. He struggled out of his seat and came into the cabin. He said: 'For God's sake, Ryk, what have you done to your face? Did you fall out of a tree?' It was James Murray. Van Dalen almost wept with relief and pleasure at the sight of him.

'Is this the laddie? How is he?' enquired Murray, peering at the stretcher. He looked tired.

'He's out cold, sedated,' said Van Dalen. 'My God, I'm glad to see you.'

'And so you should be.' Murray seated himself. 'Now listen, here's the score. What that stand-off was about down on the ground there was that the local fuzz have finally figured out that your laddie is the white man who was helping the rebels, so all hell has broken out. They're after him and they want you too. Colonel Steiner's hoods helped you through Kisangani, but Zairean police and army people are waiting for you in Kinshasa. You've got to get out of Zaire, so we're flying you next door to Brazzaville. There's a chartered Lear jet waiting for you there with a full medical team on board, including a doctor, to fly the laddie to London, making only a fuel stop in Nice.'

'Thank you, James. You've gone to enormous trouble.'

'Not so much as you might be thinking. That Lear jet was not hired by the embassy, although we are co-operating, on instructions from the Foreign Office. It's chartered by the *Daily Courier*, which also arranged the medical team and came in last night with your own people on board: the editor and the foreign editor, as well as the managing director. They are meeting you in Brazzaville.'

'I'm impressed,' said Van Dalen. 'Although it sounds a bit over-staffed and overdone.'

'Perhaps not in the circumstances. You see, Lord Walmer has died.'

'My God,' said Van Dalen. He looked down at the stretcher. 'So what we are transporting here is the new Lord Walmer.'

'Precisely,' said Murray. 'The king is dead, long live the king – and his court has hastened to Africa to take delivery of him.'

'Yes, I see,' said Van Dalen after a moment's thought. 'It's a time when courtiers must secure their jobs at all costs.'

'Quite so,' said Murray. 'Now, I need his passport if he still has it.'

'He had no documents on him when he was captured,' said Van Dalen, 'but I've got his backup passport.' He delved in his shoulder-bag and handed Murray the passport he had found hidden in Walmer's hotel room in Lusaka.

Murray paged through it. 'No Congo-Brazzaville visa,' he said. 'No matter, we should get round that. The Congo is a friendlier place than Zaire. Nevertheless they must move him on to London quickly. There's only a river between Kinshasa and Brazzaville and I can't guarantee no effort will be made to extradite him.'

There were no problems in Brazzaville. Murray's advance arrangements worked well. Following control-tower directions the Beechcraft taxied to where the Lear jet was parked. The doctor and other medical crew were waiting beside it, accompanied by Resnick, McCrae and Woodley, wearing almost identical white linen lightweight suits and Panama hats. There were also Congolese immigration and customs officers and two officials from the British consulate in Brazzaville.

The three newspaper executives rushed to the side of the stretcher as it was lifted from the Beechcraft and clucked and fussed over it while it was being transferred to the Lear. Stephen was emerging from sedation but was still too confused to converse, or even to recognise them.

John Resnick hurried over to Van Dalen and shook his hand. 'My dear chap. Your poor face, whatever happened?' Without waiting for an answer he went on: 'We are so grateful for all you have done. Marvellous fellow, marvellous fellow. Now if you don't mind I must be with His Lordship.' He hurried up the steps of the Lear in the wake of the stretcher.

McCrae shook Van Dalen's hand and seemed genuinely concerned about his appearance. 'Great work, Ryk. But you look in bad shape. Something awful must have happened. But our doctors on the plane can have a look at you during the flight.'

'Thank you, Gordon, but I'm OK, and I will not be coming with you. You have him now and there is no need for me to return to London immediately. I'll be going on to South Africa for the time being.'

McCrae gave him a hard, steady look, then shrugged. 'I wish you well,' he said. He shook hands again and boarded the plane.

David Woodley had hung back, but now stepped forward, sweating profusely, and drew Van Dalen into the shade of the wing of the Lear jet. 'We are all very grateful for what you have done, Ryk. I rather wish though that you had kept in more regular contact.' His voice lapsed into its usual whine. 'After all, you know, I had to deal with all the questions and panic in London. Not nice.'

Van Dalen made no reply.

Woodley continued: 'I think you should know how we are proceeding in this matter. We are getting a lot of nonsense enquiries about Stephen being actively involved in combat situations. All a lot of crap of course. So we are running an exclusive page-one splash on him being invalided out of Africa after being wounded on assignment. You understand?'

'I understand perfectly,' said Van Dalen, coldly.

'Good. And another thing ...' He looked around him and lowered his voice. 'We are not paying the balance of that outrageous ransom demand. We have him back now and it's diabolical that we had to pay anything at all! Do you know that they are debiting it to my foreign budget?' His tone became a snake-like hiss of indignation.

Van Dalen's stomach churned. 'David, I cannot believe what I am hearing! If you break the deal these guys will come for me! They might even go for you!'

Woodley brushed it aside. 'It's your problem, Ryk. And I can't see anyone being in danger at our end. There's law and order in England. The fact is that we are not doling out any more money. So whatever arrangement you are involved in at your end, you'll have to handle it.'

Van Dalen went cold with fury at the hint that he had a part in the ransom.

'You are getting it wrong, David, and you are seriously underestimating these people.'

He looked desperately at the door of the Lear, but Woodley read his mind and snapped: 'Forget it. Talking to John and Gordon would be a waste of time. We are all in agreement on this. Goodbye, Ryk.' He strutted self-importantly to the steps and boarded the aircraft without looking back. The door closed behind him and the steps were wheeled away.

Murray, who had concluded formalities with the Congolese officials, said: 'I need a drink.' They were given a lift to the passenger terminal by one of the consular officials.

While Murray hung back to talk to his colleague, Van Dalen sought and found the bar.

As he ordered a beer Benatar, wearing the inevitable dark glasses, moved quietly from a corner, carrying a familiar-looking suitcase. '*Bonjour, mon ami.* I have been observing the condition of your face, which I think tells a story. I regret that you had trouble. But I think all is now well. I took the liberty of settling your hotel bill at the Memling and packing and bringing your belongings across to Brazzaville on the ferry.' He handed Van Dalen the suitcase. 'You should not return to Zaire until this matter is long forgotten. I suspected that they probably kept your passport at the airport when you arrived, but decided it would be prudent not to enquire after it. You will have to abandon it. I am sure your consulate here will replace it.'

They shook hands. 'I am deeply obliged to you for everything,' said Van Dalen.

Murray was walking towards them. 'No, do not introduce me to Murray,' warned Benatar. 'We have much in common but, like secret lovers, we are strangers in public.' He walked away swiftly.

Murray gratefully accepted Van Dalen's offer of a beer and mopped his brow. He gave no indication of having seen or recognised Benatar.

Van Dalen explained his passport difficulty. 'No problem,' said Murray. 'I'll have a word with immigration and the consulate here and they'll give you a new passport today.'

There was a roar outside as an aircraft took off. It was the Lear jet. As they watched its ascent Murray raised his glass. 'Good riddance, if you don't mind my saying so.' He turned to Van Dalen. 'Well now, laddie. What're you going to do with your life?'

'I'll take the Air France flight that goes through here tomorrow for Johannesburg. Got a couple of things to do there. Then ... I've been thinking it might be a good idea to take a few days' rest in Nairobi. What do you think the climate's like there at present?'

Only someone like a canny Scot could have picked up the quiet desperation lurking beneath the casualness of the question. After all, Van Dalen knew Kenya's weather conditions even better than he did. Nevertheless Murray gave an appearance of giving the question serious thought. Then he replied just as casually: 'I think it will be a good climate for you. But I'd wait a few days until your face looks better. You don't want to give the lassie a fright.'

Van Dalen checked into Brazzaville's best hotel for the night and luxuriated in a shower. He examined his face in detail in a mirror for the first time. 'Jesus,' he muttered.

When he unpacked his suitcase he found a batch of now outdated querulous telex messages received at the Memling Hotel during his absence and found by Benatar stuffed under the door of his room.

They were all from Woodley, and they served now only to intensify the tumult and anger in his mind over the blatant reneging on the deal with Steiner. He sat on the edge of the bed for a few minutes with his head in his hands until a thought struck him. Then he lifted the telephone beside him, called the hotel switchboard and asked: 'Can you get me a call to Johannesburg?'

When he arrived in Johannesburg the following afternoon he was met again by Marius Retief who commiserated on the condition of his face while he drove him to his hotel. '*Yerra* man, it wouldn't look so bad if they hadn't painted you with that red *kak*. What happened to honest-to-goodness iodine? At least it would have matched your tan.'

Van Dalen gave him a brief account of his trip and Marius shook his head. 'That fucking Steiner,' was the only comment he made at one stage of the story. He then said: 'Anyhow, Ryk, the Doctor presents his compliments and says to tell you he received your telephone message from Brazzaville yesterday and the package was sent off to the foreign editor, Woodley, as you requested by priority-express courier service and indicated as coming from you. He should have it by now. And the Doctor also says he'd like to have lunch some time. He'd like to hear about your trip. Here's your hotel. Have a good rest, man.'

That David Woodley had received the package was confirmed minutes later at the reception desk of the hotel as Van Dalen checked in.

'There's a message coming over for you on the telex right now, Mr Van Dalen,' said the desk clerk. 'It's marked urgent.' She went into an inner office, returned, and handed him the telex slip.

Van Dalen read it and smiled grimly. It bore the usual foreign-desk codes and was addressed to Ryk van Dalen. It was slugged: 'URGENT-URGENT-URGENT (HOLD FOR ARRIVAL).' It said, simply and curtly: 'SECOND INSTALMENT PAID. WOODLEY.'

As Van Dalen read the message in Johannesburg, David Woodley, foreign editor of the *Daily Courier*, 6 000 miles away in London, returned from the communications room from where he had just sent the telex. He closed and locked the door of his office and, unlocking the bottom drawer of his desk, took out the large brown courier package with the red priority stickers that had arrived from Johannesburg two hours earlier. Slowly he again drew from it the photograph that had been sent to him at Van Dalen's request.

It was the picture that showed the then Honourable Stephen Walmer, his chief foreign correspondent, now Lord Walmer, the new proprietor and chief executive of the *Daily Courier*, in camouflage fatigues standing over a bloodstained corpse. Like the others about him in the photo Walmer was laughing and holding an AK-47 assault rifle. He had one foot on the dead man's chest.

Woodley was still seething with the inner fury of a man who had just been aced and who would now have to pay out half a million dollars.

But it was an anger cooled somewhat by his pleasure at what he held in his hands. In the merciless jungle called Fleet Street, more merciless than the jungles of Africa, evidence of this kind, astutely used, could provide career security and promotion. Yes, God-damn-it promotion – right to the very top!

For several more minutes he studied the photograph, fascinated. Then he slid it back into its envelope and stood up. He walked to the safe in the corner of his office, placed the envelope carefully inside it, closed the door firmly and spun the combination lock.

7

Meeting the chief

I was in the Congo in February 1962 when the *Daily Mail* abruptly yanked me to London. The message from the foreign editor, Denys Fisher, said: 'EDITOR WANTS YOU LONDONWARDS IMMEDIATELY FOR MEETING WITH CHAIRMAN STOP HAVE BOOKED YOU SABENA FLIGHT 312 TONIGHT CONNECTING BRUSSELS-LONDON 0900 TOMORROW STOP HURRY REGARDS FISHER.'

Catapulted from the Congo's 102-degree heat and 90 per cent humidity into a British mid-winter, I arrived in London the following afternoon, shivering in work-stained tropical wear.

The assignment in which I had been engaged had not allowed for a wide range of clothing. It was a rough job which resulted in a story about Belgian refugees escaping from rebel soldiers, smuggling their children and pets (including dogs with their muzzles bound to keep them silent) down a cliffside at night onto waiting boats that took them across Lake Bukavu to the safety of Shangugu on the opposite bank.

It had brought praise from the *Daily Mail*. In fact I'd had an extremely lucky run of good stories and the 'hero-grams' (as they were called) had been tumbling in.

To be 27 years old and Fleet Street's youngest foreign correspondent in the rarified and heady atmosphere of those days of war assignments for a London daily, and to get such praise was stimulating stuff. As my good friend and chief competitor, John Monks of the *London Daily Express*, used to exult: 'This is a hell of a lot better than working!'

Now had come this urgent and mysterious message, exploding with potential and possibilities. A meeting with The Chief? What could it mean? I arrived in London wet, cold but agog with excitement.

The *Daily Mail*'s editor at the time was William Hardcastle, a plump and jovial man who welcomed me warmly but gazed askance at my clothes. 'Look, he wants you to spend the long weekend with him at Daylesford. We'll have to get you fitted out quickly,' he said, and I was rushed off by his personal driver to Moss Brothers, the emergency tailors and stockists of the right clothes for all occasions.

In an astonishing flurry of sartorial sleight of hand I was fitted out in 24 hours with a dinner jacket, a grey flannel suit (for relaxed occasions which nonetheless might require a suit) a dark suit (in case required for church), a Harris tweed jacket and grey flannels for casual wear and shirts and ties and shoes for all occasions. I was also provided with a winter overcoat. All problems solved.

I was taken to lunch the following day by the editor for what I expected to be a full briefing on what it was all about.

I was perplexed to learn that he did not know why the chairman wished to see me. 'He just phoned up and said he wanted you here by the weekend and it was urgent,' said Bill Hardcastle. 'That's all he said.' He shrugged. 'I don't suppose you have any inkling, do you?' He shot me a quick look across the table.

I then realised that the editor himself was perplexed at the situation. He could hardly be blamed. He had been ordered to haul one of his correspondents off a highly active story at a moment's notice and brought to London at considerable expense to his budget without any reason given. And he was, after all, the editor.

'Didn't you ask him why?'

His reply was terse. 'You don't ask Lord Rothermere why. He either tells you, or he forgets to tell you or he has a good reason not to tell you.'

I was now getting a definite vibe that there was some general unease over my sudden summons to London. I had picked up the first tendrils of this on the editorial floor on my arrival without becoming really aware of what I was noticing. The usual bonhomie among those I knew was in some instances more effusive than usual, in other cases a trifle restrained.

I was young and had a lot to learn in what was probably the world's toughest and most ruthlessly competitive workplace. But I already had some knowledge of the way jobs came and went and loopy-the-loop type appointments made at the whims of capricious Fleet Street proprietors.

Against such background here was I, having had a run of success, being brought in mysteriously to spend a weekend with the chairman at his country estate. If neither my editor nor I knew why this was happening it was a fair guess no one else did. I wasn't sure if anyone felt actually threatened by my presence. Nevertheless unlike earlier more relaxed visits, on this mystery-shrouded exercise in the neurosis-ridden Fleet Street publishing world I was a possible predator who needed to be watched.

I was expected at Daylesford, Lord Rothermere's country estate in the Cotswolds the following day – a Friday – and after our lunch the editor took me to the upper executive suite in Northcliffe House and introduced me to one of the chairman's secretaries, a charming lady called Jennifer. It was she who would now brief me on travel and protocol. I sat down at her desk.

'Here is a first-class rail ticket to Daylesford,' said Jennifer. 'If you are sent back in the Rolls, please let me have the return portion back.' I nodded. Okay, I thought, that's sound economics.

She leaned her elbows on the desk, folded her hands beneath her chin and looked me deep in the eyes. 'I need to give you some cautionary advice,' she said.

I gave her my full attention.

'The gentleman who will meet you at the entrance of the mansion will not be Lord Rothermere. It will be Stevens, the butler.' This was, I came to realise later, not merely guidance for a simple colonial boy from the veld. Stevens was a large and impressive looking man who dressed grandly. There had been embarrassing past occasions when visitors had mistaken him for Lord Rothermere and shaken him enthusiastically by the hand.

Lord Rothermere made a practice of not meeting guests on arrival. The butler did that and you met his lordship later when you came downstairs to tea or for dinner.

According to Richard Bourne, author of the Northcliffe and Rothermere family, biography, *Lords of Fleet Street*, even Queen

Mary, then the Queen Mother, was unmet at the threshold by her host when she visited Daylesford – but he got soundly rapped for that one.

'Now here's something very important,' said Jennifer, and I leaned forward attentively.

'Do not under any circumstances mention in Lord Rothermere's presence any of the James Bond books or movies or their author Ian Fleming.' I acknowledged assent readily, understanding the reason. His wife, the famously beautiful Lady Ann Rothermere had left him to marry Fleming after a lengthy affair. It had been a shattering experience for him, and for years afterwards newspapers in the *Mail* group never reviewed a James Bond novel or movie.

'And he doesn't like to talk about television,' concluded Jennifer. She offered no explanation but I discovered later that it had to do with Associated Rediffusion, the TV monolith created by Rothermere whose shares he sold in a panic when they near collapsed, only to see them rise spectacularly in the end.

Thus briefed I arrived at Daylesford, the impressive Rothermere country place in the Cotswolds, created and formerly owned by Warren Hastings, first Viceroy of India.

I acknowledged, gravely, the greeting of the butler, making it clear that I knew he was the butler and was shown up to a room that overlooked the church and village of Daylesford, which were part of the estate.

I emerged from the bathroom to find a footman laying out my clothes and glancing cynically at the profusion of Moss Brothers labels. Such matters bring colour into the lives of footmen and I could imagine the news whizzing about the staff quarters. Later I dressed for dinner and went downstairs to meet my host.

I found him mixing cocktails. He welcomed me genially and announced: 'I am the best martini maker in Britain. Do you want a martini?' After that it was impossible to refuse, although I would have preferred a sherry.

As we sipped our drinks on couches in a reception room filled with fine paintings and magnificent artefacts he said: 'I suppose you are wondering why I have brought you here?'

'Well, yes, sir, actually I have been wondering ...'

'Well, you see, it's a long weekend and I have my grandson here, and some of his friends from Eton and I thought it would be a jolly good idea if you came and told them – well, I mean, all of us of course – some stories about Africa.'

I must have stared at him uncomprehendingly for a moment because he said: 'That all right with you?'

'Yes, of course, sir. Fine. Absolutely. I'll certainly do my best.'

'Well then that's splendid. Let's have another drink!'

Well at least that settles a lot of things, I thought. It's not the editorship or an assistant editorship or the foreign editorship. Or the Washington Bureau. Or Moscow. It's just Africa stories for the grandson and his friends. All right, then. I began to relax, and think of more mundane things – like the cost of this frolic – and how matters were back in the Congo, hoping things stayed relatively calm there until I could get back.

I thought of the guys back at Northcliffe House. I wondered if I should call them and say: It's okay boys, relax. It's only about bedtime stories for the kids.

I wondered if the visit could not have been planned in a more conventional way. Why the drama and mystery? Why not an invitation with its reasons given right from the start? At least I could have honed up on the best African stories – and flown in with some props, like a parrot or a carved elephant-headed ebony walking stick.

I thought especially and with some sympathy of Bill Hardcastle. If this was part of what being editor of a Fleet Street newspaper entailed, well then ... hell.

Other guests were emerging. I was introduced to Lord Rothermere's daughter, Lady Esme Cromer, wife of Lord Cromer, Governor of the Bank of England, her son Rowland with two friends from Eton, for whom were destined the stories of Africa, and her daughter, Lady Lorna Baring. We were joined later by a bluff Scottish gentleman in kilted dinner dress who had brought for the occasion a freshly caught salmon which was being prepared below in the kitchens even as we spoke. There were other guests whose names I cannot recall but who appeared to be neighbours from an adjoining estate.

The dinner was an interesting affair and the salmon was delicious, served by the liveried footmen who stood behind our chairs.

The conversation was scintillatingly social, switching from one celebrity to another, some of it bitchy. Someone referred to several times as 'Dickie Bird' turned out to be Lord Snowden, husband of Princess Margaret.

Our host informed us that he had an 'absolutely splendid' movie for our later entertainment and we later viewed it in his luxurious private cinema, where the projector was manned by Stevens the butler himself, who enjoyed operating such equipment and who good humouredly endured the cries of dismay whenever a reel had to be changed.

Lord Rothermere had me seated next to him and leaned over at one stage to whisper: 'We always have a sentimental movie when Winston (Churchill) comes to visit. He's usually better entertainment than the movie itself. Can't handle the sentimental stuff. Blubs like a baby.'

It was a pleasant weekend of gracious hospitality. Tours of the delightful Cotswolds in the Rolls Royce. Visits to pubs. Long, rambling walks on the estate set around a lovely lake. Fine dinners, excellent luncheons, sumptuous teas and enormous breakfasts.

Lord Rothermere had bought the stately home when it was in a very run-down condition and dedicated himself to its restoration. He had immersed himself in the history of Warren Hastings and it was rich in Hastings memorabilia, including paintings of India by William Hodges RA, commissioned by the former viceroy himself.

The home contained an immense wealth of art by famous artists. Showing me around, Lord Rothermere asked me what art I preferred and I was immediately on thin ice. It was a subject I liked but had never got deep into. After a desparate pause I said, 'I like the French impressionists. Do you have anything by Lautrec?'

'No,' snorted his lordship. 'He painted whores. I wouldn't have him in my house!'

He took me for a long stroll around the estate and quizzed me about the possibilities for investment in Africa. Here too I think I was a disappointment to him. 'I'd keep out of Africa,' I said.

'Even South Africa?'

Well ... I had a momentary wild fantasy about brokering a deal to get him to buy the Argus group. It would have been a chance to level some old scores.

'I'd keep out of newspapers,' I said, finally. 'Financial and trade publications would be a safer bet.'

'Thompson (Lord Thompson) has got all those,' he said glumly. We left it at that.

When we returned to the house he went upstairs and I met Lady Esme in the drawing room, reading the morning newspapers. She smiled knowingly. 'This must be hell for you,' she said.

'Not really,' I said. 'But I'm going to have a cup of tea.'

That afternoon we were ordered to swim. Literally ordered. 'We shall all swim this afternoon because swimming is good for you,' said Lord Rothermere. Footmen issued bathing wear, beach towels and we dutifully reported to the indoor swimming pool. There I was on more familiar territory and executed some dramatic dives, if somewhat lacking in style.

'Bravo!' applauded my host. 'Jolly good show!'

Some more friends came to visit that evening and after dinner Lord Rothermere, in festive mood, said, 'Let's play the book game. Get *the book*, Lorna!'

Lady Lorna, his granddaughter, raced upstairs and came back with an impressive-looking tome. It turned out to be the definitive authority on the zodiac and a ritual commenced which was clearly a favourite family game. Every person present was asked their date of birth whereupon they were looked up and their character and life prospects were read out by Lady Lorna, to much nodding, exclamations and chirrups of 'That's right!' and 'My goodness, that describes you exactly!'

I was the last to be thus researched. When I informed him what my date of birth was Lord Rothermere hooted: 'Aha! Scorpio! That's the bad one! Go on, read him out, Lorna!'

The recital began and droned on to much nodding, eyebrow-raising and expressions of 'hmmm' and 'really?' and ended in dramatic silence at the last line which said: 'People born under this star tend to suffer from diseases of the sexual organs.'

I looked up, startled. They were surveying me with expressions of mock horror.

'Good heavens,' I said, not quite knowing what else to say. And I adopted a hangdog look.

The following day proved to be Stories From Africa Day. The boys approached me and said: 'Please sir, what about the stories?' We had just had breakfast and I glanced at the formal decor around us and felt it was not the right setting.

I didn't want the grown-ups butting in either. 'Let's go to the woods,' I suggested. We bundled up because it was cold and headed for the copse beside the lake. The trees were winter-bare, the sky was dark and promising snow, and the atmosphere in the woods was appropriately spooky.

'Let Rowland go and hide wherever he wants to and I'll show you how quickly we can find him,' I said. Rowland sped off. We gave him a few minutes, then followed.

'He's behind that tree over there,' I said, pointing to a distant oak. They rushed off and flushed Rowland out. 'How did you know?' they chorused.

'You have to work it out,' I said in my gravest manner. When you hunt or when you are planning an attack of any kind, it helps to put yourself inside the head of your quarry or enemy. You try and think as he would think. So I figured that Rowland wouldn't hide under a bush because the ground is pretty damp and unpleasant. He wouldn't hide behind a bush because there's not much leaf in wintertime. Likewise he wouldn't climb a tree because the bark is slippery and there's not much foliage, meaning we might see him too easily. So I figured he'd just stand behind a tree and probably choose the one with the fattest trunk – and that's where we found him.' Behind my back I had my fingers crossed. It had largely been guesswork, but it had paid off. They were impressed, and it was a good beginning.

I told them about the Nguni tribes and how although they were found to be illiterate by our standards they had a sign language by which they could send messages to each other by drawing pictures. I sketched some of the signs they used in the sand. 'It's picture language – the same sort of principle by which the Chinese developed their own literature,' I pointed out. 'And no one ever regarded them as illiterate.'

I was thankful for a childhood involving relatives who had farmed in Namaqualand and the Swartland of South Africa. There are few storytellers like the old Afrikaners from those parts and they had given me tales that now saved this day for me. It was a successful morning.

Two other guests and I were chauffeured back to London in the Rolls Royce the following day and I dutifully surrendered the unused portion of the rail ticket to Jennifer.

I visited the editor in his office. 'How did it go?' he asked.

'Interesting,' I said. 'Did you know that Scorpios tend to suffer from diseases of the sexual organs?' He shook his head in disbelief.

'What do I do now?' I asked.

'You hotfoot it back to the Congo,' he replied. 'All hell has broken loose there again.'

I met Lord Rothermere again several years later when I was the *Daily Mail*'s bureau chief and White House correspondent in Washington DC. He paid frequent visits to the United States on which occasions I had to go to New York where he preferred to stay and brief him on inside political events and White House gossip. He particularly liked the gossip, and hooted with delight at the story that at the height of his election, Richard Nixon's spin doctors had tailors brought in to alter his suits so that the collars did not pop up around his ears when he raised his arms and wiggled his forefingers at election rallies.

He had recently remarried at the age of 66 and the new Lady Rothermere, half his age, an American lady of distinction (formerly Mrs Mary Ohrstrom, daughter of a Texan oil millionaire who divorced her husband, a Virginian businessman, to marry Rothermere) seemed to have brought him a certain happiness and relaxation that had been absent when I was his guest at Daylesford. It confirmed what many suspected, that Esmond Rothermere, a shy and reserved man, often regarded by business associates and employees as distant and aloof, was most at ease as a family man. And Lady Mary certainly rose to the occasion by presenting him with a son, Esmond junior.

During one of our meetings in New York, when we were on our way to his club there for lunch, he insisted on paying the cab fare. 'I've got loose change here I want to get rid of,' he said. As we walked away we were followed by a stream of invective from the cab driver.

'What? What?' said Lord Rothermere irritably. 'What's wrong with the fellow? What's he saying?' He was always good at pretending to be deaf when he did not wish to hear something.

I explained: 'He's upset because he feels you under-tipped him.'

'Ha! I can never understand Americans, they're always obsessed with money,' snapped Lord Rothermere, one of the richest men in Britain. We quickened our pace to get away from the disturbance.

My last meetings with the Rothermeres were in somewhat sad circumstances after I had returned to Africa as Africa correspondent at my request for family reasons. The Mail group had gone through a bad financial patch and it had been decided to merge the *Daily Mail* with its sister paper, the *Daily Sketch* under the *Daily Mail*'s title. This involved the dismissal of some 3 000 employees, most of them printing and other technical staff, but also a large number of journalists, including the entire foreign reporting staffs of both papers. The only foreign bureaus kept open were New York and Paris.

Although involved in all the pre-planning Lord Rothermere arranged to be away from England when the painful event occurred and all the flack hit the fan. He decided to spend three months in South Africa.

His visit took nearly nine months to arrange – not so much for the travel and itinerary as for the fact that he kept on changing his mind about his accommodation – which had to be on the seaside so that the nanny could take young Esmond, now two years old, to the beach.

He would telephone me and say: 'Lord Cromer says there's a nice place called the St James Hotel which he recommends.'

'When last was Lord Cromer here?'

'In 1950, I believe.'

'Well that place has gone a bit downhill since then and has a railway line in front of it. I think you should be at the Mount Nelson Hotel.'

'Is it at the seaside?'

'Not quite, but it's definitely the place for you.'

'Out of the question. We must have a place at the seaside.'

In Cape Town we went back to the drawing board. Soon he was

on the line again. 'Lady Ashcroft says there's a nice place called the Camps Bay Hotel. What about it?'

'I don't think I can recommend it, sir. Also Camps Bay is very windy. I do think the Mount Nelson Hotel is where you would like best to be ...'

'No, no. We must be at the seaside!'

Finally we hit on the President Hotel in Sea Point, but when he did arrive Lord Rothermere stayed there less than a week, irritated by the fact that the hotel used a loudspeaker system and worried that two-year-old Esmond 'might be picking up a South African accent'.

Fortunately I had kept a provisional booking open at the Mount Nelson Hotel and we moved the family there. He was delighted. 'This is an excellent hotel,' he enthused. 'I don't know why you didn't recommend it in the first place!'

In the following weeks I steered him around the diplomatic circuit and arranged courtesy meetings with the prime minister, John Vorster and other high-ranking government officials. 'Curious cove,' was his thoughtful comment after meeting Vorster.

He and Lady Rothermere embarked on the Blue Train to Johannesburg to visit friends and there we encountered a hiccup in the generally smooth flow of events. I had arranged for him to be met at Johannesburg station by Michael Keats, the UPI bureau chief who was also our stringer. Keats is an Australian who has a total disregard for rank and treats everyone with a friendly but earthy bonhomie and I realised in retrospect that I should have briefed him more carefully on protocol. Lord Rothermere's first question on his return to Cape Town was: 'Who was that dreadful man you had meet us in Johannesburg?'

I telephoned Keats for an explanation. He said: 'Well, the guy's supposed to be a multi-millionaire but he arrives here without any cash in his pockets and can't tip the porter ...'

'Christ, Mike, YOU are supposed to tip the porter!'

'Well thanks, mate, NOW you tell me. Anyway all I said was, "What's the matter, your lordship, forgotten which pocket you've got the millions in?" And he got kind of shirty. So I helped him out with some cash – which I'm putting on expenses by the way – and after that I thought we got on rather well, actually. Hullo? You there, sport?'

'Goodbye, Mike,' I said and put the phone down wearily.

It was now common knowledge in Fleet Street that the *Mail* and the *Sketch* were going to merge and in due course my official dismissal notice arrived accompanied by a truly handsome severance pay cheque. I immediately used it as a down payment on the purchase of a farm that I had coveted for a long time. It was called Kleinbosch, was the birthplace of the founding father of the Afrikaans language and its centrepiece was a delightful old Cape Dutch homestead that was a national monument. I was probably the only happy retrenched member of the *Daily Mail*'s staff, especially as I had other prospects in mind.

The fact that the Daily Mail management had retrenched me while I was hosting the proprietor was indicative of the chaos in London at the time. Lord Rothermere himself certainly didn't seem aware of it and I was careful not to raise it.

As D-day for the merger approached he became subdued and reluctant to accept social engagements, causing the British ambassador to telephone me to inquire after his health. I assured him all was well.

My wife and I had him and Lady Rothermere around for dinner more frequently and they both seemed to prefer the quieter lifestyle. Lady Mary Rothermere was a charming woman and noticeably concerned about her husband. She confided on one occasion that the events in London were heavily on his mind. One had to sympathise. It was a famous and influential newspaper group and a family dynasty that was at stake. Lord Northcliffe, his uncle and the first Viscount Rothermere, his father, had been its founders. The responsibilities now lay on his shoulders.

What we did not know at the time was that the pressures of publicity about the approaching merger and the difficulties with the unions were becoming so intense that it had been decided to pre-empt the expected merger date.

The decision was suddenly taken several days earlier at about four o'clock in the afternoon. Most of the home reporting staff on both newspapers had been kept in the dark about their prospects until, on the *Daily Mail* editorial floor, a management executive climbed onto a desk and began to hand out dismissal notices.

The scene went something like this: 'Here's one for you, John, sorry old boy. And one for you too, James, tough luck old man. No, Harry, I haven't got one for you and I suppose that means you're staying on ...'

There was pandemonium and loud expletives as enraged staff members vented their anger at being fired and the way it was being done.

Trapped in the mêlée was a group of frightened schoolgirls who had been in the process of an educational tour around the *Daily Mail* printing works and editorial floors to see how a great newspaper functioned.

Opposition Fleet Street newspapers splashed the story on their front pages the following morning. One paper headlined their report: 'NIGHT OF THE LONG KNIVES AT THE DAILY MAIL.' The satirical magazine *Private Eye* went one better by calling it 'NIGHT OF THE COMBINED HARVESTER.'

Lord and Lady Rothermere dined with my wife and me at our home in Cape Town that evening. A call came through from the *London Daily Express* requesting an interview with him. I held my hand over the mouthpiece and said: 'It's the foreign editor of the *Express*. He asks how you are and wants to speak to you. What should I say?'

Without raising his eyes from his plate Lord Rothermere replied: 'Tell him I am dining with you, that I am well and that I have nothing to say.' I relayed the message.

Two days later at a luncheon at the Mount Nelson Hotel he seemed in much better spirits. With the merger accomplished, the new *Daily Mail* launched, there was action in the air and the first step towards the great recovery that the group would make had begun.

'You will like David English, the new editor. He's a good man and you will get on with him famously,' he said.

The time had clearly come to clarify my position as delicately as possible. 'I know David English well, sir, but I won't be working with him. I have been retrenched.'

He was acutely embarrassed and for several seconds searched for words. 'Good heavens, I didn't know that. No one informed me ... I am terribly sorry. But my dear fellow, don't you worry. I shall have you reinstated immediately!'

A great panic overwhelmed me at the prospect of having to pay back the severance pay, which I had already spent. I assured him that I was happy to be unemployed, and I told him about the farm and that I wished to devote myself to farming for a while. He was visibly grateful at being relieved of the problem.

He and Lady Rothermere then asked to visit the farm. They did so a few days later, bringing with them two yellowwood saplings which they insisted on helping me plant on either side of the entrance to Kleinbosch.

Private Eye came to hear about the yellowwood saplings and reported that after the Rothermeres returned to London I kicked them to death, which was totally untrue. It is true that one became diseased some years later and died, curiously in the same year that Lord Rothermere himself died.

The other has grown into a fine stalwart tree and stands there to this day, growing taller all the time.

8

Trying to beat the system

The fears and the bad memories seem to come in the dark hours before dawn as one grows older. It's usually then that I am visited by the recollection of how Howard Lawrence died. I tell myself that what I did was well intentioned and that what resulted was not my fault, and I blame the system as it then was. But I also know it may have been the stupidest mistake of my life. It is then that the guilt seeps through the barriers I have tried to build against it.

Howard was an outstanding journalist, although when we first met I never realised it because he had a problem. It was an evil little gremlin that perched on his shoulder when he sat down at his typewriter and tried to write a story. The gremlin just wouldn't let him do it. It sniggered in his ear and created a mental block, and Howard just couldn't get the ideas in his head onto the blank sheet of copy paper in his typewriter.

He would sit for hours, chain-smoking cigarettes and just staring at that sheet of paper, sometimes writing a line, only to tear it out of the machine, screw it up into a ball and chuck it on the floor. Finally he would get up in exasperation and rush out to get a drink.

Howard's gremlin also created problems for me. I was Cape Town editor of *Drum* magazine at the time and the gremlin caused havoc at edition times, holding up Howard's stories when we needed urgent copy.

I remember assigning him to write a story about a gangster called Barney Bosman who had been shot by the police. When I called for his copy Howard was gone. Written on the sheet of paper in his typewriter was a single line. It said: 'Barney Bosman is dead. Thank God he's dead ...' I could only curse and reassign the story to someone else.

Happily Howard overcame his problem. I came into the newsroom one morning, returning from holiday, to find him pounding away at his typewriter like a man demented.

'What's happened to him?' I asked.

'Who cares?' replied my assistant editor, looking jubilant, although a trifle uneasy. 'He's writing great stuff.'

'What's that smell?' I asked. There was an embarrassed silence. Then I understood. The gremlin had been blown away by dagga (marijuana).

The penalties for being found in possession of drugs, including dagga, were horrendous in those early days of the Afrikaner nationalist regime. As a publication serving mainly a black readership we were disliked by the government and regularly raided by police. If the cops arrived, recognised the smell (as they surely would) and brought in the dogs, we would all end up in the slammer, the office would be shut down and we would be presented in court as a national disgrace. I had to tell Howard to get rid of the joints.

Fortunately, the dagga seemed to have broken the spell: Howard managed to freewheel on without it and the gremlin never came back. I have ever since read reports of the medicinal properties of marijuana, whatever its evils, with some respect.

Howard had a superb news sense and great contacts and I ended up gaining not only a wonderful friendship but also a valued colleague. Those were the early years of apartheid and South Africa was becoming a major international news story as a result of institutionalising a despised racial policy.

I had become a stringer, a part-time correspondent, for the *London Daily Mail* and, because of my connections with *Drum* magazine and the contacts made with the assistance of Howard and other black colleagues on our staff, I was dispatching stories that were getting good display in Britain.

These were not only the routine fare of racial politics and police violence. Howard introduced me to the exciting world of underground theatre and nightclubs that enriched Cape Town at that time – underground because they were attended by adventurous whites in defiance of the apartheid laws, which forbade whites and non-whites to socialise or enjoy entertainment or cultural events together. It was even illegal, at that time, for whites and blacks to drink alcohol together anywhere at any time.

The world-famous jazz pianist Dollar Brand, who later changed his name to Abdullah Ibrahim, was then a virtual unknown, playing regularly to an illegal multiracial audience in a murky nightclub in District Six in his native Cape Town. The first time I went there with Howard – who was a close friend of Dollar Brand's – a lot of people dived out of the windows.

'What's going on?' Howard asked as we ourselves began edging back outside.

The proprietor, a man called Solly, said: 'Your friend here,' pointing at me, 'is big and white and has a short haircut and everyone thinks he's a cop. You should have warned us you were bringing him.'

Howard and I drove to Worcester one hot day with a photographer called Ralph Matudi to report on an outbreak of rioting in the black township near the white town. We had a *Drum* magazine press sticker on our windscreen to reassure angry or suspicious blacks but, at the entrance to the township, encountered a truckload of white vigilantes armed with shotguns who became inflamed at the sight of the *Drum* sticker, 'arrested' us and took us to the local police station.

There we encountered a malevolent white duty sergeant seated in the charge office, stripped to the waist, his shirt and uniform jacket draped over the back of his chair, wearing a holstered pistol strapped across his hairy chest. He shouted: '*Julle kak gaan nie vanaand hier moeilikheid maak nie!*' ('You shit are not going to make trouble here tonight!')

We were jailed for the night. There was some confusion when they sought to place us in separate cells in accordance with the complicated apartheid regulations – Ralph in a cell for blacks, Howard in one for coloureds and me in one for whites. But because of the day's events all the cells were crowded with blacks. Ralph was dispossessed of his camera equipment and pushed into a cell already overcrowded with blacks while Howard, assessed as not black enough to accompany Ralph, was locked up with me in a small windowless room that appeared to be generally used for radio equipment, off-duty clothing and other police junk.

It was not a comfortable situation. We slept on the floor and were given no blankets. Fortunately, it was a warm night. We were allowed water but offered no food. Howard's cigarettes and lighter were taken away from him 'in case you burn the place down, you stupid coon'. My demands to use a telephone were refused.

Howard proved a wonderful prison companion. His infectious sense of humour and gift of anecdote dispelled all sense of discomfort and stress.

He had a thin, lanky frame that doubled up when he laughed, with the laughter usually ending in a fit of coughing because he was a heavy smoker with lungs in a permanent state of protest. He would tell a story, ending it with the laughter, which wheezed into congested coughing as he slapped his thigh. Some of his stories were outrageous but, if he sensed any disbelief, he would adopt a serious expression, his light-brown eyes suddenly hooded, and say: 'True's God man, true's God.' When he recalled a funny event he would say: 'Man, that time I really crashed myself.' That meant he had been so amused that he had broken up with laughter.

Howard crashed himself repeatedly that night as he told of past experiences, a cheeky childhood in Cape Town's sleazy but colourful District Six, run-ins with the police and extraordinary story assignments for *Drum* magazine – like when he dressed in silken Arab robes and headdress to breach the racial barrier at a posh whites-only Cape Town hotel by presenting himself as a Saudi prince: 'Man, they were in such a state. They didn't like my colour but they didn't want to risk a diplomatic incident either. Finally they let me in and the manager showed me up to a suite, bowing and scraping like a lackey. Just for fun, I tipped him one rand. He must have thought Saudi princes were the meanest bastards in the world. After he left I just sat down and crashed myself. Man, did I crash myself. True's God!'

Throughout the night we swapped stories and we were both crashing ourselves – so loudly that a cop came and hammered on the door and shouted: 'If you two don't shut up I'll throw you in with the Kaffirs!'

They released us the following morning with dire threats and foul epithets, giving Ralph his cameras back only after stripping the film out of them. We drove back to Cape Town still crashing ourselves.

When the Sharpeville massacre happened Fleet Street invaded South Africa, sending in top foreign correspondents with well-known names. In the weeks that followed I scooped them frequently, not through any special talent but because *Drum's* black reporters were always on the inside track of events, knowing what was going to happen before anyone else did, and they kept me well informed.

On the day I achieved not only the front-page splash and led the foreign page as well as the main feature page with three separate dispatches, the *Daily Mail* asked me to join their staff as a foreign correspondent to cover Africa and the Middle East. I accepted and departed for Nairobi, which was to be my base for the next several years.

It was sad parting from my friends on *Drum* magazine and in the final week I had a memorable night out on the town with Howard and the boys, ending in Solly's Jazz Club with Dollar Brand hitting the ivories at his best. Man, did we crash ourselves. True's God.

I did not return to live in Cape Town until 12 years later. Howard Lawrence was still there. But not quite the same old Howard. He'd had some bad times. The security police had pulled him in for interrogation under the iniquitous 90-day Detention Act, which meant solitary confinement and forbade access to family, legal counsel and the law courts. They had tortured him. His hands still bore the scars where they had burned him with lighted cigarette ends.

He was still lanky but a little paunchy. There were some grey streaks in the curly black hair and the mouth under the wispy moustache drooped a little to one side, giving him a slightly cynical look. I learned later that they had beaten him senseless on one occasion in prison and he had suffered a mild stroke. The eyes were a little harder but could still crinkle in fun and after a drink or two the old Howard would emerge – and he could still crash himself, rocking back and forth in laughter that always degenerated into a wheezing, hacking cough. He still smoked too damned much.

On the happier side, he had married and had a delightful family. They lived in Noordhoek, from where Howard trundled into the city most days in a beat-up old car.

He was freelancing, but was a bit down on his luck. For me it was a pleasure to give him a desk in my office. I was now working for *Newsweek* as well as fulfilling a new contractual arrangement with the *Daily Mail*, and Howard provided valuable assistance.

As in the old days, he accompanied me on some assignments, and in many long conversations I was distressed although not surprised to discover the extent to which the burden of apartheid, along with the torture and the beatings he had suffered in prison, had worn down his spirit.

'You know,' he said, one day, puffing on the inevitable cigarette, 'in the beginning it was a kind of joke. They were so ridiculous, the way they applied their stupid laws, that all you could do was crash yourself. But after a while it wasn't so funny. For me the arrests and the prison were bad. I am ashamed to say they broke me.' He did not enlarge on that, but he was silent for more than a minute as he seemed to wait for a surge of bad memories to pass.

Then he took another draw on his cigarette and said: 'But you know when I was hurt most? It was actually after I was released from prison and I was driving my children past a park where a lot of white kids were playing – on swings and see-saws and so forth – and having a good time. We could hear their laughter. My own kids got excited and said: 'Daddy can't we go and play there? Please Daddy please!' I had to tell them that they could not play there because it was a play park for white children only. That was how they found out, for the first time, about the sort of life they were going to have in their country. I can still remember the incomprehension on their faces, and I can remember the pain and the anger I felt, and the guilt – guilt that I had brought them into a country like this. Guilt that I had not been able to take them to another country where such things did not happen.'

It was not long after this discussion that Howard came into our office while I was working at speed, trying to meet a deadline. I said hello and went on typing.

He sat down in the chair on the other side of my desk without saying anything, so I looked up – and then took another look. He had gone a funny, pasty colour.

'What's the matter, Howard? Are you alright?'

He shook his head, as if puzzled. 'I feel as though I want to puke, yet I don't want to puke. It's sitting right here.' He placed his hand on his chest.

'Indigestion?' I suggested. 'Hangover? Too much curry?' Everyone knew his love of spicy foods.

He shook his head, got up abruptly and left the room. I assumed he had reached the point of no return and was hurrying to the nearest toilet to throw up. I went back to my typing.

Five minutes later he was back and sat down opposite me again. I looked up and this time I was startled. He looked terrible and he was sweating profusely. 'I've got a helluva pain in my chest,' he said. Suddenly it dawned on me that he could be having a heart attack.

'Stay here,' I said, and rushed out of my office into the next-door office, where John Stewart, Cape editor of the *Financial Mail* was working. I said: 'John, I think Howard is having a heart attack. I'm going to get my car. Get him downstairs and I'll meet you at the main door.'

I was at the front door of the building within four minutes. John assisted Howard into the car and sat with him on the back seat.

This was happening at a bad time. The late-afternoon rush hour had begun and we used up 30 valuable seconds discussing the options. Groote Schuur hospital, world-famous for its advanced cardiac unit, was the best choice, but was situated on De Waal Drive, where traffic congestion would be building up. Somerset Hospital was much closer and the traffic on that route would be less dense. We decided to go there.

I drove at high speed, weaving in and out of the traffic, with my hand on the hooter and my flashers on.

'He's getting worse,' John reported from the back seat. 'I think he needs oxygen or something.' So I went faster and raced through red lights at intersections, causing a lot of swerving and bad-tempered reaction from other motorists.

We raced into the Somerset Hospital grounds and it was there that I made my mistake. We were confronted by the inevitable signs and arrows that said 'CASUALTY WARD FOR WHITES' and 'CASUALTY WARD FOR NON-WHITES'.

I decided on the spur of the moment that apartheid was not going to get Howard this time. In hospitals, as elsewhere, the separate facilities for whites were usually better than the facilities for non-whites. Right now I wanted Howard to get the best possible medical attention, so I drove to the casualty ward for whites.

We assisted Howard out of the car and up the steps into the reception area. 'My friend is having a heart attack or something,' I said. 'Can we please have a doctor immediately?'

As inevitable as the apartheid signs was the man behind the desk – that certain type of civil servant trained to enforce the regulations relentlessly. 'This man is coloured,' he said. 'You must take him to the non-white casualty ward.'

Something seemed to snap in my head. I leaned forward, seized him by the lapels and dragged him towards me so that our faces were inches apart and he was lying on his belly on top of the reception desk. 'Are you mad?' I said. 'This is an emergency. This man may be dying, and he needs a doctor!'

I felt John's hand on my shoulder, restraining me. The receptionist had put his hands against my chest, trying to fend me off. I felt his jacket tearing.

Then I felt someone hanging onto my other shoulder. It was a woman in a white coat with a stethoscope around her neck. 'Bring him in here,' she said.

I dropped the receptionist and we took Howard into the casualty ward, where attendants lifted him onto a trolley. 'Now get out,' snapped the lady doctor as she went to work on him. We went outside. As I looked back I saw them place a mask over Howard's face and begin hooking him up to a machine.

I was calmer, but the man behind the reception desk was not. I heard the words 'assault' and 'police' mentioned as he spoke urgently, in Afrikaans, into a telephone. I avoided his glare and walked away, leaving John to deal with him.

The hospital's loudspeaker system came alive and said: 'Dr

Pienaar to casualty, please.' A senior-looking man, dangling a stethoscope, arrived, walking swiftly, and hurried into the casualty ward. Minutes later the loudspeaker blared again: 'Dr Webster to casualty!' Another doctor arrived and, as the door opened briefly, we saw him join the group around Howard.

About 15 minutes passed. There was a very long, poorly lit corridor at Somerset Hospital linking the white and non-white divisions and we were actually standing in this thoroughfare, pacing up and down anxiously. I happened to be facing down it when I saw the double doors at the distant end open and four coloured nurses emerge, running fast and pushing along between them a machine on rubber wheels. They passed us at an urgent pace and took it into the ward where Howard was.

The indications were that further urgently needed equipment had been called for to help Howard and we began to realise that things were really looking bad.

Twenty minutes later, the lady doctor emerged, avoided our inquiring stares and walked away. A minute later the senior-looking doctor came out and walked over to us. 'I'm sorry, we lost him,' he said. 'A massive cardiac arrest. There wasn't much we could do.'

After a few more words of commiseration he turned to walk away, and then turned back towards us. 'By the way, why was he brought here? It would have been better if he had been taken to the non-white ward. Our resuscitator broke down and we had to send for theirs.'

I suppose I looked stricken because he added kindly: 'Not that I think it would have made much difference.'

My God. What had I done? How much difference was 'not much difference'?

John and I walked silently out of the hospital, in grief over the loss of our friend and myself further devastated by the realisation that I had possibly contributed to his death.

We drove to Noordhoek to break the news to his family. Margie and the three young children greeted us cheerfully, looking behind us as we walked in to see if Howard was following because sometimes, when his old jalopy broke down, we did bring him home.

Then Margie read our faces and said: 'What's wrong? For God's sake, what's happened?' We stood there, tongue-tied, unable to cope with the awfulness of what we had to tell her.

Then she understood and her chin lifted almost imperceptibly as she gathered her courage. 'He's dead, isn't he?' We could only nod, and she turned abruptly and went into an adjoining room to grapple with this thing, away from the children.

The children stared at us wide-eyed. Tania, the eldest, flung herself into my arms and wept uncontrollably. I broke down and wept too. We all wept.

The small Catholic church at nearby Kommetjie was filled to overflowing at Howard's funeral. Most of Cape Town's journalistic fraternity was there, including editors and proprietors, as well as diplomats and even members of the government. The bewildered priest began the service by saying: 'Howard Lawrence never came to church. But today the church is not big enough to accommodate those who have come to pay tribute to him. This is the only indication I have ever had of what sort of a man he was.'

The memories of Howard slip into my mind every now and again, and along with them comes the guilt.

I try to blame apartheid, and of course the system was indeed at the root of it all. Those were the times when drivers of ambulances reserved exclusively for the use of whites would, if called to a road accident, refuse to transport the injured to hospital if they were found to be non-white – the official term for blacks, coloureds (mulattos), Asians, Chinese and Japanese. Many seriously injured people died as a result of this demented and unforgivable racial discrimination. And it was common knowledge, too, that in the overworked casualty wards of the general hospitals life was at a lower premium in the non-white wards than in the white wards.

So I have tried to find comfort in telling myself that my action was not only well intentioned but justified. But the other side of the coin is that dedicated medical staff, including white doctors, also worked in the non-white wards and Somerset Hospital had a high reputation. And nothing can alter the fact that the only functioning life-support equipment available at the time was where, according to the law, I should have taken Howard.

I sometimes wonder what Howard would have thought of all this. He would probably have crashed himself. I can't. True's God.

9

The oasis

When Wouter Steyn took his newly wed wife, Marietjie, home to the family farm in the Great Karoo, the east wind was blowing. They had been travelling for six hours since leaving Beaufort West at 8 a.m.

They had headed west and the last dorp of any consequence they had seen had been Fraserburg. They had crossed the Riet River, almost not noticing it because it had run dry. There had been a hamlet called Bonekraal. Since then they had seen no more human life. They had not seen another vehicle for the past hour.

The land was flat and semi-desert, to give it a polite description. The sun was merciless. Occasionally a mirage would focus and become a group of semi-withered bluegums, always leaning towards the west, as if pointing the way for the east wind. Twice a homestead had appeared in the distance yet near enough to see that it was derelict and abandoned.

The powerful Mercedes 600 droned on steadily, its wake of dust hanging only an instant above the rutted dirt road before being snatched away by the east wind. Wouter drove fast to ensure smoother passage. That way the car skimmed over the ruts, so that their shuddering effect became a mere tremble.

'Where are we now?' Marietjie asked brightly. Her cheeks were rosy with love and the newness of the adventure of marriage.

'Steynskraal,' replied Wouter. 'This is our land.'

She laughed. 'You said that nearly an hour ago!'

'Yes, but it's true. We have been driving on our land for the past hour.'

'Where does your land end?'

He pointed ahead to the faint blue of peaks. 'Those mountains. They are called the Bastersberge – Mountains of the Bastards.'

'Your land goes right to those mountains? Gosh, Wouter, how absolutely *feudal*!'

'To the other side of them, actually. The mountains are on our land.'

'Wow!' Then she was silent, trying to absorb the size of a ranch that seemed the size of a country.

They drove on in silence for a while. Another derelict farmstead hove into view.

'Why are all these farmhouses abandoned?'

Wouter explained: 'When the bottom fell out of the wool market some years back many of the sheep farmers in the Great Karoo and the Little Karoo went bankrupt. So my father bought most of the farms in our neighbourhood. They now form part of our land.'

'Gosh, did he need more land?'

'I suppose not. But he said they were going too cheaply to ignore. Anyhow, in these dry times we move our herds onto them. We need all the grazing we can get.'

They rounded a low swell of terrain that was almost, but not quite, a hill. A mirage ahead focused into a grove of bluegum trees surrounding a beautiful and elegant homestead built in the Cape Dutch style, against a background of what seemed to be a small village of outbuildings and corrals.

'We're home,' said Wouter. 'Welcome to Steynskraal.'

That arrival had been 14 months previously. The joy of marriage no longer shone in Marietjie's eyes. The bloom had left her cheeks. She had lost weight. There was a listlessness about her and a reluctance to get out of bed in the mornings.

She had never been of large build. Somewhere between petite and of medium height, she had always been slim, but with a well-rounded, pretty figure. There had been a freshness about her fair-haired, blue-eyed beauty. She had a skin that responded delight-fully to the sun with a light tan but needed protection from too much heat and wind. Marietjie's beauty was of the sort that would be at its best with a wide-brimmed straw hat bearing a ribbon of blue and with a basket of newly picked roses on her arm as she strolled through an English garden.

But there was no rose garden at Steynskraal and the freshness had gone. Marietjie had become thin. She was sick.

Wouter drove her to a doctor in Fraserburg who diagnosed low blood pressure and prescribed medication. To cheer her up Wouter bought her a horse, a lovely chestnut mare called Tina, and this worked well. She now rose early and eagerly each morning and would find Tina saddled and bridled, waiting for her, held by Koos, the stable-hand appointed to the horse, who would gravely hand her the reins. She rode far out into the Karoo until the sun drove off the morning chill and its heat turned her back to the homestead.

The early morning rides were the high point of her day. She was delighted with the mare and its affectionate nature, and the way it whinnied with pleasure at the sight of her and nuzzled her. She liked animals. There was only one dog at Steynskraal – an elderly Rhodesian ridgeback called Hansie. Wouter explained that only one dog at a time could be tolerated. 'Otherwise they pack and attack the livestock.' There were other horses, but they were rough-and-ready bush ponies used for cattle and sheep-herding and each one responded only to its regular rider.

She was irritated by the fact that she could not have the total privacy she wanted on the morning rides. Two mounted farm hands always followed her, albeit at a distance.

When she asked Wouter about this he said: 'Oh yes, Krisjan arranged that. I have to ask you to accept that, Marietjie. It's for your own safety.'

'But it's not dangerous here, is it? All I ever see are sheep and cattle.'

'It's tricky country. You could get lost and we might have difficulty finding you.'

'Tina would find our way home.'

'I can't rely on a horse in this matter,' he replied curtly. 'You could get lost or you could have an accident. Please leave it the way Krisjan has arranged.'

So it was Krisjan who had arranged it, she thought. She had wondered at times about Krisjan, the quiet, almost taciturn farm manager at Steynskraal. He always greeted her politely, touching the brim of his weathered old felt hat, but avoided conversation unless absolutely necessary. He would reply, respectfully, to her direct questions, but offer no information other than that. And he would excuse himself and withdraw at the first opportunity.

'He's shy,' explained Wouter. 'He means no offence.'

Marietjie had been astonished at the scene on arrival at Steyns-kraal. Wouter and Krisjan had hugged each other joyfully, like brothers long parted. Krisjan had wept, and Wouter had gently patted him on the shoulder, and had then hugged him again. She had been astonished because Krisjan was a coloured man and it was a time in South Africa when such contact between a white man and a coloured man was rarely seen.

It was evident that it was Krisjan who ran the vast Steynskraal estate and attended meticulously to the daily details of its affairs. Sometimes he was absent for long periods, supervising work with the herds in the veld. At other times he worked closer to the homestead, coming and going in a work-worn Landrover pick-up, or trudging back and forth between the corrals and the shearing sheds, directing the branding and dipping operations. Or conferring with the mechanics in the vehicle shed. He was a short, thickset but powerfully built man who walked with an odd rolling motion, due (she later heard) to a shortened leg, the result of a long-past accident. He usually wore a work-stained khaki shirt and shorts, and veldskoens without socks. He was darkly bearded and his slate-grey eyes, sinister against the dark olive of his skin, were narrowed from a lifetime of scanning the horizons of the Great Karoo under the African sun.

Krisjan also spent long hours conferring with Wouter in the large, cool study, fascinating with its smell of ancient tobacco, the glass-fronted gun cases, the heavily framed paintings and old family photographs, the worn leather furniture, the large desk and the heavy square yellowwood conference table scattered haphazardly with Wouter's untidy mess of papers. They would sit and smoke while they talked – Wouter a cigar and Krisjan a pipe – or they would stand before the floor-to-ceiling wall map of the Steynskraal grazing lands and plan the movement of the herds.

In Marietjie's stressed state she resented Wouter's long hours spent with Krisjan. In the first few months following her arrival, she had accompanied Wouter on visits to various cattle outposts

148

in the semi-desert of the vast Steynskraal estate. Sometimes they would stay in one of the abandoned farmsteads where one or two rooms were always kept suitable for accommodation. At other times they would camp. The vehicles would be loosely formed into a laager and tents pitched within the circle. Food would be *braaied* over open fires. The searing heat of the day ended almost abruptly with the setting of the sun and was replaced by the cool of the desert, which swiftly became cold as the east wind's hot day breath became bitingly frosty at night.

Marietjie liked these safaris, especially the evenings when the grim rough work of rounding up livestock was replaced by relaxation and the laughter and chatter of the men. She was awestruck by the fact that each day began with a sunrise that was vivid – almost startling in the way it lit up the veld – and ended with a sunset even more dramatic in its colours.

She stood watching one such sunset when a voice behind her said: *'Regtig die hand van die Here.'* ('Truly the hand of God.') She turned and found Krisjan standing close behind her, his eyes fixed on the sunset. Before she could reply he turned and walked away, leaving her unsure of whether he had spoken to her or himself.

She found other aspects of the trips into the vastness of the Steynskraal lands less attractive. The heat, the dust, the distances, the flatness of the Karoo veld touched her with the melancholy of its emptiness. The monotony was broken at intervals by the tall, stark structure of a clanking windmill water pump, its blades whipped by the east wind as it sucked up precious water from deep down in the dry earth and deposited it, in meagre spurts, into a cement reservoir at its side, which, in turn, fed the low drinking troughs for the cattle. Usually there was a single shack nearby, built of stone, brick or corrugated iron, Spartan in its provision only of shelter and little else for the attendant herder. Close by would be a *boma*, a circular construction of thorn bush, for the protection of his horse at night, for the occasional lion still roamed the district and leopards sometimes visited from the Bastersberge.

These single-manned water points were the cattle stations and the visit to each one entailed getting the herder's report and inspection of the water supply, as well as the count of the livestock, which never roamed far from the water. Again it was Krisjan who directed operations, while Wouter merely watched. Sometimes Krisjan would refer something to him, but it seemed only a matter of formality because Wouter usually nodded and said little.

After a while Marietjie lost interest in the field trips and stayed home. There, too, was a monotony. The old manor house, bearing the date 1881 on its gable, was beautiful. It was kept in immaculate condition and whitewashed on a two-yearly cycle. Nothing grew around it except the grove of tall bluegums within which it stood. In a stark way, it enhanced the clean beauty of its fine proportions.

And, as Wouter once remarked, it was at its best in moonlight. A full moon, it was said, bathed the Great Karoo in a light so mysterious and gave the night such clarity that at such times there was no place in Africa – maybe nowhere else in the world – to compare with it, and artists came from afar in attempts to capture this special quality on canvas. At such times, especially in winter and if the night was windless, Steynskraal, the old homestead and the outbuildings surrounding it, became magical. The bluegums were tall, stark sentinels against the pale night sky, their leaves touched with silver. The walls of the great house were bone-white in the moonlight, the doors and shutters etched in deepest black, touched here and there by the soft orange glow of a lamp behind a window. And the lunar-lit frost on the ground was like a billion pinpricks of light, presenting Steynskraal as a fairyland on a jewelled carpet.

The interior of the homestead was impressive. The entrance hall was paved with huge Batavian floor tiles, sent as ballast in wooden ships from the Far East to the Cape and hauled from there to Steynskraal by wagon in the last century. Two great copper-bound chests of ancient oak stood in the hallway and splendid armoires and four-poster beds of Burmese teak, Cape yellowwood and stinkwood were in the bedrooms. Fine old wall cabinets and corner cabinets, their immaculately tooled wood inlaid with mother-of-pearl, adorned the reception rooms, which were lit by great brass chandeliers. Persian carpets and rugs, worn but still warm in their colours, covered some areas of the old wide-planked yellowwood floors. The kitchen, with its stone-tiled floor, huge range and old copperware, contained items of furniture that Wouter's great-grandfather, Andries Wouter Steyn, had brought with him on his wagons when he had arrived as the founder of Steynskraal in the 1860s. It also contained furniture and other items that had been made and forged on the farm at that time and since then.

Later, when the cattle herds expanded and the demand for meat grew urgent during the Anglo-Boer War, and when railways were extended to the railheads at Bonekraal and Steynskraal, Barend and Anna Steyn – Wouter's grandparents, clearly people of some taste – had brought in the finer pieces of furniture by rail.

In terms of valuable antique furniture and art, the house was a veritable museum. The paintings on the walls included some by Pierneef and Naudé and other important South African artists. Marietjie, while admiring a particularly outstanding work by Pierneef soon after her arrival, suddenly realised that it was a painting of the Steynskraal homestead.

'He visited here several times,' Wouter said. 'He and my grandfather were close friends. That painting was a gift for my grandfather on his fiftieth birthday.'

It was not long before Marietjie came to realise that Steynskraal was not what she had expected her home with Wouter to be. It was the subject of their first row. 'I don't feel like the mistress of this place,' she complained tearfully. 'I feel more like the custodian of a museum.' There was an element of truth in her outburst. There was no question of moving anything. Every item of magnificent furniture seemed rooted to its spot by tradition.

Even the running of the home eluded her. Lena, the cook, ruled in the vast kitchen like a queen of her domain, and a crusty old biddy called Gertruida led a housekeeping team who kept the place spotless. They were all friendly and courteous – but there seemed a conspiracy to allow Marietjie no part in the running of the home. It seemed neither a hostile nor a sinister conspiracy. Rather, it seemed a design of kindness, as though they were anxious for her not to be inconvenienced. It was a well-intentioned impasse that she had not yet been able to penetrate. She felt, nervously, that if she attempted to break through it too brusquely, some delicately balanced inner wheel of the system would be thrown out of gear.

One morning, she found Krisjan in the house. He was standing in the *voorkamer*, staring thoughtfully at a stain on the carpet. When he saw her he greeted her respectfully. 'Gertruida asked me to look at this and see if I had anything that could fix it,' he said.

'That's a red-wine stain and I spilt it!' she said angrily. 'Just leave it alone and I will attend to it!'

Krisjan almost reeled at the intensity of the anger in her voice, as if his face had been slapped. Muttering an apology he left the room hastily.

Marietjie stormed through to the kitchen and confronted Gertruida in front of the other staff. 'The next time you have a problem in this house you tell *me*! You don't call in the farm manager! Do you understand?' The housekeeper shrank back in fright. '*Ja* madam,' she said. The others watched open-mouthed. Marietjie walked out, trembling with rage.

In a colourful account of the incident later, Lena the cook said: 'Her eyes flashed and she shook like a leaf. She's not as quiet as she looks. She can be wild, that one.'

Marietjie knew she had overdone it. But when she told Wouter about it he merely laughed. 'It's not important,' he said. 'Anyhow, you should have left it to Krisjan. He attends to everything.'

She was silent. Why didn't he understand? Suddenly she felt isolated, as if she was alone on an island and her last communication with the outside world had faded. If Wouter didn't understand, whom could she turn to with these strange feelings of confusion and loneliness building up in her?

Wouter's sister Karina came to visit, and it helped. Karina, tall, dark-haired and attractive, had a wit that could lighten any situation, no matter how doleful. It did not take her long to sense that Marietjie was in trouble.

The morning after her arrival she strode up and down the *voorkamer*, long-legged in weathered jeans, smoking a cigarette. 'That lummox of a brother of mine,' she said. 'I told him not to keep you here for long periods. Steynskraal has its points, but it is, after all, in a bloody desert and you need to get away for breaks.'

'He can't leave here now. It's the annual stock count,' said Marietjie.

'Bullshit!' hooted Karina in her forthright manner. 'This place ticks along whether he's here or not. Krisjan attends to everything.'

'Krisjan,' said Marietjie wearily. 'It's always Krisjan. I'm not sure I like the man. He seems to take up so much of Wouter's time.'

Karina drew on her cigarette and studied Marietjie thoughtfully through the smoke. She had stopped pacing and had flung herself into an armchair, one long leg looped over its side.

'Don't knock Krisjan, sweetie. He's a gem of a man. Painfully shy, but terribly loyal. He'd lay his life down for Wouter – which means he'd do the same for you.'

Marietjie remembered: 'They hugged each other like brothers the day we arrived.'

Karina nodded. 'As kids we all grew up together. We played together, ate together. Krisjan sat at the table with us. It didn't matter that he was a Baster. My parents adored him. Wouter had no brother. There was only me – the evil sister. Krisjan became his brother. My father taught them both how to run Steynskraal. I think Krisjan was the better student. When my parents died in that awful car crash and Wouter was at university, Krisjan took over and things here didn't miss a beat. So take it from me, Wouter can take you away for a spell and nothing here would suffer.'

Marietjie was silent. She thought of her own childhood in Stellenbosch. An unhappy childhood with a father whom she loved and a stepmother who disliked her. When her father, a manager on a leading wine estate, had died after a short illness, she had inherited enough money to take her through Stellenbosch University where she had met Wouter. She had fallen totally in love with this tall, rangy engineering student with his quiet manner and shy smile. She had not known so much happiness could exist. Where had it gone? Would her life now always be with a preoccupied husband in a desert? Suddenly she missed, desperately, the great spreading oaks and the green vineyards of Stellenbosch. The green, the green. God, how she missed the green. Her eyes filled with tears. She came back to the present with a shock. Karina's hazel eyes were still fixed on her with growing concern.

'A baby would help? No sign yet?'

Marietjie shook her head.

'Steynskraal needs children. When we were kids we rode and we hunted and we rounded up cattle and we partied with the kids on other farms and they came and partied with us. You'll see, when you have children it will all come right. Meantime I'll tell that idiot brother of mine to take you on a holiday!' Karina got up and stubbed out her cigarette in an ashtray. 'Where the hell is he?'

Karina had her discussion with Wouter and it seemed to go vigorously. Marietjie heard them shouting at each other in the study. Karina emerged, rolling her eyes heavenwards. 'He says sure, but he has to finish the stock count. So I told him he'd better bloody well hurry it up! Anyway, honey, I've got to fly – literally. Have to make Groenfontein before dark. Don't have a night-instrument licence yet. Will you drive me to the landing strip? He's sulking now. Bloody men!'

Before she clambered into the Cessna she said: 'You could come with me, you know. But our farm's also in pretty much of a desert. I think what you need is something different. Right?'

Marietjie smiled and nodded.

'Yep. Well, hang in there honey – and have a kid!' She boarded her aircraft, taxied to the end of the strip and roared past on take-off, a hand raised in farewell.

Marietjie waved back and watched the plane until it vanished from sight. Have a kid. Ride horses. Hunt. Round up cattle. Have parties. She sighed. She hadn't even bothered to remind Karina that the farms around Steynskraal were deserted. There were no longer neighbours and kids near Steynskraal to party with.

The day after Karina's departure, the east wind began to blow remorselessly, as it sometimes did. During the night that followed it sighed and whispered through the tall bluegum trees that surrounded the homestead. The isolation of Steynskraal seemed to close in, as if the wind drew it around the house like a shroud.

Wouter rose silently in the early dawn hours to drive to Fraser-burg to attend a cattle show. He took care not to wake Marietjie and she took care not to let him know that she was awake.

She remained in bed until late morning, refusing Lena's offers of breakfast. The groom brought the saddled mare to the front door as usual but, after waiting an hour or more, walked it back to the stable.

When Marietjie did rise, she neither showered nor washed, but went to sit on the stoep, wearing only a dressing gown over her nightdress. The midday sun shone but without effect because the Karoo winter had set in and the east wind was cold. Marietjie seemed not to notice.

The house staff, curious and concerned, kept watch over her from the windows but did not know what to do. So they sent for Krisjan.

When he arrived she had risen and was standing at the edge of the stoep, her eyes fixed on the vast expanse of the dry winter veld. Krisjan removed his hat and went to stand beside her. '*Mevrou*, are you all right?' he asked respectfully.

Without looking at him she said: 'The rose gardens will still be blooming in Stellenbosch. The roses bloom late in the Boland, you know. Even when the autumn leaves fall and the first rains begin.' She touched her cheek and it seemed as though she had wiped away a tear. A long silence followed.

Krisjan shifted awkwardly. 'We used to have roses here ... when we had more water,' he said. 'Over there.' He pointed to an area below the stoep.

'Many of the big old oaks will still have their leaves,' said Marietjie. 'The vineyards will be changing colour. The leaves of some will have turned golden by now. Others will have turned red. The Cabernet Sauvignon in the Cape – their leaves turn red in the autumn. The wine farmers will have sown the cover crops – the rye – between the rows by now. It will be coming up and ... and it will be green. Green ...'

Krisjan held out his hand. '*Mevrou* ...'

She turned towards him. Tears were streaming down her face. With a sob she laid her head on his chest. His arms closed about her and she felt him tremble.

There was a clanking sound as a farm hand drawing water from a tap some distance away dropped his bucket and stood gaping in astonishment at the sight of a white woman in the arms of a coloured man. Krisjan turned his head to look at the man and sighed. There would be talk about this.

He called Lena and she and Gertruida came to help him take Marietjie inside where the two women put her to bed.

Wouter returned late that night and two days later drove her to Fraserburg where the elderly physician referred her to a colleague in Beaufort West who, in turn, referred her to a psychiatrist in Cape Town who hospitalised her.

'It's a bad case of cabin blues,' he told Wouter.

'Cabin WHAT?'

'Cabin blues. That's what the Americans call it. Loneliness from living in a remote place, like a cabin in the Rocky Mountains of Colorado or the Appalachians in Kentucky. In this case it's a matter of the Karoo blues.'

'But I'm there – and there are lots of other people around her.'

The psychiatrist shrugged. 'Sometimes it's more complicated than that. It becomes a matter of circumstances, environment. She speaks at great length about a need of green fields and flowers. Forgive me for asking, but is your terrain very forbidding?'

'No,' said Wouter, irritably. 'It may be different, but it's very beautiful.'

'Well, it will be necessary to convince her of that.'

'And how long will that take?'

'It may take a long time. She certainly should not return there now.'

Wouter wrote to Krisjan two weeks later. 'It seems this will take many months to come right. I am taking her to a clinic in Switzerland. I am sorry, old friend. I can only ask that you help us in this matter. Please take care of everything. You have done it before and I know you can do it again.'

Krisjan read the letter sitting in front of the fireplace of the modest cottage on the estate where he lived alone. He read it a second time and then sat staring into the fire.

It was close to midnight when he walked across to the deserted manor house in the cold moonlight, his feet crunching on the frost that was already forming on the ground. He let himself in by the kitchen door and walked through to the study where he switched on the overhead and table lights and swivelled the desk lamp to light up the wall map of the Steynskraal lands to maximum clarity. For more than an hour he studied the map, almost motionless in his concentration. Then, abruptly, he switched off the lights and returned to his cottage.

The next morning he briefed Konrad, the head herder, on the requirements of the day and said: 'I will be away until tonight. Look after everything well.'

He went to his cottage, packed sandwiches and a thermos flask of coffee and placed them in his Landrover, along with a map. Then he drove into the veld. He headed for the Bastersberge.

The rough road became a rougher, little-used trail that pounded his vehicle severely. Krisjan kept a steady speed. When he reached the foothills the trail disappeared into shale with no recognisable track, and the Landrover began to slew. Krisjan stopped, adjusted the front-wheel slots and proceeded in four-wheel drive. The faint trail reappeared and it began to climb. The air became cooler and patches of green vegetation, not seen on the Karoo lower veld, began to appear.

Rounding a sharp bend, Krisjan suddenly came upon a small valley that contained trees, green pastures on which cattle and sheep grazed, and a collection of small, simple, whitewashed cottages. He drove past the first three cottages and stopped outside the fourth. A man, similar to Krisjan in build and of about the same age, came out and they shook hands. '*Langtyd, Broeder,*' ('Long time, Brother,') said the man. He pronounced the word not as *broer* in Afrikaans, but in the original Dutch language, elements of which still lingered in the speech of the Basters.

'*Langtyd,*' replied Krisjan. He slapped his brother, Konrad, on the shoulder and they went inside where he was greeted effusively by his sister-in-law, Anna. The men drank coffee and smoked. They had maintained their family ties and friendship even though their parents had quarrelled with the Steyn family many years previously and moved back to the Bastersberge. Krisjan, then aged 16, had elected to remain at Steynskraal, his attachment to Wouter being the reason.

'What brings you?' asked Konrad.

'I want to see the secret,' said Krisjan.

Konrad studied Krisjan carefully as he lit his pipe. 'Why?' he asked.

'I'll tell you when we get there.'

Konrad continued to study his brother, his eyes slitted against the smoke of his pipe. Then he rose to his feet. 'All right, come,' he said.

They walked out to the Landrover and Konrad climbed into the passenger seat. Krisjan turned the vehicle and drove back the way he had come for several kilometres until they reached a narrow turn-off between two tall rock-faces. The Landrover needed all its four-wheel drive traction as it whined and pitched up a defile. They came to a clearing where the vehicle could go no further. There was rock-face all about them.

Krisjan took a flashlight from the dashboard compartment. They climbed out of the Landrover and walked to where part of the rock-face was obscured by bushes.

'You remember when Pa first brought us here,' said Konrad. Krisjan nodded. Holding branches aside as they climbed, they forced their way up into a narrow crevice that became a cave. As the light faded and the gloom deepened, Krisjan switched on the flashlight.

He could hear the running of the water. He could smell the water. Within a minute they came to it, an underground stream that cascaded vigorously from a shelf on one side of the cave and disappeared into a crevice on the other. They knelt beside the water.

'It's running as strongly as ever,' said Konrad. 'Even after three years of drought.'

Krisjan scooped up a palmful and tasted it. 'Pure and sweet,' he said, as always in wonderment. 'Not like our *brak* water on the veld.'

Konrad looked at him, quickly and suspiciously. 'Why did you want to see it?'

'I need this water at Steynskraal.'

Konrad stood up swiftly. 'This is Baster water – not Steynskraal water!'

Krisjan sighed. 'You sound like Pa used to sound. Listen man, this is Steynskraal land. The whole Bastersberge belong to Steynskraal. It follows therefore that this water belongs to Steynskraal. I don't have to bring you title deeds to prove it. You know what I am saying is true.'

'Pa always said it was our water. No Steyn ever knew of it – not even Wouter knows it exists. It's our secret!' Konrad was growing angry.

'You cannot deny legal ownership,' said Krisjan. 'Anyhow, you don't use it. You have enough water in the valley. You have never used this water. You don't even know where it comes from or where it runs to. Down on the plain we now need it.'

Konrad turned and made his way out of the cave. Krisjan followed him. They stood beside the Landrover, scowling at each other. Both of them had the slate-grey eyes of the Basters of the Bastersberge, but no brotherhood showed in their eyes now. All that showed was the cold, grey slate.

'Only a fool gives up water, whether he is using it or not,' said Konrad, and there was a finality in his tone. So Krisjan played his last card.

'Do you remember when I saved you from the stallion and he trampled me instead, smashing my hip?' he said brutally.

Konrad said nothing, merely watching him.

Krisjan said: 'Later in the hospital you said that I had saved your life and you hoped that one day, somehow, you could make this up to me. Do you remember?'

Konrad said nothing.

'Well,' said Krisjan. 'You were very young ... anyhow, I am now calling in the debt because I need this water, and rather than calling in lawyers and police, I want you to help me take it.'

Konrad still said nothing. He turned and got into the Landrover. Krisjan turned the vehicle round and drove him back to his cottage.

When they arrived there Konrad asked: 'How are you going to get the water to Steynskraal?' Krisjan sighed with relief at his brother's acceptance.

'I'm going to pipe and channel it.'

'Are you mad? The distance from here to Steynskraal is more than 80 kilometres!'

'Nevertheless I will do it. I will use people and mechanical diggers.'

Konrad shook his head. But Krisjan took from the Landrover the map he had brought and spread it out on the bonnet of the vehicle.

'Look here. About halfway between here and the homestead we have a windmill pump on a borehole that has run dry. There is already an old water sloot that runs from that borehole almost to

159

the house – a distance of some 40 kilometres – that old man Steyn built. It took him 11 years, but that was before the days of mechanical diggers. He obviously thought that water source would last forever, but it didn't. All we have to do is clean out that sloot. Then we link it up to here with a pipeline, which must be buried. I want to give the impression that the water rises at the old borehole. I see no reason why the true source of it should not remain a secret. That way Pa can rest easy in his grave.'

Konrad snorted. 'And how do you think you will keep the laying of a water route in the Karoo for nearly 100 kilometres a secret?'

'By having it laid by Basters under your charge. Basters know how to keep a secret. And having you in charge makes it doubly safe.'

'There are not enough people here to do this work. Our community is too small.'

'Then get more from Rehoboth. There are a lot of people out of work there. We will pay them well. And we will pay you especially well.'

'It'll take me a week to bring enough people from Rehoboth. I'll need at least three trucks.'

'You can have three trucks.'

Konrad shook his head, nonplussed. 'You must need this water very badly.'

To this day people speak of the astonishing events at Steynskraal in the winter of that year. It was, of course, impossible to keep it a secret that Krisjan was piping water from a hidden source in the Bastersberge. The curious, ranging from Water Affairs inspectors to other Karoo farmers and even a reporter from a newspaper in Beaufort West, came prying. Even aircraft came swooping low at times in a region where planes were hardly ever seen.

But by the time the news got around, the pipe was well out of the mountain range and buried, and the disturbed soil smoothed by the east wind, so that its exact source remained secret. Those who tried to trace where it began were met by taciturn Basters who refused to answer questions – and even threatened violence when pressed.

Krisjan stormed ahead with the laying of the pipe. Konrad had trucked more than 100 Basters down from Rehoboth across the border in southern Namibia. They worked in shifts around the clock, flailing away with picks and shovels. But the heavier work was carried out by 26 mechanical trench diggers that Krisjan railed in from a contractor in Beaufort West. The project crept ahead at the rate of nearly a kilometre a day.

When the pipe, laid and covered, reached the dry borehole, it linked with an inlet pipe that connected with the borehole's reservoir. From that point the water would continue by open channel to Steynskraal. Soon the diggers and the mechanical trenchers were cleaning out the old channel and the work was proceeding at a faster pace.

Given the time of the year, the days were not excessively hot but the nights were bitterly cold. Krisjan set up diesel-fuelled generators that lit up arc lights and he lit fires along the work line. He organised relays of food and coffee to keep the night shifts going.

The Basters worked willingly. They did not know why they were doing this work or why it had to proceed at such speed. The pay was good so they asked no questions. But there was more to it than that. Somehow they gained the impression – or had been given it – that this was something personally important to Krisjan and Konrad, that it was in some way a Baster thing. So they gave the work their loyalty and passion, which was worth more than money could buy.

This is the way of the Basters, one of Africa's smallest and more curious clans, existing in small pockets of communities in the western Karoo and up the west coast of southern Africa. Their name, literally translated from Afrikaans, means 'bastards', but they bear the title with pride. The local historical origin of its meaning was simply that they were a racial mix of the indigenous inhabitants of the Cape and the first white settlers who arrived there in the seventeenth century. Thus a word that carried a social stigma elsewhere became for them a proud identity.

During the eighteenth century and later, the Basters trekked away from white colonial rule, setting up small, sometimes tiny, settlements of their own in various places of lesser menace in the arid and semi-arid west-coast regions, culminating in Rehoboth in southern Namibia. Some of the smaller settlements were absorbed or vanished. A few, like the Basters in the Bastersberge, flickered on the brink of survival. In Rehoboth they remain a tenacious people with a homeland of their own, defiantly independent, intensely religious, rarely marrying outside their community and fiercely loyal to each other.

This was the calibre of the team that had been fetched to assist with the waterway to Steynskraal and, as they saw it, Konrad the Baster had brought them to help Krisjan the Baster and it was therefore a Baster affair, so they gave of their best, without question.

While the pipeline team toiled ceaselessly, Krisjan organised Steynskraal workers into another squad that began to dig a tight and intricate grid of irrigation channels around the homestead, which grew steadily outwards.

He was now getting anxious inquiries from the firm of accountants in Cape Town that handled the deeper financial affairs of the Steynskraal estate. The latest statements received from the bank in Beaufort West indicated unusual expenditure well over budget estimates, and Adriaan van Duren, the senior partner, wanted to know why. Krisjan replied tersely that he was catering for urgent water needs.

The firm contacted Karina about the matter, and two days later her Cessna was circling the homestead, waggling its wings for transport to be sent to the landing strip. On this occasion, catching sight of the activity around the house, she swooped lower than usual for an aerial inspection. Krisjan drove to the landing strip himself to meet her.

'Krisjan, what the HELL are you doing?' Karina yelped as she leaped from the aircraft.

'Let me show you,' he said.

She puffed agitatedly on a cigarette as they drove to the house. 'I've had old fussypants Van Duren on the phone complaining that you seem to have gone on an unauthorised spending spree and he thinks you may have gone nuts,' she said. Krisjan said nothing.

Minutes later they stood on the front stoep of the homestead, where Karina stared at the criss-cross pattern of trenches already extending some 200 metres into the veld.

'I'm making a garden,' explained Krisjan. 'For Marietjie.'

Karina stared at him, speechless.

'For Marietjie, so that she will be happy here, and then Wouter will be happy and everybody will be happy and they can have children and Steynskraal will return to normal.'

Karina felt the need to sit down and found her way to a stoep bench where she sat holding her head between her hands.

'Krisjan,' she said, wearily, 'are you crazy? Even if Van Duren agrees to the cost of all this, where the hell do you think you are going to get the water for a garden this size?'

So he told her about the water.

She was immediately on her feet. 'Are you telling me that you and your family knew there was this amount of water in those mountains and you never told my family?'

'It would only have led to trouble with the Basters.'

'My father would have shot the Basters!'

'That was the trouble,' replied Krisjan. 'And that would have led to a very bad situation.' His slate-grey Baster eyes locked calmly with her own angry, now smouldering, hazel eyes.

'Listen Karina, Steynskraal is a very rich place. It became rich even without the water from the Bastersberge. Never mind the past. The water is now here and what is important is what we do with it. Come with me. I want to show you something.'

He led her indoors to the study. The long yellowwood table was laden with books, illustrated brochures and sales pamphlets dealing with flowers, shrubs and trees that Krisjan had sent for and accumulated over the past several months.

'I'm arranging for trees and shrubs and flowers to be sent by road,' he told Karina. 'But I would be thankful for your help with the roses. It is better that the rose plants arrive quickly. You have an aeroplane.'

He picked up a brochure from the table. 'There is this place in Grabouw called Duncan's Roses. They are famous for the quality and varieties of their roses. I would be very grateful if you would help me to order the rose plants ... we need many roses in the garden ... what I want to know is, will you please help me order the rose plants and fly them here in your plane?'

Karina sank into one of the big old leather armchairs, closed her eyes and placed a hand over her brow as if to ward off a migraine. After a while she said: 'I will do what you ask for one reason only. It is that I think you have gone mad and if I do not help you, you might do something worse.'

After further thought she added: 'God knows what I'll tell Van Duren.'

Krisjan said: 'I think when Van Duren hears about the water he will forgive everything.'

Three weeks later the diggers reached Steynskraal and the final pipes were laid. The Bastersberge water was on tap. Konrad had the main body of Basters trucked back to Rehoboth and those from the Bastersberge were camped at Steynskraal, where they helped with the planting of the trees and shrubs that had begun to arrive from the Cape.

Krisjan laid out the rose beds in front of the homestead. Directly below the stoep were the Peace roses, renowned for their fragrance, so that it could drift into the bedroom.

'The first thing she will be aware of in the mornings will be the scent of the roses,' he explained to Karina, who stood aside, arms folded, watching him in silence.

Beyond the Peace roses were the Duftwolke reds, the Queen Elizabeths and the Coral Sunsets. Fuchsias were to one side, where he had planted false olives for shade. 'The fuchsias need partial shade,' he explained. 'Especially from the midday sun in summer.' Karina nodded politely, as if humouring a lunatic.

He had also needed to replace some of the ancient tall blue-gums in front of the house, which he had felled with pangs of regret and a feeling of defiling history. But it had been necessary for the broad purpose of his plan, for nothing grows beneath bluegums except more bluegums.

To make up for their loss he had replaced them with fully grown coconut palms. It had also been necessary to excavate and remove the soil soured by the bluegums and replace it with many tons of earth trucked in from afar and abundantly laced with lime and phosphate. The expense had been enormous and Van Duren in Cape Town had howled in despair when he had received the bills.

Paved footpaths led between the rose beds to a lake that he had stocked with water flowers and fringed with papyrus reeds, arum lilies and willows. Krisjan planted trees beyond the lake, grouping them so as to protect the inner garden from the east wind but also leaving spaces between them to preserve glimpses of the veld. There were conifers and poplars on the outside of the grouping with an inner lining of Cape ash, flamboyants, Africa flames, Cape chestnuts and acacias – all trees eager for the water he had now made available, yet sturdy enough to withstand the east wind.

The men from the Bastersberge were sent home except for a few who became attached to the permanent staff of Steynskraal as gardeners.

Karina flew in one day to inform Krisjan that Wouter had written to say that he and Marietjie would not be returning as early as expected. 'She's mending,' said Karina. 'But it is going to take more time. Another year, perhaps.'

Krisjan's first reaction was disappointment. Then he said, almost eagerly: 'It's alright, it will give time for the garden to develop ... the trees to grow.'

Karina said: 'He enclosed a letter for you.' She handed it to him.

Krisjan read it that night by his fireside. Marietjie was slowly improving, Wouter wrote. The clinic in Switzerland had worked wonders. Now it was a matter of rest. They were in the south of France. It was springtime. Marietjie was entranced by the way the olive trees grew with fields of lavender beneath them. He wrote warmly of how he looked forward to their return to Steynskraal.

The next morning Wouter telephoned nurseries in the Cape to order olive-tree saplings and lavender plants. He planted olive groves beyond the trees that surrounded the lake, with lavender between them. He planted ten hectares. Labour was brought from the Bastersberge to help with the planting.

Krisjan the cattleman had become Krisjan the gardener. The books and the loose-leaf literature in the study grew pile by pile. The ranching operations at Steynskraal did not falter. His overall sense of commitment did not allow any lapses. He had to delegate more than before but he kept control. The garden, however, had become his passion – for the sheer love of it and for the purpose of it.

And the water from the Bastersberge flowed bountifully, fulfilling every need of the garden: seeping through intricate earthen channels where required and distributed by overhead sprayers, drip systems and microjets elsewhere – and what was left over was extended into the veld to enrich pastures for the cattle.

Arriving on a visit, Karina found Krisjan engrossed in a new book entitled *Microclimatology within the Garden*. It had to do with a secluded hectare of the Steynskraal garden where he had hemmed in the *klimaat*, as he called it, by the dense planting of trees, trapping the heat of the veld, blocking out the east wind and humidifying the area with microjet irrigation. 'Here we can experiment with subtropical plants,' he told her excitedly. He rattled off the names of exotic flora he had ordered. 'Can you fly them up for me? I cannot risk having them come by road. They may not survive the journey.'

She smiled wearily. 'Of course I can, and I'll bring you a couple of dinosaurs for that special corner of the garden,' she said. 'Meanwhile here's another letter for you from Wouter.' He read it eagerly and, again, disappointment furrowed his brow. They were not coming home yet. They were in Italy. Wouter informed him they had rented an old villa surrounded by cypress trees for the summer. 'It's a beautiful place and Marietjie has fallen in love with it,' he wrote.

The next day Krisjan telephoned the Forestry Department nursery at Wolseley in the Cape and ordered cypress trees. He planted a group of them at the corner of the homestead and balanced it with another group close to the lake. He stood back and surveyed them, visualising how they would look when they had grown taller. 'They will look good,' he muttered to himself. 'And I always thought they belonged only to graveyards.'

A miraculous thing now happened in the garden. Birds came to it in their hundreds. They came in increasing numbers and varieties. In the mornings, whereas there had before been only the sighing of the east wind in the trees, there was now the glorious chorusing song of birds. To Krisjan they seemed to be messengers carrying a divine blessing for what he had done, and he was awestruck. They also opened up for him an entirely new realm of pleasure. He sent for a copy of Roberts's *Birds of Southern Africa*, for he was seeing birds he had never seen before.

First had come the birds most common to the Karoo and which were therefore no strangers to Krisjan. But they came in profusion: the sand martins, the white-throated swallows, the finches, the Karoo larks, the willow warblers, the Karoo robins, the pipits and the flycatchers, and others.

Karina now found herself being led on bird-watching expeditions. She was irritated on one occasion, when she stayed overnight, at being woken at six in the morning and cajoled into accompanying Krisjan into the garden. 'Look!' he said excitedly, handing her a pair of binoculars. 'It's a Kalahari robin. It's the only one I have ever seen this far south. Our own Karoo robins are grey-brown, but this one is a paler colour and it has more music in its song. Listen!'

'*Ag* Krisjan, that's wonderful. Can I go back to bed now? I'm cold.'

He hardly heard her as he listened, fascinated, to the soft 'kuh-woo' of a Namaqualand dove. 'These doves hardly ever come this far south,' he said. But she was already on her way back indoors.

The geese he had introduced into the lake had been joined by a variety of wild waterfowl: francolin from the Cape, Egyptian geese, moorhens, harlequin quail and, to his delight, he found, one morning, a pair of blue crane pacing imperiously in the reeds beside the lake.

He stocked the lake with fish and was rewarded by the arrival of kingfishers. He set up beehives and was gratified to see swallow-tailed bee-eaters, rarely seen south of the Orange River. One night he heard the hoot of an owl that sounded different from the usual, and a day later found the nest of a family of Cape eagle owls never before seen nearer than in the Bastersberge.

The highlights of his life became the arrival of these feathered newcomers to Steynskraal. But they were highlights that remained spaced by the sadness that the main purpose of his garden remained unfulfilled. Wouter and Marietjie had not returned to see it.

'It's been seven years,' he said one morning as he and Karina walked in the garden. 'I cannot believe that seven years have passed since they left. Sometimes I wonder if they are ever going to come back.'

Karina's visits to Steynskraal had become more frequent as she had gradually become drawn into Krisjan's passion for the garden. He was always asking her to bring some new variety of plant or some new item of literature. She had been walking beside him on this morning, not saying much. She no longer teased him or made cynical remarks about the garden.

They had walked through the full expanse of it: from the stoep, through the rose beds, to the lake, between the trees that now grew tall and provided shade – among the song of birds – to the olive grove and the lavender, which grew in profusion throughout. The air was heavy with fragrance.

She turned towards him and said: 'You have created a miracle here. What you have done is more important than whether they come back or not.'

He shook his head. 'No. It was done for a purpose and the purpose is not yet fulfilled.'

She asked, very gently: 'Do you love her, Krisjan?' She stopped walking and turned towards him to compel a reply. She had known him for most of their lives – since they had played together as children – and she felt she could ask this of him.

He returned her gaze without hesitation. His pale Baster eyes were expressionless, showing neither resentment nor embarrassment at the intimacy of the question. 'I love them both,' he said.

A distant mutter of thunder intervened and she said: 'I must go. There is weather building up.'

After he had driven her to the landing strip and seen her off, Krisjan returned to the garden. The Karoo was about to experience one of its rare rainfalls and he didn't want to miss it.

As the first drops fell and became a deluge, he stood bareheaded among the trees and the flowers, and allowed it to drench him, inhaling deeply as the fragrance of the enriched soil and all he had created filled his senses. Rain in the desert had always been good. But this was holy beyond words.

Two years later, after a total absence of nine years, Wouter and Marietjie Steyn returned to South Africa. Krisjan first received news of it in a telephone call from Cape Town. It was Karina. 'Krisjan, they are back! I met them at the airport an hour ago! They will arrive at Steynskraal tomorrow!'

He was speechless with the suddenness, the unexpectedness of it. There had been no forewarning.

Karina said: 'They asked me to fly them home but I said I couldn't. They will be motoring up.'

His gratitude went out to her. 'Thank you,' he said. There was no need to say more. She knew that he had always hoped that they would arrive by road, and his work in the past two years had been to design and establish an entrance avenue to the homestead, first through the lavender-cosseted olive groves, the conifers and poplars and the flowering trees, then past the gentle beauty of the lake and its chorusing birds, through the palms and the clusters of flowering shrubs, to a parking area riotous with purple and red bougainvillea. There they would alight and walk beside the blue marguerite, the magnolia, the African daisies and the marigolds and among the scented rose beds clustered below the stoep of the majestic old house.

It was, of course, spectacular. To have arrived by air would have diminished the impact of the first sight of the garden by far.

So it was that when Wouter and Marietjie rounded the bend and slight descent of the low hill before Steynskraal, they were met by an extraordinary vision. The accustomed mirage that Wouter expected to shiver and jump into the clear outlines of the Steynskraal complex seemed to have difficulty focusing. When it finally did clarify, what appeared was not a cluster of buildings but a forest: olive groves and taller, greener trees beyond, through which the tips of the roofs of the homestead and outbuildings emerged as in a Mediterranean village.

Wouter jammed on the brakes of the car in bewilderment. Marietjie raised her hands to her face. For several minutes they gaped at the sight. Wouter, struck by the possibility that he had lost his way, looked about him, searching for familiar landmarks.

Marietjie, the first to recover, said in tones of wonderment and shock: 'They've planted trees ...' Even as she spoke she realised the extent of her understatement.

Wouter went on staring at his home, struggling to relate the way it had been all his life to the way it was now.

The Karoo rancher in him finally burst to the surface. 'Water!' he exclaimed. 'How did he get water to do this?'

He started the car and entered the olive grove. The scent of lavender beneath the trees was exotic. Marietjie gasped in delight. 'It's exquisite!'

Their amazement grew as they drove between the trees, past the flame lilies, through the palm grove and past the lake, sending up a flurry of waterfowl from the reeds. Finally they came to the house.

Krisjan and the house staff awaited them on the stoep. Only old Gertruida was not there, having passed away three years earlier. Wouter and Krisjan embraced. 'My God, Krisjan, what have you done here?' was the only greeting Wouter could muster.

It was when she saw the röse beds that Marietjie realised what had happened. Placing a hand on his arm she asked, simply: 'Did you do this for me, Krisjan?' Then she repeated the question: 'Did you do this for us?'

He shifted his feet and hung his head, like a schoolboy caught out, saying nothing. She took his head between her hands and kissed him on both cheeks. 'What can I ever do or say to thank you for this?'

'Please, just enjoy it,' he mumbled, embarrassed and conscious of the stir and audible murmur that had arisen from the assembled farm hands, none of whom had ever seen a white woman kiss a coloured man.

For the next week, Wouter and Marietjie did little else but roam constantly through the garden, frequently calling or sending for Krisjan to explain this or that flower or shrub. Karina, who had arrived a day later by plane, joined them.

But, as the hours passed, Karina found herself watching Marietjie more than the garden. There was no doubt that Marietjie was restored to health. The girl who had left Steynskraal broken and bewildered by a terrible depression had returned as a beautiful woman, with an air of confident self-assurance that was almost formidable. Her skin bore the glow of constant attention. She was stylish and elegant, appearing each morning immaculately turned out, no matter how casual her attire. If the mornings were cool she wore designer jeans, silk shirts and light sweaters in pastel shades. As the day warmed she appeared in cheerful T-shirts, her shapely legs clad in shorts of the latest fashion. In the chill of the evening she switched to well-cut trousers or a fine woollen skirt and jackets of Kashmir wool or Scottish tweed. 'My God,' muttered Karina to herself, 'it's like turning the pages of *Vogue.*'

Walking with Karina during a moment alone, Krisjan said: 'Marietjie seems different.'

'She is different, Krisjan. She is cured, thank God. She has also become a very stylish lady.'

Almost anxiously he asked: 'Do you think she likes the garden?'

'She adores the garden! Good heavens, can't you see that? Everybody loves your oasis!'

He smiled with pleasure, then said: 'Wouter also seems different.'

'Yes, he has changed ...' She sought for words to describe how.

Krisjan provided them in the simplest form possible. 'He used to tell her what to do. Now she tells him what to do.'

Karina laughed. 'I think that sums it up pretty well.'

That evening Krisjan sat before the fire in his small cottage. He was alone but he was at peace. Suddenly a great happiness overwhelmed him as he savoured the fruit of his nine years of dedication and the pleasure it had given the two people he loved most. Above all his heart sang with the fact that they were, at last, home and that the garden he had made for Marietjie would guarantee her happiness. He was not an overly religious man but throughout his life, on rare occasions of grief or serious crisis or joy, he had prayed. Now, impulsively, he moved from his chair and knelt on his hearth and gave thanks.

At the same time Wouter stood before the open window of the bedroom where he and Marietjie were preparing for bed. Although the early warmth of the evening had faded and the east wind had brought the chill of the night, the air was still heavy with the scent of roses and magnolia.

Marietjie sat before her dressing table looking intently into the mirror as she applied face cream from a jar bearing the name of a famous French cosmetics house. 'Close the window, Wouter!' she said. 'I'm getting cold!' He did as he was told and sighed.

'I just cannot get over the wonder of what Krisjan has done,' he said. 'He has created an oasis here in which we can now live happily, and for that I will be forever grateful to him.'

171

She replied a trifle impatiently: 'For heaven's sake, Wouter. You know we can't live here. You know I will never live in a dry climate. We've been here for only ten days and look what it's done to my skin!'

10

The battle for Bakwanga

There finally came a time when the great Congo story of the early 1960s waned and major news media began to close down their coverage. As usual the television reporters and their crews pulled out first, followed by the foreign correspondents of major newspapers.

The life of any big news story ebbs and flows according to its topicality and news value, and the story finally dies. Transporting foreign correspondents, especially TV teams, and billeting them in five-star hotels, along with their usually awesome expense accounts, is hideously expensive. If the story is no longer making headlines or lead time, the editors want the correspondents either home or elsewhere, being more productive.

That's the way it was in Elisabethville in the Katanga province of the Congo in 1961. The story, in all its gruesomeness and with its bizarre events, had been belting on for nine months with scarcely a break. Some correspondents had moved on to events elsewhere in the world but had been replaced because the Congo story was considered 'unsafe' to leave without staff. Others remained trapped on the story for the entire period, including Christmas, and were understandably edgy. Marital strains, affairs and divorces – all the usual happenings when foreign correspondents are kept away from home too long – were beginning to emerge.

But suddenly the story began to wobble. TV footage was being shelved and the story was moving to the inside pages of the major newspapers. John Osman of the *Daily Telegraph* and Len Ingles of the *New York Times* were ordered home. Richard Kilian of the *Daily*

173

Express was told to file 'only on request'. Donald Wise of the *Daily Mirror*, turning to his newspaper's well-known love of animal stories, had filed dispatches for two successive days on the plight of an elephant starving in the unstaffed Elisabethville zoo until he received a terse cable saying: 'EDITOR SAYS UNELEPHANT STOP PROCEED BEIRUT.'

After that there was a general exodus. First by the TV networks, then the newspapermen in singles, pairs and groups – until only three correspondents and a photographer remained in Elisabethville: George Bingle of the *Daily Banner*, Roger Crawley of the *Daily Clarion*, Ray Maloney of *United Press International* and Horst Faas of the *Associated Press*, whose outstanding pictures were later to win him a Pulitzer Prize.

Bingle and Maloney sent plaintive messages asking to go home. Bingle received a curt refusal while Maloney received a kinder reply saying: 'WANT YOU KEEP STORY WARM.' Crawley of the *Daily Clarion* kept silent. He was having an affair with a Sabena air hostess and wanted no immediate change to his situation. Faas received word that he would be relieved 'soon'.

The sort of melancholia and mild insanity that afflicts correspondents when left forgotten and inactive on a story began to set in.

Bingle got drunk most days while Maloney took to moodily wandering the near-deserted corridors of the Leopold Deux Hotel in his dressing gown, with a cigarette holder clenched between his teeth. Crawley lounged contentedly beside the swimming pool at the Sabena Club with his Belgian girlfriend, while Faas spent long hours playing German martial music on a record player in his bedroom and marching up and down to its beat. This disturbed Bingle, when sober, who had the room below, but there was not much he could do about it. Faas was a big man.

But all this changed suddenly when President Moise Tshombe, leader of the rebel province of Katanga, called a dramatic press conference.

Tshombe, flanked by ministers of his cabinet and senior army officers, introduced at the press conference a tribal leader from the region of Bakwanga, situated around the town of that name about 120 kilometres north of the Katanga border.

He introduced his guest as 'King' Albert Kalonji, monarch and leader of the 'Bakwanga nation' which, he said, had just proclaimed itself a sovereign state adjacent to Katanga, adding that the two 'nations' would thus share a common border. Furthermore they would be allies in the war against the evil forces of Premier Patrice Lumumba, leader of the Congo, from which Katanga had seceded some months previously. They would be militarily and economically supportive of each other.

A praise singer, in tribal dress of monkey skins and beads and a feathered headdress, then leaped forward and, in a tribal dialect, sang the praises of King Kalonji. By his gestures he appeared to be making references to a rod being held by the king. It was about a metre long and appeared to be made of ebony and decorated with copper rings and ivory inlay. His Majesty, dressed in a pin-striped grey business suit and wearing dark glasses, held it under his arm rather in the style in which a British army officer holds a swagger stick.

One of the creepy Belgian aides who always seemed to be hanging around the Tshombe entourage translated to the press in whispered French that this was the king's 'Ibi stick', which had magical powers and would 'strike dead' anyone who tried to harm the king. The foreign newsmen present exchanged glances at this information, but the local Katangese press, more familiar with local culture, seemed impressed.

After his praises had been sung King Kalonji addressed the media. A large photographic blow-up of a map of the Congo was wheeled in on a stand and His Majesty pointed out the borders of the new state. He went to some lengths to emphasise that it was 'kidney-shaped' and carefully, with his magic Ibi stick, traced out the heavily stencilled lines of its borders.

It was indeed kidney-shaped and it was interesting for those who were familiar with the region to observe that the kidney shape included all the diamond mines for which that part of the Congo was noted. It became quickly apparent that the proposed alliance of Katanga (which already contained all the copper mines) and Bakwanga would be hogging the major part of the total wealth of the Congo.

A local journalist asked if the population within the kidney shape had indicated its support of the new state by popular vote or any other democratic means. The king pointed his Ibi stick at the questioner, who reeled back in fright. *'C'est pas d'importance!'* ('It's not important!') he snapped.

Ray Maloney, the crew-cut, hyperactive UPI correspondent, had meantime been screwing up his eyes at the map and pointed out that Lumumbist forces were encamped at Luluabourg, which didn't seem very far from Bakwanga, and he asked if the new independent state had enough military muscle to withstand an attack.

The king said he was glad Maloney had asked that question as he was about to address the conference on that very subject. He said he had an army, already secretly trained and equipped, and barracked on the very outskirts of Elisabethville itself – and that it would embark by train for Bakwanga the following day, not only to defend the independence of the new state, but also to engage the forces of Lumumba and drive them out of Luluabourg. Military training and assistance had been given to his forces by Katanga, and President Tshombe had very kindly provided arms. Tshombe, his big moon face split by a friendly grin, nodded his head in assent.

The foreign press corps left the conference with mixed feelings. On the one hand they wanted to go home – on the other hand here, for the first time in several weeks, was a story of substance. It was not every day that a new country was created overnight – even in Africa. And an army on the move was always good copy. Maloney, Bingle and Crawley drove to the battle-scarred Elisabethville post office to bribe the Congolese telex staff to get the telex machines in the sweaty communications room working and began to compose their stories. Faas departed grumpily to the Leopold Deux Hotel to telephone his office. He really wanted to go home – not mess with another Congo caper.

In London foreign editors honed by long and hard experience sniffed at the story cautiously. Bingle had a reputation at the *Banner* for getting carried away on a story, especially when he had a beer or two under his belt. His value to his newspaper was that he was a colourful and entertaining writer, but he needed careful management.

Crawley was on his first foreign assignment and had not yet

won the total confidence of his foreign desk – and there was another problem at the *Clarion*. The newspaper was in financial trouble and all its foreign correspondents were on freeze at that time, although they had not yet been told the reason why.

Yet another problem was that big news was coming out of the Middle East and to have a Congo story butting in at this stage was almost an irritation. Added to this was the fact that, while great news stories frequently and undoubtedly came out of Africa, some leaned towards the surrealistic, and it wasn't always easy to tell the difference. This one certainly had an air of surrealism about it. A country created overnight? A king with a magic wand? What the hell ... Was Bingle pissed again? Was Crawley malarial? Their copy was passed back and forth on their foreign desks and weary night editors scratched their heads.

The upshot was that Maloney's story on the new Bakwanga, competing against heavier stuff from the Middle East and elsewhere, was put out briefly and used scrappily by most UPI subscribers. Bingle and Crawley received messages to say that their stories were unused and they were warned to avoid expense and keep communications costs to a minimum – and Crawley, in particular, was told to sit tight and file only on request. Faas was told to go home.

But the next day the new Congo story took off like a fireworks display.

A military band came marching through the main street of Elisabethville, playing loudly and discordantly. It was followed by motorcycle outriders who were in turn followed by President Tshombe's official open state car, a white Continental, in which stood Tshombe and Kalonji, the leaders of the two allied secessionist states, side by side, waving to cheering bystanders. The presidential vehicle was followed by an officer in splendid uniform bedecked with medals yet to be won astride an agitated horse that he was struggling to control. This was the army's commander, General Alphonse Murumbi, who a year previously had been a stretcher-bearer in the Medical Corps of the Belgian colonial armed forces of the Congo. The commander was followed by his troops – a motley column of about 800 men (battalion-strength, as Bingle expertly observed) marching gloriously out of step, some of them lurching drunkenly and singing loudly songs of various choice but all at the same time.

This was King Kalonji's army – and they were off to war.

But the first thing noticed about the army was that there were no guns. There was not a single weapon in sight, other than a pistol being worn in a holster on the hip of the commander on his prancing horse.

In other respects, however, the troops appeared well provided for. Many were carrying bottles of beer in their ammunition pouches, and loaves of bread and other goodies peeped from beneath the flaps of tightly crammed rucksacks. Some had live chickens, tied by their feet, hanging upside down from their webbing belts. The chickens, perplexed at their plight, squawked piteously, adding to the general pandemonium. There were also women, marching in tight embrace with some of the soldiers, while others capered alongside shrieking and ululating in delight and clapping their hands. This war was obviously going to have in it something for everyone.

'Christ Almighty,' said Crawley, who had not yet seen an army going off to war and had not imagined it could look like this. Faas was busily taking pictures. Word passed that the column was headed for the railway station, and the journalists leaped into their vehicles and headed for the station.

Sure enough the column duly arrived, and indeed there was a motley train of coaches, vans and open cattle trucks waiting for it, headed by a puffing, wood-burning locomotive already stoked up and ready to go.

The column came to a shambling halt and NCOs hysterically shouted commands, which were largely ignored. The troops surged aboard the train, dragging women with them and battling for the best seats. Those slower than the rest ended up in the cattle trucks.

Attempts were made to get the horse up a ramp into a closed truck, but the animal, rolling its eyes at the prospect of going any further with this army, broke free and bolted down the railway track. Soldiers ran after it, but the commander shouted: *'Laissez le cheval!'* ('Leave the horse!') He was obviously glad to be rid of it.

'I wonder what the Duke of Wellington would have thought of this lot,' said Bingle.

The press approached Tshombe and the king on the station plat-form. Tshombe received the press smilingly. Kalonji was sullen.

'We would like to ask His Majesty why his army has no guns,' said Bingle.

The king waved his magic Ibi stick nonchalantly and everyone moved back uneasily. '*C'est pas d'importance,*' he said. It seemed to be his stock answer for everything.

But the journalists grew restive. An army off to war without guns needed an explanation.

Tshombe came to the rescue. 'Arms are being sent to Bakwanga by separate transportation,' he said. 'We don't want them to be seen here. They include secret weapons.'

Secret weapons? The reporters scribbled busily in their notebooks.

The train pulled out to the accompaniment of warlike whoops from the troops and loud applause from the crowd at the station. Kalonji and his military commander remained behind with Tshombe, announcing their intention to fly direct to Bakwanga to take command of the troops on their arrival there.

'When will your troops go into action?' asked a member of the local press.

'Immediately,' replied the Commander.

'It is a military secret,' the king corrected, looking at his com-mander balefully. The commander, realising he had boobed, broke into a sweat and looked at the Ibi stick, which was twitching.

They then joined Tshombe in his limousine and drove away, the motorcycle escort thundering ahead of them, sirens wailing.

The foreign press returned to the Leopold Deux Hotel and ordered drinks.

Bingle went up to his room and returned with a dog-eared road map of the Congo. 'Bakwanga ... Bakwanga ...' he muttered. 'Yes here it is. Christ, those troops will be there by tomorrow evening and it'll take us two days to get there by road. It's got to be a char-ter flight.'

Everyone filed a story and requested instructions.

Faas received a cable sent overnight ordering him to go to the Middle East urgently. With a whoop of joy he packed and raced to the airport before the Bakwanga army pictures he had just sent caused a change of mind.

Shortly after midday Bingle got a scratchy telephone call from his foreign editor, Bill Haines, who said: 'Listen George, what the fuck's going on? There's this king with a magic stick and an instant kingdom and there's this army going off to war with chickens but no guns and now you want to chase after them. How seriously do you want me to take this? You're not pissed are you – or getting high on the local ganja?'

Bingle replied: 'I can't help what goes on here, Bill. This is Africa, as you well know. They do things differently here. Look at it this way: if it's not going to be a serious war at least it will be a funny war. Either way it makes a good story.'

There was a long silence from the foreign editor. A colleague had passed to him a batch of Faas's pictures just received from *Associated Press* showing Kalonji's army marching to the railway station. He stared at them in fascination. Correspondents might exaggerate or cajole, but photographs don't lie.

'How much will it cost?' he asked Bingle.

Bingle had it all worked out. 'About 600 pounds for the plane and plus-minus 1 000 for everything else.'

'Holy shit!' said Haines.

'C'mon Bill,' whined Bingle. 'This is heart-of-darkness stuff, I don't know what's waiting for me there.'

'Hopefully little pygmies with hissing blowpipes who'll put a poisoned dart up your arse,' said Haines, playing for time to think as he flipped through Faas's pictures.

'Maybe I can beat the charter company down on the flight,' said Bingle, sensing that the story with its rich promise of profit on expense account might be slipping away.

Haines deliberated, astride the knife-edge on which foreign editors frequently find themselves: reluctant to miss a good story but equally reluctant to waste money on one that may bomb out. Too many errors either way could be career-threatening.

'All right George – go for it. But I'm telling you now: you drop me in the crap on this one, I'll have you fired. Got it? You're promising me a war, so I want a war, OK? No war, I'll have your balls for a necklace, OK?'

Bingle gulped. 'OK,' he said. What else could he say?

He went to the local charter company in Elisabethville to confirm a Cessna for take-off to Bakwanga the following morning at first light.

Ray Maloney, because of his day-to-day and hour-by-hour agency responsibilities and fearing the likely lack of communication in Bakwanga, had arranged to cover the story as best he could from Elisabethville, using United Nations sources. The UN, which was in the Congo to attempt to secure a peaceful end to the secession of Katanga, had so far proceeded no further than engaging in armed clashes with Katangese troops aided by mercenary forces. But in the process it had established bases throughout and beyond the province that provided a sometimes useful if not always accurate network of information filtered through its headquarters in Elisabethville.

Roger Crawley, meantime, was disconcerted and despondent over having had no acknowledgement of his story or response to his messages about the latest development on the Bakwanga story. Communications by telephone out of Elisabethville were difficult and, unless his office called him, as Bingle's had done, he had little hope of talking to them on the phone. In fact the *Daily Clarion* had used his latest story but, in the mania over cost-saving as the newspaper neared its demise, was not even bothering to communicate with its correspondents. Although he didn't know it, Crawley was about to be recalled and his newspaper was days away from shutdown.

That night Bingle decided to have a heart-to-heart talk to Crawley.

'Listen, Roger, why don't you come with me on this story? We can share expenses on the aircraft. I can get a duplicate bill from the charter company and we can each charge our papers the full amount. Good profit, old man.'

Crawley listened to the voice of the seducer with some doubt. 'I don't know, George. I've got strict instructions to stay put and file only on request.'

Bingle sighed. He was a big man and, although not yet middle-aged, much beer had given him a paunch, which tended to hang over his belt and strain the middle buttons of his shirt, sometimes leaving a gap through which his hairy navel could be seen. This had come to be known as Bingle's Third Eye. He was round-faced and sandy-haired, and his blue eyes were small and shrewd. He was of the seen-it-all, done-it-all breed of hack and wore his cynicism on his sleeve.

He sighed again. 'It's like this, Roger, and you can take it from me as coming from someone who knows. Those guys on the foreign desks are arseholes. They commute every day between Surbiton and their jobs and they've got no idea of what goes on in the field and the problems we have. All they worry about is money and how to balance their budgets. Their worries usually get in the way of a good story. Most times they just can't see it. That's when we have to take the initiative. Now, you come along with me and I will guarantee you a great story on this one. Then you will be a hero and they will forgive you everything. In fact your foreign editor will probably take the credit for sending you even if he didn't!'

The words of Bingle, the wily serpent, worked on Crawley's senses like opium. The only real achievement so far of this, his first foreign assignment, had been his conquest of the Sabena air hostess – which, of course, was not what his editors had had in mind when they had assigned him. As far as the story itself was concerned, he was feeling highly insecure. He had yet to get anything substantial into his newspaper and, unaware of the basic problems back at the office, he was misinterpreting the long silences from home as a criticism of his lack of input. Dark-haired, slight, intense in a way women found attractive, Crawley fidgeted as he listened to Bingle. It would be nice to have a front-page splash. He almost salivated at the thought. To return home without having achieved at least one front-page lead would be humiliating. Bingle's words had an element of truth. In the highly competitive world of foreign reporting those who took bold risks tended to get the best stories.

'OK, George, I'll go with you,' Crawley said.

They took off the following morning at first light.

Within two hours they were circling over Bakwanga. The pilot made three low passes over the town, examining the people who looked up curiously at the aircraft, some of them waving at it. 'I see no sign of troops. There does not even appear to be anyone at the police station,' he said.

He buzzed the nearby landing strip to clear it of a flock of large birds and landed, cursing, as the rutted, ill-kept field shook up his aircraft cruelly. 'I will not land here again. This strip is no longer safe,' he announced to his shocked passengers.

'How do we get back?' demanded Bingle. 'We have a return-trip contract.'

'You must come back by road, river or railway,' said the pilot. *'C'est votre problème, non*? I will not risk anymore to crash my plane for you.'

'We've paid for two ways,' bawled Crawley.

The pilot shrugged. 'You can collect the return-trip money when you come back to Elisabethville.'

They climbed from the plane disconsolately. Without waiting for further discussion, and gesturing at heavy cloud building up on the horizon, the pilot spun the aircraft, trundled it down to the far end of the landing strip and then roared back for a bumpy take-off.

'Belgian bastard!' said Bingle. 'No wonder everyone despises these Belgians!'

It was intensely hot. The air was heavy and humid. Although only about 1 000 kilometres from Elisabethville, the climate was already tending towards subtropical and the vegetation was more lush.

The landing strip possessed a threadbare windsock, now hanging limply from its blistered mast, and a vandalised hangar that may once have housed the local aero-club trainer. There was no person in sight and no one had driven out from the town to express any interest in their arrival.

There was a sign that bore a faded arrow and the words *'À la ville'*. They began to walk, carrying their portable typewriters and overnight bags.

Five kilometres and one-and-a-half hours later they arrived, sweat-sodden, in Bakwanga. It had once been a pretty village shaded by jacaranda trees. Most of the trees appeared to have been chopped down, presumably for firewood. Blacks standing in doorways or lounging on shabby verandas watched their arrival with faint curiosity. Some came up and asked aggressively for money and cigarettes. Their eyes roved over the visitors' wrist-watches and the Nikon camera carried by Crawley. Bingle grew nervous and said: 'Keep moving.'

They came to the hotel, but found that its management had long ago departed and the entire establishment had been taken over by some of the local populace who were apparently living there free of charge, had turned it into a tenement and had chopped up the furniture and part of the veranda for firewood.

They visited the police station but found it shut.

It was clear that Bakwanga had not fared well after nine months of independence. The white Belgian population had clearly abandoned it. The few village shops were either boarded up or empty, or vandalised or occupied by blacks living in the premises and cooking on the sidewalk.

'*Où est le gendarmerie?*' Bingle inquired of one of a number of blacks who had begun trailing around behind them.

He replied that the police were now at the '*Palais du Président*'.

'And where is the palace of the president?'

Without bothering to take his hands out of his pockets the man pointed the way with his chin in the irritating manner in which the Congolese give directions.

Still sweating profusely Bingle and Crawley walked in the direction he had indicated, up a hill between pleasant villas, some of them unoccupied, with untended lawns and gardens, and others invaded by new occupants who, judging by the number of children about, were clearly living several families to a room.

At the top of the hill was a near-mansion, the home of the mayor, who had departed in the general exodus following the army mutiny and the start of the civil war.

Here some slight semblance of order prevailed. President Kalonji had made it his residence and headquarters and had transferred to it (wisely) whatever remained in Bakwanga in the way of vehicles, firearms and beer. It had also become the new headquarters of the police. A strange black flag bearing a design of red stars grouped around something that may have been intended to resemble the president's magic Ibi stick fluttered from a pole that once bore the Belgian flag and, more recently, but briefly, the flag of the newly independent Congo republic. Three Landrovers, a fairly reliable-looking Peugeot and a battered Deux Chevaux pickup stood in the grounds of the house. The puttering sound of a diesel-driven generator came from somewhere behind the house.

Two slovenly sentries wearing the familiar grey uniform of the Congo police, but looking as though they had slept in them for several weeks, stood on the veranda at the main entrance, carrying sub-machine guns. But their shoddy tunics bore bright new gold-coloured epaulettes and clean-looking scarlet armbands. They were, it later transpired, members of Kalonji's newly formed Presidential Guard.

At the sight of the two journalists both the sentries rushed indoors and emerged within seconds accompanied by a hatless, dishevelled officer in an unbuttoned tunic, waving a pistol. He pointed the gun at the two newspapermen and shouted: 'Stop! You are spies! You are under arrest!'

'Shit!' cried Crawley. 'We're going to be shot!'

'Shut up, Roger,' said Bingle. To the officer he said in his passable French: 'We are British journalists. We have come to see President Kalonji, who knows us well. Please take us to him.'

The officer's pistol wavered only slightly as he advanced on the newsmen, until he was a mere two feet away from them. Bingle, looking directly into the man's eyes, noticed that they were blood-shot and wild. The situation was made more alarming by his body odour, which was a pungent blend of sweat, beer and marijuana.

At that moment a white man, stocky, balding and sallow-complexioned, appeared in the doorway behind him. 'It's all right, Captain. These men are not spies. They are indeed journalists. We have been expecting them. With your permission I will deal with them.'

The captain lowered his pistol sullenly. 'If I am not kept informed of these matters how can I be expected to handle my responsibilities?' he asked. He bellowed at the sentries to resume their posts and lurched back indoors.

'Thank you for that,' said Bingle.

'It is nothing,' said their saviour. 'But you had better come with me.'

He led them through a foyer where more members of the Presidential Guard in old police uniforms given new life with gold epaulettes and red armbands lounged in easy chairs drinking beer. The captain rejoined them, paying no further attention to the newsmen.

They entered an office where paintings and photographs shared space on the wall with a map of the Congo. There was a desk surrounded by comfortable chairs. Their benefactor produced glasses and cold Simba beer from a refrigerator disguised as a cabinet. He introduced himself as José Carvalho, a Portuguese national who owned a trading post 20 kilometres away on the bank of the Sankuru River. 'But,' he said spreading his hands apologetically, 'I have been co-opted as Minister of Economic Affairs in the new state of Bakwanga. But as there is no economy, there is not much for me to do, so I am at your service.'

Bingle said: 'We have come to report on an impending battle. We saw King Kalonji dispatch his army by train from Elisabethville to defend Bakwanga against attack by the Lumumbistes. They should have arrived by now, but we see no troops in the village ... er ... capital. Where is the army now?'

Carvalho spread his hands helplessly and was again apologetic. 'They have *disparu* – disappeared.'

'The army has disappeared?'

'*Oui.*'

'Where to?'

Carvalho shrugged and spread his hands again. 'Who knows? The train brought them to Dibaya from where they were intended to march to Bakwanga. But when they disembarked they all disappeared into the bush. Many of them were drunk and there were women with them. Need I say any more?'

'But where did they go?' asked Crawley, as Bingle held his head in his hands.

'In my opinion they have all gone back to their various tribal villages in the region,' replied Carvalho.

'But ... but we were told that they would receive their arms and ammunition on arrival. Was no one there to meet them? What's it all about?'

Carvalho pursed his lips. There was a long silence as he played with a pencil on his desk and appeared to be trying to come to a decision. Finally he said: 'Very well, I will tell you what it is all about – provided only that you do not reveal me as your source of information. Is that agreed?'

The journalists nodded eagerly.

Carvalho prepared for discussion by refilling everyone's glasses and producing and lighting for them thin Brazilian cheroots, which were accepted even by Crawley, who did not smoke, so anxious was he not to interrupt Carvalho's mood of revelation.

The Portuguese drew on his cheroot, exhaled and began: 'What it's all about is, of course, diamonds. There are seven very productive diamond mines in this region. They are owned by associate companies of the same Belgian mining group that owns the Katanga copper mines, which are, as we all know, propping up the Tshombe regime and financing Colonel Mike Hoare's mercenary unit, which is the nucleus and only really effective fighting force of the Katangese army.

'Well, Tshombe and King Kalonji, the senior tribal leader in the Bakwanga region, put together this plan to create the independent state of Bakwanga and ally it to Katanga with the main aim of securing the diamond mines and defending them against attack and seizure by the army of Lumumba.'

Carvalho pointed to the map on the wall. 'As you can see the new nation of Bakwanga is outlined there in the shape of a kidney, which I assure you does not evolve from a love of anatomy. Our new nation's borders are cunningly designed to incorporate all the diamond mines.'

Bingle said: 'Yes, King Kalonji himself introduced us to this kidney-shaped map and it was not difficult to conclude that the diamonds influenced its design. But our assignment here directly concerns the army that was sent to defend it. We are devastated to learn that it has disappeared because we have come all this way to report on the war.'

'*Aaah, hélas! Tiens-tiens-tiens,*' tutted Carvalho sympathetically. 'However I must tell you that while that army was recruited, trained and dispatched with – shall we say – the best of intentions and for the sake of appearances, no one in his right mind was going to rely on it to resist the more experienced and better-equipped forces of Patrice Lumumba.'

'So who *were* they going to rely on?' asked Crawley, bewildered by the growing complexity of the story.

Carvalho spread his arms wide. 'Why, none other than the mercenaries of Colonel Mike Hoare, better known to us all as *Les*

Affreux – the Frightful Ones! They, after all, have been the ones mainly responsible for defending and maintaining the secession of Katanga. Only they could be relied on to ensure the defence and independence of the new kidney-shaped state of Bakwanga!'

Bingle asked the obvious question: 'So where the hell are the mercenaries?'

Carvalho sighed. 'We now come to the tragic part of this story,' he said. 'Let me replenish your glasses so as to fortify you for the news I must now tell you.' So saying, he produced three fresh bottles of beer from the refrigerator and refilled all three glasses. He then offered fresh cheroots, received no takers and lit one for himself. He leaned back in his chair, blew a cloud of smoke at the ceiling and said:

'Colonel Hoare, whatever one might think of some of his men, is, as you must know, a good officer. He decided to allocate a force of 100 men to the defence of Bakwanga. They were scheduled to arrive here to synchronise with the arrival of Kalonji's troops on the train from Elisabethville. They were to arm and organise the troops on their disembarkation from the train, advance with them the short distance to Bakwanga and take up positions in and around the capital – in general, be the backbone of the defence and protection of the state of Bakwanga, including of course the diamond mines.

'For reasons best known to himself Colonel Hoare decided on a three-pronged operation. He requisitioned the little river steamer that goes up and down the Lulua River between Mwimba in northern Katanga and Dibaya. He placed 30 men on it and sent 40 men in a convoy of three trucks and an armoured car by road. A third group of 30 men was arranged to go by aircraft in one of the two old Dakotas being flown by mercenary pilots under the title of the Katanga Air Force. All three expeditions were planned to arrive at Dibaya more or less simultaneously with, as I have said, the army on the train from Elisabethville.

'Unfortunately what was either unknown or overlooked was that an Indian patrol of the UN peace-keeping force assigned to the Congo was encamped on the bank of the Lulua River at Luiza. When the river boat came past laden with armed mercenaries the UN patrol was understandably curious and hailed it to stop. The mercenaries ignored the UN signal so it was decided to fire a warning shot across the bows of the craft. All that the UN force had available for this purpose was a trench mortar. The mortar crew tried very diligently to fire a shot up into the air that would drop somewhere in front of the steamer. Unfortunately they succeeded in doing what they almost certainly would never have been able to accomplish had they thus aimed. The mortar shell dropped right down the funnel of the boat. It exploded in the engine-room and the vessel sank within minutes. Seventeen men were killed, some of them seized by crocodiles as they struggled in the river. Of the survivors several were wounded, three seriously. The wounded mercenaries were flown to Elisabethville by UN helicopters for hospitalisation.

'Meanwhile the mercenaries advancing by road got bogged down in heavy rain at Kaniama, and for all we know may still be there.

'The Dakota aircraft carrying the remainder of the mercenaries arrived on time at the Dibaya airstrip but, finding no one there, flew back to Elisabethville.

'It was several hours later that Kalonji's army arrived, belatedly and drunkenly, on the train from Elisabethville. I suppose one can't blame them for disappearing. There was, after all, no one to meet them. No mercenaries, no members of their so-called government – and their arms, which were being transported to them by the river boat that had been sunk by the UN, were now at the bottom of the Lulua River.

'It has all been, as you say in English, a fuck-up.'

Thus concluding his narrative, Carvalho poured himself another beer and puffed at his cheroot disconsolately.

'What is the situation now?' asked Bingle.

'The situation now, *messieurs*, is that the new state of Bakwanga appears no longer to have an army or a government. We have not seen King Kalonji or any other members of his cabinet for several days and here in this place we appear to be the sole representatives of the kidney-shaped state of Bakwanga. That is to say, myself the Minister of Economic Affairs and the élite Presidential Guard, seated outside, getting drunk.'

Carvalho, loosened by alcohol, was not making much effort to hide his disgust.

'What's the strength of the Presidential Guard?' asked Bingle.

Carvalho grinned. 'Their total number is 11, under the command of a captain ... and you have seen the captain.' He studied the ash on the tip of his cheroot. 'I should add that there are three battalions of Lumumbiste troops at Luluabourg, 60 kilometres away, preparing to advance on Bakwanga.'

'Good God!' exclaimed Crawley. 'Shouldn't we be getting out of here?'

Carvalho replied: 'I was actually on the point of leaving when you arrived. I suggest you come with me.'

Bingle said: 'We need transport and communications. We have to send a story. And we have to find means of getting back to Elisabethville ...'

'My old Deux Chevaux outside is the only vehicle left in Bakwanga that has fuel,' said Carvalho. 'The other vehicles, which are the entire official fleet of the state of Bakwanga, including of its armed forces as we now know them, are almost empty of petroleum – which is why no one rushed out to meet your aircraft. And there are no communications except at my trading store, where I also live, just outside the town. Thanks to the ingenuity of Belgian technicians before they fled from here and with whom I was personally friendly, I can still make contact with Elisabethville and Brussels so long as my generator keeps working. For the present I suggest you come with me. We will have to leave the problem of getting you back to Elisabethville until later.'

Suddenly departure seemed imperative. Carvalho picked up a briefcase and they left his office.

The majority of the Presidential Guard in the foyer appeared to be asleep. The captain was stretched out on the floor. The others took no notice of their leaving. The sentries outside were flopped in reclining garden chairs. One of them saluted Carvalho without rising. The other raised a half-empty beer bottle in acknowledgement.

They climbed into the Deux Chevaux, which started reluctantly, and Carvalho nudged it down the hill. On reaching the main street they were set upon by bystanders who hammered on the vehicle and at one stage even rocked it, shouting various demands like '*Quelle nouvelles, monsieur?*' and '*Où est le président?*' and '*J'ai faim!'* and *'Donnez-moi du pain!'* A cripple seated in an old squeaky-wheeled perambulator and paddling it along with a plank as though it were a canoe tried to keep pace with them, screaming obscenities. Carvalho kept his foot down on the accelerator and finally got through the mob. He was sweating profusely and he shook his head sadly.

'What will happen to these people when the Lumumbistes come?' asked Bingle.

'Oh, they'll kill as many men as they can and rape as many women as they can,' said Carvalho. 'As usual,' he added.

'What about the Presidential Guard?'

'They will run away if they are sober enough to get to their feet. If not, they will be killed. The Lumumbistes will be especially angry if they find they have drunk all the beer.'

Carvalho told them something of himself as he drove out of town. He had flown his wife and children to Lisbon before independence. 'I saw this excrement coming,' he said. 'I was prepared to stay to see what could be retrieved here, but not with the family. I will join them in Portugal and maybe I will come back after a while to see how things are – but I don't think it will be safe enough, ever again, for the family.'

It was clear that he was one of the remarkable tough breed of traders so often found in remote corners of Africa – usually Portuguese, Greek, Indian or Arab – who tenaciously and miraculously survive, sometimes becoming part of the kaleidoscopic pattern of African politics and even becoming wealthy. He was the only white man left in Bakwanga and was now about to leave. He would probably be the first white man to return if it ever became possible for whites to return.

They arrived at Carvalho's trading store, a warehouse and office close to a pleasant villa on the bank of the Sankuru River which passes by the town. A servant opened the gate to the security fence that surrounded the compound. The steady beat of a diesel-powered generator sounded nearby and Bingle was silently thankful. Hopefully it meant communications, cold beer and maybe even air-conditioning. His optimism was met on all three counts. Carvalho unlocked the office, switched on the air-conditioning, switched on a telex machine and produced Simba beer from a refrigerator.

'I will leave you to your work,' he said. 'Come over to the house when you are finished.'

The moment he was gone Bingle gave vent to his frustration. 'Bloody hell! We've got to put together a war – but quick!'

'You mean the mercenary caper?' inquired Crawley.

'No, fuck the mercenaries. That river skirmish is three days old and anyway it was hardly a war, and also Maloney may have picked that up already from his UN sources in Elisabethville. What I mean is we've got to put Kalonji's army into action against the Lumumbistes and have a real war. That's what we're here for.'

'But George, the army has disappeared – you know, *disparu*! You heard what Carvalho said!'

'Yeah, well, only we know that. Meanwhile my foreign desk is waiting for a war.'

Crawley held the cold Simba beer bottle against his forehead for solace. He had heard of Bingle's occasional wild forays into fantasy and fiction, and he felt uneasy.

'Look, George, we've got a pretty good story if we just tell it the way it is. I mean Carvalho gave us a good fill-in and all that diamond stuff and the politics and the strategy and the atmosphere in this place are interesting and I actually think the army buggering off into the bush is quite amusing ...'

'No, Roger,' said Bingle, firmly. 'It's all very well for you. Your paper has pretensions of grandeur and gives you more space. My paper has readers who move their lips when they read and I have to tell everything in 300 words and I have to keep it down to one simple thought. Furthermore I have been warned by my foreign editor that if I don't produce a war he will (and I quote) have my balls for a necklace and he will probably fire me. Also, let us not forget that the bigger the action, the bigger the expense account we can put in. Trust me on this one, Roger. We're in a country four times the size of France and it's mostly jungle and everything has gone to hell. We've got plenty of slack to play with. No one is going to care much about this story except about the action.'

Crawley wilted before this avalanche of logic and was silent.

Bingle drew from his bag his dog-eared road map of the Congo. 'Now let's see,' he said. 'I'm going to be the commander of Kalonji's army and you can take command of Lumumba's forces.

My troops have just disembarked from their train at Dibaya. I am going to move my men swiftly across into a defensive line here 20 miles west of Bakwanga town to block the advance of the Lumumbistes on the capital. I have ordered them to fight to the death for their king and country.'

Crawley said: 'As I recall your troops have no guns.'

'Ah yes,' said Bingle, thoughtfully. 'Thank you for reminding me of that.' He was silent for a moment. Then he said: 'Caches. That's it. Arms were awaiting my troops in secret caches close to Dibaya. We armed rapidly with automatic rifles, mortars and rocket launchers – and, of course, ammunition. Lots of ammunition.'

Crawley took reluctant command of the Lumumbiste forces. 'We moved out from Luluabourg at dawn. We advanced as King Shaka's Zulus did in days gone by – the main body forming the head of the beast, with two flanking units as the horns ...'

'Shit, that's good,' said Bingle in tones of respect. Then his blue eyes hardened. 'The armies clashed at midday beneath the burning African sun. The Bakwangese reeled back at the onslaught of the Lumumbistes, fighting with demented courage, stoked up with marijuana and spiced by the promises of their witchdoctors that the bullets of their foes would turn to water and thus would not harm them ...'

'Oi, I'm commanding the Lumumbistes, not you!' complained Crawley.

'OK,' said Bingle. 'Anyway, I'm ready to file.' And he launched himself at the telex machine – only to find that it was completely dead. Bingle howled in dismay. Then he ran to the door, opened it and screamed, 'Carvalho-ooo!' into the night.

José Carvalho, unfamiliar with the reaction of a foreign correspondent when communications break down on a hot story and alarmed by the panic in Bingle's yell, came running from the residence, carrying a pistol.

Bingle pointed wordlessly at the telex.

'*Merde!*' said Carvalho. '*Tiens-tiens-tiens!*' He pecked away at the machine for several minutes and finally shook it, but all without success. '*Alors* – we will try the telephone via Elisabethville,' he said. He dialled a number repeatedly, clearly without much hope – but suddenly he grinned broadly.

'Aha! An operator answers.' He spoke rapidly in French and hissed triumphantly at Bingle and Crawley: '*Ça va!* They are connecting me with Brussels. Quick, give the numbers of your newspapers. Brussels will connect us.'

There followed 10 anxious minutes of Carvalho shouting: '*Allô Bruxelles!*' into the telephone while Bingle paced up and down in agitation. Crawley was calmer, half hoping the communications would fail. He was not entirely happy about what he had been led into.

The Brussels connection was made and minutes later the *Daily Banner* was on the line. Carvalho handed the receiver proudly to Bingle who said: 'Foreign copy, please, and tell the desk I'm about to dictate from this telephone number reachable via Brussels and also on ...' (he peered at the telex switchboard) '... telex Bakwanga 14 when it works.'

Joe Bailey, one of the *Banner's* two foreign-desk night copy-takers came on line. He sat side by side with Barney Stubbs, the other night copy-taker. In between eating sandwiches and drinking coffee they had been taking telephoned dispatches from foreign correspondents for many years. The experience had left them taciturn and cynical. They had long ago ceased to become breathless with wonder at what they heard. Great events – including wars, rebellions, mutinies, assassinations, Olympiads, sporting triumphs, and cliff-hanging conferences such as peace treaties and councils of war, and natural disasters such as earthquakes and volcanic eruptions and foundering ships – had passed through their earphones and clattered onto their worn typewriters. They had become calloused by history, unmoved by drama and indifferent to sensation – even when delivered in the purple prose of some of the *Banner* reporters.

It did not mean that they were entirely bereft of feeling. They could still muster sympathy for a young correspondent out on his first foreign assignment and struggling to file a dispatch from hastily compiled notes – or no notes at all – under genuinely hostile conditions. In such circumstances a gruff kindliness could emerge, even to the extent of a helpful phrase being offered to a novice tongue-tied by tension or shell shock.

But they tended to regard the older and slicker hacks like Bingle more critically, sniffing at the well-worn phrases of popular journalism with a disdain that they never dared to express but often inferred tonally. It came across as a terseness that some correspondents in the junior and middle leagues often found disconcerting. But hardened veterans like Bingle regarded copy-takers as the carthorses of newspaper communications and shrugged off their taciturnity as an oddity of temperament.

'Yep,' said Joe Bailey when Bingle announced himself.

'GEORGE BINGLE. BAKWANGA. CONGO,' said Bingle.

'Hold on,' said Bailey.

Bingle sighed.

'OK, carry on.'

'GEORGE BINGLE BAKWANGA ...'

'Yeah I got that.'

Drop dead you old bastard, thought Bingle.

In the customary manner of the reporter dictating a big story through a difficult telephone connection his voice moved to a higher pitch as he launched into his tale:

'FORCES OF CONGO PREMIER PATRICE LUMUMBA ENCOUNTERED FIERCE RESISTANCE FROM THE ARMY OF THIS VAST TERRITORY'S NEWEST SECESSIONIST LEADER KING ALBERT KALONJI TODAY AS THEY ATTEMPTED TO INVADE HIS NEW COUNTRY THE KIDNEY-SHAPED STATE OF BAKWANGA ...'

'Hang on,' said Bailey. 'You're going too fast.'

I wish they'd retire this old fart, thought Bingle.

He resumed: 'BAKWANGESE TROOPS HOWLING WITH RAGE AT THIS RAPE OF THEIR NEWLY FOUND NATIONHOOD POURED HOT LEAD INTO THE ADVANCING LUMUMBISTES.'

'Yep,' said Bailey.

'THE CHARGING LUMUMBISTES BEGAN TO FALL AND TAKE COVER AS THE HAIL OF BULLETS SCYTHED THROUGH THEM.'

'Yep.'

Bingle, growing irritated, as he always did, at the monotony of the monosyllabic responses, threw in a line off the cuff designed to induce some respect. 'A SCREAMING, WILD-EYED, DRUG-CRAZED LUMUMBISTE SOLDIER FIRING PROLONGED BURSTS FROM AN AK-47 CHARGED STRAIGHT AT ME.'

'Yep.'

'BUT HE DROPPED DEAD, SHOT THROUGH THE HEAD, A MERE YARD FROM ME.'

'Yep.'

Bailey put his hand over the mouthpiece and said to Stubbs out of the corner of his mouth: 'Any moment now he's going to give us his usual shit where he crawls along the ground with bullets flying over his head.' Stubbs picked up the earpiece extension and listened in, grinning.

Bingle dictated: 'I DROPPED TO THE GROUND AND CRAWLED ON MY HANDS AND KNEES FOR COVER AS BULLETS FLEW OVERHEAD ...'

'Hang on. Changing paper.' The two copy-takers exchanged a high handclasp and shook with silent laughter before Bailey slipped another sheet into his typewriter.

Bingle ground on: 'AS THE BATTLE RAGED I MADE MY WAY THROUGH HEAVY JUNGLE TO A REMOTE TRADING STORE TO FILE THIS DISPATCH.'

'Yep.' Bailey put his hand over the mouthpiece again and said out of the corner of his mouth: 'I'll lay you five to one we're going to get a crocodile-infested river out of this one.'

Bingle continued: 'TO REACH THIS VITAL COMMUNICATIONS POINT I HAD TO SWIM ACROSS THE CROCODILE-INFESTED SANKURU RIVER.'

The two copy-takers engaged in another high handclasp and shook with more silent laughter.

Bill Haines, the foreign editor, burst into the copy room. 'What's going on here? We're close on deadline. How's that Bakwanga story coming along?'

'I think he's just finishing, sir,' said Bailey, poker-faced. 'An exciting story, if I may say so. I think they'll be creaming themselves on the underground tomorrow morning.'

When Bingle had finished Carvalho volley-talked with Brussels international again and got Crawley connected to the *Daily Clarion*. While that was going on Carvalho drew Bingle into a quiet corner of the office and hissed at him: 'Monsieur Bingle, this war I hear you reporting – where is it? Why am I not aware of it?'

Bingle felt genuinely embarrassed. Generally he preferred not to be around if doubts were cast on any story of his. He spread his hands. 'Don't worry too much about it, Monsieur Carvalho. You see, I was sent here to cover a war and that is really the story my editors are expecting.'

'But Monsieur Bingle, what about all the information I have given you? That is the true story. With respect, I do not think the story you have sent really happened.'

'Well, I know what you told me is true ... but it is a very complicated and unusual situation, with mercenaries on the way and not arriving, and a boat blown up because a mortar shell drops down the funnel, and an army that disappears into thin air, and a government that appears and then disappears, and a king with a magic stick who appears and disappears. It is all so unusual that it is becoming just about unbelievable. I just know that my newspaper would prefer a simple story the way I have told it.'

Carvalho was silent for a while. Then he said: 'So what you are telling me is that rather than send a true story for fear that it may be disbelieved you prefer to send an untrue story in the hope that it will be believed?'

'Well, yes ... something like that.'

'I see,' said Carvalho, although it was clear that he did not.

When Crawley finished his dispatch Carvalho took the now tired newspapermen over to his residence overlooking the river for a simple meal prepared by himself. 'My cook and other house staff have already fled because they fear the arrival of the Lumumbistes,' he explained apologetically. 'Only my warehouseman, office clerk and the askari on duty at the gate remain because I think they intend to loot the premises after I leave and escape across the river with whatever they can load into a boat.'

Later, as they enjoyed cigars and cognac on the veranda, listening to frogs and a vast variety of other night river sounds, Carvalho said: 'I am still thinking about your dispatches.'

'Yes?' said Bingle, guardedly.

Carvalho spoke solemnly. 'I see historians, in about 100 years from now, trying to piece together this period of events in the Congo and coming across your published reports in the course of their research. The battle for Bakwanga you have described may be immortalised in the history of the Congo. You will have created history. Truly is it said the pen is mightier than the sword.'

The newspapermen sensed the cynicism in his remarks and carefully remained silent. Crawley hung his head.

'Well,' said Carvalho, placing the remainder of his cigar to rest in an ashtray. 'I think it is time to retire. Let me show you to your bedrooms.'

After Carvalho had left them for the night Crawley said: 'I'm not sure that man likes us.' Bingle yawned.

The next morning, while they were breakfasting on the veranda and watching the lethargic Sankuru River swirling by some 20 metres away, Carvalho's office clerk, Jean-Baptiste, arrived to tell him: 'Monsieur, the telex, it speaks!'

They all hurried to the office and found a message for Bingle, which he tore off the machine and read. It said: 'BINGLE YOUR EXCELLENT BAKWANGA BATTLE SPLASHED FRONT PAGE ALL EDITIONS CONGRATULATIONS EDITOR DELIGHTED STOP OFFICIAL UNITED NATIONS AND DIPLOMATIC SOURCES DENY KNOWLEDGE OF WAR SO YOU STILL EXCLUSIVE STOP INFORMATIVELY ALL MAJOR OPPOSITION NOW RUSHING CONGO-WARDS TO COVER BAKWANGA WAR STOP REGARDS HAINES.'

Bingle's broad smile at the first part of the message was eclipsed by an expression of horror when he read the last part. It was such an expression of dismay that Crawley broke all protocol and snatched the message from Bingle's hand and read it. He went ashen-faced and began to keen and blubber.

'Oh my God, Bingle! Oh Jesus! Now look what's happened! Your stupid fucking story has woken up the whole of Fleet Street and they're all on their way here expecting to find a real war! Fuck it, George, I *told* you we shouldn't have done this. What are we going to *do* George? What are we *going to do*? This will cost me my job – and I'm damned sure it's going to cost you yours!'

Carvalho, never able to stand the sight of grown men weeping, discreetly departed.

Bingle, his face screwed up in fierce concentration of thought, was looking out of the window as Crawley continued lamenting and walking back and forth, wringing his hands.

Suddenly Bingle spun around and snapped: 'Shut up, Roger! How can I think with you wailing and whining all the time? I'll think of something, but just shut up, will you?'

Crawley collapsed in a chair and buried his face in his hands. 'What are we going to do?' he whispered through his fingers.

Bingle snapped his fingers and said: 'I've got it! It's so simple. All we have to do is have Kalonji's army defeated and have it disappear back into the bush. It'll take those bastards from London at least two days to get here and all we have to say to them is: "Sorry, mates, you're late as usual. It's all over."'

'You're going to make a whole army just disappear?'

'Well, it disappeared once before didn't it?'

'Yes, but we never got around to saying that. We have now got it on record as dug in around Bakwanga defending king and country, with our readers hanging on every word and expecting to read about another bloody battle tomorrow morning. Now – whoosh! You want to make it disappear like a fucking magician popping rabbits in and out of a hat! Jesus, George, this is a whole army, not a rabbit. How long do you think our editors are going to buy all this shit?'

Bingle sighed patiently. 'Listen, Roger, this country is about the size of the whole of Europe and it's one big fucking jungle. If there is one thing I like about the Congo it's that you can lose an army in it. So let's make the most of it. There's no one here to gainsay our stories. Not even the UN or the agencies have been able to get here or reach these communications yet. We've had a jolly nice war. Let's end it now, lose Kalonji's army and get the hell out of here.'

Carvalho reappeared. 'Messieurs, I am driving towards the town to assess the situation there. Do you wish to accompany me?'

'No thanks, Monsieur Carvalho,' said Bingle. 'We have a complicated situation here to deal with and a story to write.'

'I fully understand,' said Carvalho. 'You do not wish to be confused by the facts.' He departed, shaking his head.

'That bugger's getting cheeky,' muttered Bingle as he drew out his dog-eared road map of the Congo and spread it out on a table. Now let's see, Roger. I suggest we say that Kalonji's army was wiped out in a dawn attack by your Lumumbistes. It was a savage onslaught. They took no prisoners. They gouged out the eyes of those they killed and castrated them ...'

'That's a fucking lie!' said Crawley, angrily. 'No one under my command committed such atrocities!'

Bingle stared at Crawley in alarm and then leaned over and

rapped him on the head with his knuckles. 'Steady on, Roger, it's only a story, mate. You're not getting to believe it, are you?'

Crawley was close to tears again. 'Well I don't know, George. You've got me so confused I just don't know what's real and what's not anymore.'

Bingle grew anxious. 'Take it easy, old mate. Don't you go having a nervous breakdown on me now. Tell you what – why don't I just eliminate my men, most of them killed by your blokes here, just west of Bakwanga?' He jabbed the position on the map with his forefinger. 'You have your guys storming triumphantly into Bakwanga and I'll have the remnants of Kalonji's men retreating to the crocodile-infested Sankuru River, throwing away their guns and swimming the river. Some get eaten by crocs and those who don't disappear into the jungle on the other side. All gone. End of war, end of story. OK?'

'OK,' said Crawley, listlessly.

'Well then,' said Bingle as he rose to his feet and guided his colleague gently to the telex. 'Let's file.'

As Bingle and Crawley set about the final annihilation of King Kalonji's army, desperate scenes were in progress at London's Heathrow Airport. A number of distraught Fleet Street correspondents were jostling each other in their attempts to invade the first morning flight to Brussels to connect with the first available Sabena flight to the Congo. The British Airways counter clerk ignored those who leered and made lewd promises in exchange for a ticket and tossed her head angrily at others who nastily threatened to arrange her dismissal if she did not allow them to crash the wait-list.

In between cajoling and heckling the clerk the correspondents lamented to each other the latest turn of Congo events that had disrupted their lives and got them out of bed early.

'Just got home from the fucking Congo and here we go again,' cursed Richard Kilian of the *Daily Express*.

'... in bed at midnight and on the vinegar stroke when the bloody foreign desk phones and says a war has broken out in the Congo, get there and hit the ground running,' whined Dave Morris of the *Daily Mirror*. 'And I'm supposed to be on holiday – and where is this place Bakwanga, anyway?'

John Osman of the *Daily Telegraph*, large and authoritative, boomed: 'Bloody George Bingle. I knew we shouldn't have left him there on his own. He's probably run wild again. But not even Bingle could suck a war out of his thumb.'

Horace Morley-Brown of *The Times*, peering through horn-rimmed spectacles and not yet quite awake, said: 'Bingle ... Bingle. Isn't he the fellow who nearly got killed reporting that bomb attack in Cyprus last year?'

'Bullshit!' snarled Richard Kilian. 'The only bomb that could have killed Bingle in Cyprus would have had to be thrown into the foyer of the Ledra Palace Hotel in Nicosia, bounce up three flights of stairs, negotiate a way into his bedroom and explode under his bed.'

As the Fleet Street supremos battled for flights at Heathrow, Bingle, in Bakwanga, dumped a pile of soiled Katanga currency notes in front of Carvalho's clerk, Jean-Baptiste, to motivate him into assisting with communications. With surprising alacrity Jean-Baptiste activated the telex and raised the *Daily Banner* via Brussels and Carvalho's secret link with Elisabethville. Bingle sat down and typed his dispatch live into the *Banner* communications room:

'FROM GEORGE BINGLE, BAKWANGA, CONGO: CASTRATE ONE: HOWLING DRUG-CRAZED LUMUMBISTE TROOPS EGGED ON BY CAPERING WITCHDOCTORS LAUNCHED A DAWN ATTACK ON BAKWANGA ARMY POSITIONS TODAY DRIVING THE ARMY INTO FULL RETREAT.

'THE PANIC-STRICKEN BAKWANGESE SOLDIERS FLED, THROWING THEIR WEAPONS AWAY – BUT FEW ESCAPED DEATH AND SHOCKING ATROCITIES. THE ATTACKERS CASTRATED THEIR VICTIMS AND GOUGED OUT THEIR EYES WITH THEIR BAYONETS. BAKWANGESE SURVIVORS REACHING THE BANK OF THE CROCODILE-INFESTED SANKURU RIVER PLUNGED INTO THE WATER AND SWAM FOR THE OPPOSITE BANK. SOME WERE SEIZED BY CROCODILES. THOSE WHO MADE IT TO THE OTHER SIDE FLED INTO THE JUNGLE.

'THE COLLAPSE OF KING KALONJI'S ARMY NOW LEAVES HIS NEWLY CREATED KIDNEY-SHAPED SECESSIONIST STATE OF BAKWANGA OPEN TO THE INVADING FORCES OF CONGO PREMIER PATRICE LUMUMBA.'

Bingle added a few more dramatic paragraphs and ended his dispatch.

An awed *Banner* telex operator typed back: 'DO YOU WANT FOREIGN EDITOR TO COME TO COMMUNICATIONS ROOM?'

Bingle blanched at the thought of having to answer questions and typed back hastily: 'NO. JUST TELL HIM I NOW HAVE TO FLEE THE BATTLEFIELD MYSELF TO SAVE MY OWN NUTS.' He switched off the machine.

Jean-Baptiste reactivated the telex and got the *Daily Clarion* on the line. Crawley, who had been making hurried notes, seated himself in front of the telex but before he could commence typing the machine chattered at him. He stared at the message that emerged. It said: 'FOREIGN EDITOR TO CRAWLEY: REGRET MANAGEMENT HAS ANNOUNCED CLOSURE OF DAILY CLARION FOR FINANCIAL REASONS. RETURN LONDON IMMEDIATELY.'

Crawley's jaw dropped and his eyes glazed. Bingle, watching him, came over to look at the message and was genuinely moved. 'I'm dreadfully sorry, old chap.' He placed a hand on Crawley's shoulder. 'But at least you don't have to worry about being fired anymore ... what I mean is this is a much nicer way to go.'

There was the clattering sound of a Deux Chevaux outside and seconds later Carvalho burst into the room. 'Quick, messieurs, we must depart with haste! I have just returned from the capital. The news is that the Lumumbistes are advancing from Luluabourg. The town is mostly deserted. The Presidential Guard has fled, except for one who is lying drunk on the floor inside the *Palais*.'

'But where are we going?' demanded Bingle.

'There is a special train reserved for VIPs preparing to leave from Dibaya. We can get on it if we hurry. We must go now!'

The departure took less than ten minutes. Carvalho threw a suitcase and his briefcase into the Deux Chevaux. Bingle flung in his and Crawley's typewriters and overnight bags. Crawley, who appeared to be in a state of catatonic withdrawal, was helped into the open back of the vehicle with Jean-Baptiste to look after him. The askari at the gate seemed to have disappeared. '*Alors*,' said Carvalho, leaping into the driver's seat. 'We depart!'

'Aren't you going to lock up your office and house?' asked Bingle.

'*Non,*' replied Carvalho. 'It will all soon be ravaged by thieves and looters. Locking it up will only irritate them.'

The Deux Chevaux bounced and clattered along the 40 kilometres of rutted road to Dibaya. The creepy, hair-tingling sensation that accompanied their fear that they could be ambushed by advancing Lumumbiste troops – or brigands – persisted all the way to Dibaya, but they arrived without incident.

There was an engine breathing steam linked to a tender, two coaches and a covered truck at the siding. It was a wood-burning locomotive and a group of sweating Africans in tattered blue overalls under the direction of another African in greasy grey shorts, a dirty white T-shirt, a battered khaki pith helmet and sandals was loading timber into the tender from a handcart.

Bingle noticed that a considerable area around the siding was denuded of trees. Only their stumps remained and it was obvious that for some time the surrounding forest had been used for fuel.

Carvalho spoke to the man in the pith helmet who replied volubly in what seemed a mixture of French and a local dialect.

'Who is he and what's he saying?' asked Bingle.

'He is the engine driver,' replied Carvalho. 'And he is saying that he will transport us to Elisabethville for 100 US dollars per person and he will not accept Katangese or Congolese currency. And there is a further condition.'

'What's that?' asked Bingle.

'He says he will not have enough fuel for the complete journey so when the engine runs out of wood we will all have to assist in chopping down trees at the side of the railway to refuel it.'

'Well,' said Bingle. 'In the circumstances we can hardly refuse, so tell him OK.' He drew out his wallet, extracted 400 dollars in US currency and gave the money to the engine driver. 'You have been very helpful and kind to us, Monsieur Carvalho. Please allow my newspaper to pay your fare and that of Jean-Baptiste to Elisabethville.'

'I accept, Monsieur Bingle,' replied Carvalho cheerfully. 'And your generosity will of course also buy my silence.' Bingle ignored the remark.

They mounted the leading carriage and Bingle led the way

down its corridor. He slid open the door of the first compartment he came to and stopped, astonished at what he saw.

In the dim light of the interior were seated four Africans in formal, although somewhat crumpled lounge suits and, considering the general situation and the heat, fairly neat collars and ties. All were wearing dark glasses – but Bingle had no difficulty in recognising King Kalonji. He was seated in the furthermost corner with his magic Ibi stick across his knees.

The king's immediate reaction on seeing Bingle was a reflexive movement of his right foot. It was to nudge more snugly under his seat a large and extremely full-looking leather bag. As Bingle remarked to a colleague at a later stage he would not have been surprised to discover that the bag contained at least a month's production of all the diamond mines in the now doomed kidney-shaped state of Bakwanga.

The man seated beside the king rose swiftly to his feet, his hand reaching ominously under his jacket to what was undoubtedly a shoulder-holster. '*Ce position est occupé, monsieur!*' he snapped.

Bingle ignored the bodyguard and addressed the king: 'Good day, your majesty. I am George Bingle of the London *Daily Banner*. Do you have any comment to make on the current state of affairs in Bakwanga and what your destination might be at this moment?'

The king pointed his magic Ibi stick at Bingle. '*C'est pas d'importance,*' he said.

11
Guns and roses

Professor James Arthur Dewey was in his rose garden when he got the message. His wife, Judith, called him to the telephone. It was a late Saturday afternoon.

He placed the pruning shears in the basket and removed his gloves carefully. Then he trudged to the house, a tall angular man in his early 60s, grey-haired and bespectacled. His gait revealed only slightly the stiffness of an elderly person having risen swiftly from a kneeling, working position.

The telephone receiver had been carefully laid down for him on the hall table. His wife, wiping her hands on a dishcloth, watched him from the door at the end of the hall that led to the kitchen.

He raised the receiver to his ear. 'Dewey here.'

The voice at the other end was clipped and toneless. It said: 'Call me back.' The line went dead.

Dewey dialled a number that he knew by memory. He avoided looking at his wife.

The call was answered immediately. 'One hundred hours,' said the voice. 'Usual place. Probably two days, maybe longer. Bring your man.' The line went dead.

Dewey replaced the receiver and sighed. He looked at his wife and grimaced. 'Sorry, love. I'll be gone two days, maybe longer. I'll have to take Titus.'

She shrugged wearily and went back into the kitchen.

Professor Dewey went back to the garden and stood watching the gardener cleaning up where he had pruned. 'No more today, Titus,' he said, in Swahili. 'Memsahib will finish the pruning on Monday. We leave at midnight. Be ready.'

The gardener, a thin, wiry man whose hair was tinged with grey, and who was approximately the same age as the professor, leaned on his rake and looked at him, grinning. Then he straightened up and, sloping the rake on his shoulder like a rifle, he gave a jocular military salute and barked: '*Ndio Bwana!*'

The Professor smiled briefly and walked away. Silly bugger. Always ready for a fight.

He had tea with Judith and had the sort of conversation that usually preceded departures of this sort. Sometimes, when the departures were sudden, there was time for only a few hurried words. At other times like these they were thankful for the longer notice.

'Getting chilly,' he said. 'You'll need a fire tonight.'

She poured the tea. She was slim, composed, not yet grey, but the blonde hair that once shone in the African sun had also been faded by the African sun. The sun had also punished her skin and lined it at the corners of her eyes and mouth. But the eyes remained a deep blue and the lips retained much of their fullness. She was an attractive woman, but quiet. At times like this she was quieter.

Dewey kept the conversation going. 'I'll take the Peugeot. The station wagon's due for a service on Monday. Can you take it in?'

She nodded.

'And you'll call the dean? I've got a lecture scheduled at ten. Ask him to make an arrangement with Dr Merrington. And I've got two more lectures on Tuesday. Nicola's got my schedule. I hope Merrington can help out again. The dean will have to work it out. God, we're getting so short of people.'

She rose and placed a hand on his shoulder. She stroked his hair, fluffing it over the balding spot on the top of his head in a habitual gesture of affection. 'Stop worrying,' she said. 'I'll sort it all out. And the university will cope. It always does. I'm going to get dinner ready. You must try and get some sleep before you go.' She went indoors.

Dr James Arthur Dewey, Professor of African Studies at the University College of Rhodesia, lit a cigarette and stared thoughtfully into the deepening dusk. It was four years since, like many other middle-aged and elderly men, he had become sucked into the war as the conscription demands on the country's small white civilian population became more pressing.

He went to bed at eight p.m. and rose an hour before midnight.

While Judith made coffee he went to a corner of the bedroom, opened the steel trunk that she jocularly called his 'war chest' and laid its contents out on the bed.

He showered, came back into the bedroom and put on the faded combat fatigues, the lightweight paratrooper boots and the webbing.

He checked through a small rucksack, the contents of which included minimal toiletries, sun-protection creams, lip balm, a compass and a Browning 9-mm pistol. There was also a plastic pack of special survival rations and gadgetry that he had never had to use and that he could only assume were still viable.

He went to the bedside table and transferred to the rucksack a packet of aspirin and the pills that he used for a minor heart ailment. He hesitated a moment, then slid open the bedside-table drawer and added three packets of the cigarettes he had been medically advised not to smoke.

He went into his study, which adjoined the bedroom, spun the safety combination on the full-length gun safe and took out the two army-issue FN automatic rifles and ammunition clips.

Judith came in with the coffee and they drank it in silence. He then took her in his arms and kissed her. He gathered up his equipment and trudged to the front door where they kissed again. She had become a good army wife for these occasions and showed little emotion. 'Be careful,' was all she said. But she ached as she watched him walk away. She had come to worry more about the stress of these expeditions than the events involved. She knew that he was taking strain and was very tired.

Titus, also wearing combat fatigues and carrying a pack, emerged from the shadows, and Dewey handed him the second FN rifle.

They drove to New Sarum military airport in silence. Dewey showed his security pass at the gate, drove some distance to a hangar and parked beside it. The two armed guards saw the captain's pips on Dewey's shoulder straps and saluted smartly. Nonetheless they studied his and Titus's security passes carefully before opening the heavy steel doors sufficiently to let them through. They stepped inside.

The large hangar teemed with activity. It smelled of sweat, coffee, gun oil, high-octane fuel and leather. Two aged Dakotas stood nose to tail in the centre of it and supplies were being loaded into them. A group of soldiers sat on their packs in a semicircle near the first aircraft, being addressed by an officer carrying a clipboard. Some were black and some white. They wore camouflage combat fatigues and a medley of headgear including green berets, bush hats and twin-peaked forage caps but bore no insignia or badges of rank. Some had been issued with Rhodesian government-issue FN automatic rifles but others carried AK-47 assault rifles. They were a rough and sinister-looking lot, most of them unshaven.

Dewey recognised them instantly as Selous Scouts and sighed. So it was going to be that kind of operation.

Titus also recognised them and spat. '*Hau!* The thieves are here,' he said.

'Shut up, we don't want trouble,' warned Dewey sharply.

On a previous excursion with the Selous Scouts Titus had lost a favourite knife, and he was convinced one of the Scouts had stolen it.

The Scouts were special forces, named after the famous nineteenth-century big-game hunter, Frederick Courteney Selous.

A smaller group of troops, also in full combat rig but wearing khaki bush hats, were beneath a wing of the other Dakota. A few were standing and talking among themselves, and there was a burst of laughter at something said by one of them. Some were sitting, but most of the group were asleep on the ground in sleeping bags. They appeared to have been there throughout the night.

Dewey recognised their RLI shoulder tags. 'Rhodesia Light Infantry,' he murmured. 'Fewer than three sticks.' He had become accustomed to military parlance. A 'stick' was seven men: the sections in which they were dropped in low-level parachute attacks, usually in front and behind the enemy. It was a highly effective tactic in the bush war against an enemy who usually operated in tight groups of between 10 and 40. He now estimated the RLI present at around 20.

'*Ndio,*' grunted Titus. 'The ones standing and sitting are the old ones. Those still asleep are the children.'

Dewey smiled at the accuracy of the observation. It was true that the RLI, a wholly white unit, was now taking recruits straight out of high school, sucking at the youth of the nation as the army's needs became more urgent. The white population of Rhodesia had fallen below 200 000 and recruitment had become more difficult as emigration increased and some youngsters evaded conscription, slipping away to work or for education in South Africa or overseas. The army had become desperate enough to make deals with recruits in some instances: to allow them to go to college and come back and fight during their vacations.

An RLI major hurried over to them. 'Welcome, Professor,' he said. 'Briefing at 02:00. Take-off at 03:00. Meantime have coffee.' He rushed off.

Dewey and Titus went to the trestle tables against a side of the hangar where coffee percolated and long rows of mugs stood. They helped themselves to the brew and moved to a nearby vacant wooden bench.

Titus drank his coffee, then curled up on the floor with his head on his pack and went to sleep.

Professor Dewey craved a cigarette, but smoking was not permitted in the hangar. He sipped his coffee and contemplated the snoring African at his feet, envying his ability to lie down and sleep at any given moment and place.

They had been together since the Kenya days. Dewey had been a district commissioner in the North Frontier District of Kenya, and towards the end had encountered serious problems with *shifta* – bandits – and poachers. He had sent out an urgent request for more trackers and had been sent Titus, who had turned out to be the best of the lot. Titus had served in the King's African Rifles until it had become the Kenya African Rifles under the black government of the newly independent Kenya. Like all other KAR regulars who had fought against the Mau Mau, he had been demobilised. They had been replaced by new recruits considered untainted by colonial vices. He had returned to his village in the north. He was of the Tharaka tribe, renowned as hunters, and it was there that he had heard of the call for trackers.

'It was as well that you found me,' he informed Dewey later. 'If

209

I had not come to work for you I would have become a poacher, and then you would have had much grief.'

Soon after Kenya became an independent nation Dewey was transferred to the Bechuanaland Protectorate. He was able to make arrangements to take Titus with him. When the protectorate itself became independent under its new name of Botswana, he took early retirement, settled in Rhodesia, again taking Titus with him, and embarked on formal study of the African people and the languages he had picked up during his service in the colonies. Eight years later, having acquired his doctorate, he took over the Department of African Studies at what was then called the University College of Rhodesia. Titus, now gardener, sometimes chauffeur and general factotum, had become part of his family and clearly would be so forever.

As usual when he thought of Kenya – a land he had come to love more than any other he had ever known and where he had met and married Judith and spent the happiest days of his life – he drifted into a reverie.

But his thoughts were disturbed by the arrival of Captain Porky Cronwright. Like Dewey, Porky Cronwright was a part-time soldier. Whereas Dewey felt only mildly awkward in the role, having acquired some military-related experiences as a DC, Cronwright felt intensely uncomfortable in it. He had no liking for it and he did not have the physique for it. He was plump and awkward of movement and his camouflage fatigues and combat bush hat, from under which his lank blond hair stuck out in tufts, were ill-fitting on him. With the bulky pistol that hung on a webbing belt beneath his paunch, he looked as though he had kitted up for a fancy-dress parade. He was a Billy Bunter-looking caricature of the middle-aged citizens who had to perform their quota of military service to back up the regular army.

They had become hilariously known as the Salusa Scouts, named after a popular energy tonic for the middle-aged sold in local pharmacies called Salusa 45, providing a wordplay on the far more sinister and ruthless Selous Scouts. It was also joked that more Salusa Scouts died of heart attacks in action than were killed in action. Normally the Salusa Scouts were used for guard and base duties, communications and transport, and only rarely in front-line combat.

But rather like Professor Dewey, Porky Cronwright had specialised gifts that had resulted in his being seconded to Military Intelligence and sometimes getting him involved in special ops like the current one. It was on these occasions that Dewey sometimes met him. Captain Cronwright was, in civilian life, a mining inspector and this gave him intimate knowledge of certain terrain. This was the knowledge he had that the army valued.

He was now relieved to see a fellow member of the quasi-military. 'Hullo, James, old boy. I've been sent to get you. Briefing's starting. Come now.'

Leaving Titus to snore away, Dewey accompanied Cronwright to the sealed-off office area of the hangar outside which an RLI guard stood duty.

They entered a room where a shaven-headed major of the RLI was standing before an enlarged wall map. 'All here now?' he said, irritably, not removing his eyes from the map, as soon as Dewey and Cronwright had entered. 'All right, shut the door and pay attention.'

He pointed to the wall map. The briefing was short and to the point. 'Dak one will drop the Selous Scouts into Sontu. It's a village across the border here between Tambare and Chemba. There are terrs coming across through that village and we intend to ask the chief there to assist us in our enquiries.

'Meantime Dak two will land the RLI and our advisers on the strip at Nyamapanda just inside our border. Two choppers will take the RLI to vantage points east of Sontu here and here to provide cover for the Scouts while they get acquainted with the villagers. We don't expect interference but we know there are terrs in the area. A third chopper will take our special advisers, supplies and backup ammo straight to Sontu. This is all that everyone here needs to know. The RLI and Scouts commanders have been fully briefed. Any questions? No? Good, let's go.'

They boarded the Dakotas, which were towed by tractors clear of the hangar, where they started their engines, revved and taxied to the take-off point. They were in the air 13 minutes after the briefing had concluded.

They landed at Nyamapanda where farmers in the area, who doubled as police and army reservists, had set up flares alongside the airstrip. The first light of day was touching the nearby mountains.

The other Dakota did not land. It flew on across the border into Mozambique where it would make a wide circle before parachuting the Selous Scouts onto Sontu to rudely awaken its inhabitants.

The RLI had piled out of the Dakota at Nyamaponda and were boarding two of the three helicopters waiting beside the strip. During the flight there had been some change of clothing and the troops had stripped to khaki T-shirts, gym shorts and lightweight canvas footwear. They carried only their FN automatic rifles. The webbing packs about their waists contained only water and ammunition clips. They were lean and light for action. Only the two light-machine-gun crews were further burdened by heavy belts of ammunition looped across their shoulders.

Porky Cronwright suddenly pointed to one of the RLI troopers scrambling onto a helicopter.

'Look, James! Isn't that Jack Corley's son? What's he doing here? He can't be more than 15 years old!'

'Yes, that's young Robert. Turned 16 in January. They only give them three months' training now. This may be his first action.'

Cronwright shook his head. 'Doesn't seem right. Seems only yesterday I was on their farm at Bindura and his father was giving him a bollocking for forgetting to take his firearm with him when he went from one room to another. He must have been about 12 then ... These kids are growing up too fast, James. It's tragic. Where has their childhood gone?'

Dewey shrugged. 'You have a point. On the other hand they seem to enjoy it. Look at the youngsters among that lot. Excited as hell. Might be going off to hunt buck for all they cared.'

The two RLI helicopters took off. Dewey and Cronwright turned their backs to the dust. The supplies from the Dakota were being transferred swiftly to the third chopper. When it was done they were waved aboard and they headed across the border, the chopper flying close to treetop level. Dewey's heart was not in this war. But now that the mission was in progress, with the thumping roar of the rotors in his ears and the treetops rushing by below him, he felt himself succumbing to the flow of adrenalin and the thrill of action. They reached their destination in 45 minutes.

The pilot turned and gave a thumbs-up signal, shouting something. 'What's he saying?' asked Cronwright.

'He says the village has been secured and we're going in.'

They landed a few minutes later.

A hut was burning, suffusing the area in smoke, through which the first rays of the rising sun spread a pattern of colours. Women and children had been herded into a group and made to sit closely together under the guard of two Scouts. A few were wailing hysterically and children were crying. The men of the village who had not escaped had been made to lie flat on their stomachs, watched by several Scouts.

Other Scouts were searching the huts. They were bringing out knives, spears, axes – anything that resembled a weapon – and dumping them in a pile in front of the hut of the village chief near a huge mopani tree that dominated the centre of the village. They probed the thatch of the huts and found more spears hidden there, which they added to the pile.

'They must dig under the fireplaces,' said Titus. 'Must I tell them, *Bwana*?'

'Yes,' said Dewey. 'Carry on.' Titus eagerly joined the action.

Two small boys and an older boy, in his late teens, who had the appearance of being a mute or otherwise mentally retarded, sat beside the growing pile of seized weaponry.

Cronwright, always concerned about children, pointed at the three and asked one of the Scouts: 'Who are they?'

'They are the sons of the chief, sir.'

A command post had been set up under the mopani tree. It consisted of the RLI major, seated in a camp chair and smoking a cheroot, watching a sergeant and two troopers squatting on the ground in front of him operating a field radio.

The village chief, an elderly grey-haired man, was being held by two Scouts outside his hut, and had fallen to his knees. One of his captors held him insolently by an ear. He was being interrogated by an officer who first tried Portuguese, then Shona and then Ndebele. At each question his ear was tweaked viciously, and the chief gasped in pain. But he said nothing.

When Dewey arrived the officer, a captain, turned to him and said: 'The bastard won't talk, Professor. Not sure whether he doesn't understand or just won't play. It's over to you.'

'Let him go,' said Dewey. The man holding the chief's ear released it reluctantly. The chief sank to a sitting position.

Dewey spoke gently in Swahili and then in Chuabo, the dialect of the region. 'It would be better to speak with us, even if you know nothing, than to remain silent,' he said in both languages. The man's eyelids flickered almost imperceptibly when Dewey spoke Chuabo and Dewey knew he had got the message across. But still the chief remained silent.

The captain walked over to the three boys seated beside the weapons pile and, seizing the middle one, aged about 12, by the arm, dragged him over to the chief. The child was sullen-faced and tense.

'Is this your son?' asked the captain in Portuguese.

Dewey repeated the question in Chuabo. After several seconds of silence the chief nodded.

'Good,' said the captain, and thrust the boy into the arms of one of his men. 'Carry on, sergeant – under that tree over there!' The child, now whimpering, was made to stand under the tree. The sergeant, with an exaggerated show of deliberation, removed the magazine clip from his weapon, glanced at it and slotted it back into position. He worked the breech and stood facing the boy in a firing position.

From the group of women came a long, high-pitched wail as the mother of the child tried to stand but was roughly pushed back onto the ground by a guard.

A Scout selected a pumpkin from a pile outside a hut and, walking over to the child, placed it on his head. The boy stood quivering, the large yellow pumpkin balancing precariously.

The captain turned to Dewey. 'Ask the chief if he now wishes to speak.' Dewey put the question in Chuabo.

The child, without moving his head, turned his eyes, the whites showing hugely, in the direction of his father, his lips quivering, tears streaking his face.

The chief seemed to have turned to stone. His face went grey as the blood drained from it. Then he raised his head and stared steadily at his son. He said nothing. As if some steely message had passed between them, the boy's fear seemed to steady into an expression of trembling defiance. His chin rose almost imperceptibly.

The captain nodded at the sergeant who raised his rifle and took aim. A loud collective wailing burst forth from the women. The sergeant fired.

The bullet shattered the pumpkin and the boy staggered back half a step. Then, drawing himself to his full height, which was not very high, he spat at the sergeant.

There was complete silence as the astonished onlookers absorbed the moment.

'Well, fuck me!' said the sergeant. 'What a cheeky little bastard! Shall I slot him sir?'

'No!' snapped the captain, visibly discomfited. 'Let him go.' Then he shouted: 'Look out, sergeant!'

The elder brother, the mute, had jumped up and seized a spear from the pile of weapons nearby and was now charging at the sergeant, the spear held at high thrust. But the sergeant, alerted by the captain's shout, whirled and emptied the contents of his weapon into the charging youth.

The mute, caught by the full burst of bullets, dropped the spear, whirled, staggered and fell to the ground, where he lay twitching, trying to rise. The sergeant furiously replaced the spent magazine with a clip from his belt, stepped up to the dying youth and pumped two more shots into his chest. Still the mute tried to rise. The sergeant shot him once more, through the head.

Again the women wailed, this time louder than before: long, high, keening cries of anguish.

Another sound added to the cacophony. One of the captive men, lying face down, shouted: *'Jeee-Yaama!'* and tried to scramble to his feet. One of the guards, who had been momentarily distracted by the action in front of the chief's hut, immediately knocked him senseless with a rifle butt.

The captain pointed at the chief. 'Get him into his hut!' he shouted. The chief, open-mouthed at the events, was dragged into the hut.

Dewey, grim-faced, unhooked the water bottle from his belt and drank from it. He looked round for Cronwright and found him leaning against a nearby hut, vomiting.

When he had finished Cronwright slid into a sitting position in the shade of the hut and gasped weakly, holding his hat in one hand and his spectacles in the other. 'I'm sorry, James. I have never seen anything like this before.'

The captain came storming out of the chief's hut. 'Captain Dewey, please come here. We need you.' He went back into the hut.

Dewey walked over and entered the chief's hut, stooping under the low lintel. The chief was spread-eagled on his back, held down by four men. A fifth was holding his head between his hands. A cloth had been placed over his face and a sixth man was pouring water onto it from a calabash.

Dewey turned and walked out of the hut. The captain followed him. 'What?' he enquired. 'What?'

'I am not going to be present at anything like that,' said Dewey, coldly. 'You can call me when he says he is ready to talk.'

'Well, fuck it, can anyone tell me why we brought you?' fumed the captain and went back into the hut.

Dewey went to stand in the shade of the mopani tree and lit a cigarette. He tried to stop his hands from shaking. Cronwright came over and joined him, flopping down into a sitting position, his back against the tree trunk, mopping his face with a handkerchief that he soaked repeatedly from his water bottle.

They were close to the command post where the radio was spitting static, punctuated by sharper static. It was a few moments before Dewey realised that the sharper static was small-arms fire. The RLI major was leaning forward, cheroot between his teeth, showing interest. The radio operators were crouched low over the set, trying to make out the message.

'What's he saying?' demanded the major irritably.

'It's Lieutenant Benton, sir. Contact with terrs, sir. Estimating between 40 and 50. Estimating about two miles from here. Enemy withdrawing – but in two different directions. Lieutenant Benton requesting permission to pursue, sir.'

'What's the score?'

'Four floppies plus two wounded sir. On our side: one dead, one wounded and one snakebite.'

The major hesitated only a moment. 'Permission to pursue refused. Disengage, repeat disengage, and await transport. I also want all enemy dead and wounded brought in. Copy that message to their chopper.'

The major got out of his chair and stretched. 'We can't hang around here too long. I don't like what's lurking around us. Dewey, go and tell Captain Borrowic to hurry up with the interrogation. If he can't get the chief to talk we can take him home with us – ah, here you are Borrowic. I was just sending Dewey to ask you to hurry up.'

Captain Borrowic responded curtly, as Selous Scout officers tended to do with officers of other units. 'The chief's dead. Heart attack, if I had to guess.' He avoided meeting Dewey's eye. 'But we've got his brother in there now, and I believe he is prepared to talk – if Captain Dewey would like to follow me.'

Dewey walked back with the captain and stooped to enter the hut. The stench was revolting. The chief lay dead, and in his dying had lost control of his bowels.

The man seated beside him appeared terrified. He had clearly been beaten. One eye was almost totally closed. The white of the other eye showed large in the gloom of the hut. He had probably witnessed the death of the chief. In the growing heat of the day and the close confines of the hut he was sweating profusely.

'Get him out of here,' said Dewey, holding a handkerchief over his nose. The man was assisted outside and lowered into a sitting position in the shade of the hut.

'Bring water for him,' Dewey said. And while water was being brought he offered the man a cigarette. Then, squatting beside the prisoner, he began the interrogation, patiently translating the questions put by the captain. He had to admit to himself that the results were good.

As they ended the questioning a Scout arrived on the run and dropped a round-shaped biscuit tin at the feet of the captain. The edges of its lid were sealed with tape and it smelled faintly bad. 'Found it in the village latrine, sir, at the end of a cord concealed by being dug into the side of the long drop.' He added, apologetically: 'We washed it clean as best we could, sir.'

'OK, open it,' said the captain.

The Scout unsheathed a knife, sliced the tape and prised the lid open.

The captain squatted beside the tin and lifted out a wad of documents. He flipped through the papers for several minutes.

217

'Bingo!' he said. 'This was worth coming for. There are maps, arms-cache sketches and orders here for the next bunch of terrs due to come through.'

He stood up. 'Let's go,' he said. He walked over to the RLI major. 'We've finished here. You can call in the transport.'

Before they left they destroyed the motley collection of weapons and burned down every hut in the village. As their helicopters departed there was fire and smoke everywhere, and the wailing of women.

They landed at the Nyamapanda airstrip shortly after the arrival there of the helicopter bearing Lieutenant Benton's section. Five bodies had been unceremoniously dumped from the aircraft and lay in an untidy heap. Two wounded prisoners, one lying on a stretcher and the other, his head bandaged and his hands bound, sat sullenly beside them.

The Selous Scouts again went busily about their work. Captain Borrowic, notebook and pencil in hand, knelt beside the prisoners and began questioning them. This time, pointedly, he did not ask for Dewey's assistance. He used one of his own black Shona-speaking men.

Borrowic's Scouts began stripping the dead men. They searched their pockets and webbing pouches, shook out their boots, examined the insides of their leather belts. They even emptied their water bottles and broke them open. Finally they fingerprinted and photographed the corpses, making certain they got clear pictures of the faces.

A Dakota landed on the strip. A wounded RLI troopie still in the chopper was carried to the Dak. Then the dead RLI infantryman was gently lowered on a stretcher and carried across to the plane.

'My God, James,' said Cronwright, going a sickly colour for the second time in four hours, 'it's young Robert Corley. Oh Jesus, James ... 16 years old. Jack and Anne will be devastated. It's their only kid ... '

Another RLI infantryman was lifted out of the chopper. Dewey walked over to help because there were only three medics, one of them holding a drip, and they were having difficulty getting the man onto a stretcher. He was a large, heavy man and his face was bluish. Yellow saliva ran from a corner of his mouth.

'Thank you, sir,' gasped the medic corporal.

'Where's he wounded?' asked Dewey, puzzled at the absence of blood or bandages.

'Snakebite, sir. Bloody puff adder. In the neck unfortunately. We've injected serum, but we're going to lose him unless we get him into intensive care quickly.'

They lifted the stretcher and took their burden to the Dakota at a trot. The plane took off almost immediately.

Captain Borrowic, now disposed to be friendly, came over to Dewey. 'It was a good hit. We got valuable information,' he said. 'I'm grateful for the help given by your man, Titus. He put us onto the latrine hiding-place trick. He seems to have had lots of experience.'

'He's been around,' admitted Dewey. 'What are you doing about the wounded prisoners?'

'One's dead. The other one is lightly wounded. We'll look after him here tonight. We need to question him some more.'

He had become curt again. 'You worry too much about these people. Think rather of what they are doing to us.' He walked away.

A group of farmers, wearing police-reservist T-shirts and carrying government-issue FN rifles, were on the airstrip. They were the same people who had set up landing flares in the predawn hours. One of them now strolled over to Dewey.

'Hullo James. Remember me? Alan Forrester. We met a year ago on Brian Hoskin's farm at Centenary. At his daughter's wedding.'

'Ah yes,' said Dewey, shaking his hand vigorously. 'Of course I remember!' Although in fact he could not remember the man, only the wedding. He hated admitting that his memory was becoming faulty.

'Listen,' said Forrester. 'Your Dak's been diverted. Alternative transport will be coming in tomorrow morning. You're stuck here tonight, I'm afraid. Why don't you come back to my place for tea and stay on for dinner?'

Dewey hesitated and then gave in to the temptation of a shower, a clean shirt, a decent meal and the chance to telephone Judith. 'Thank you, I would be delighted,' he said.

The Forrester farm was typically Rhodesian. A rambling colonial-style homestead dramatically set under the brilliance of flame trees against a koppie overlooking a valley that dipped first into tobacco plantations and then, further on, into maize fields. Then onwards to silent, brooding savannah where herds of cattle grazed, and finally rising to the blue-grey mountains about 15 miles distant, yet so splendidly etched in the evening sky that they seemed near enough to touch. Rich lawn, constantly watered, shaded by more trees, rolled about the house, encompassing the essential swimming pool and tennis court. The tobacco barns, vehicle sheds and beyond them the staff quarters spread below the farm on the western side of the hill.

That all was not well with this Shangri La was indicated by the ten-foot-high electrified security fence enclosing the complex and the sandbags that were stacked halfway up each window of the homestead and in a barricade around the stoep. The windows themselves were criss-crossed with anti-shatter tape.

'Sorry about the fortifications,' apologised Alan Forrester. 'We've had no attacks yet, but it's best to be careful. The Hendersons, only eight miles from here, got an RPG through their living-room window last week. No one hurt, thank God, but it made a hell of a mess.'

The dinner was superb. Alan's attractive dark-haired wife, Rina, served lentil soup, roast venison and vegetables from her own garden followed by home-made ice cream and a crushed fruit juice, again a home recipe.

'We owe the venison to Philip here. He shot a duiker last week,' said Rina. The 13-year-old boy at the table smiled shyly.

His sister, Fiona, a pert ten-year-old, who liked to get all the facts on record, chipped in. 'It took him two shots. He only wounded it the first time.' She got a venomous look from her brother.

'Lucky to get it all the same,' said Alan. 'The game's getting scarce. Bloody terrs are shooting it all out.'

They dined as all Rhodesian farming families now dined: with their firearms laid carefully on the floor beside them. When they moved to another room – or merely across the room – they took their weapons with them. JOC (Joint Operations Command) circulars dictated that this was how it had to be, and they did it, always alert to the possibility of a surprise attack. All the farms were linked by radio to each other and to JOC bases, and if they were attacked they could call for support. But until it got there they had to defend themselves. The small children to be secured in the safest places away from windows. The parents and the older children had to fight – and to do this they had to know how to handle the firearms issued to them by JOC. It was forbidden to eat, sleep, work, fornicate, urinate or defecate without your weapon beside you.

When the meal ended and the children had gone to bed, Alan, Dewey and Rina sat in the living room, their weapons beside them, and chatted over coffee and brandy.

'What do you think, James?' asked Alan. 'How does it look from Salisbury?'

'It doesn't look good from Salisbury. It seems Ian Smith is ready to make concessions. That speaks for itself.'

'Yes, well ... since the bloody South Africans have decided to abandon us to our fate for their own misconceived reasons, we are on our own, aren't we? I mean, they of all people ...' He shook his head in disbelief.

After a moment of hesitation he went on: 'You know, James, maybe I'm out of line discussing this with you, but I know we are talking confidentially. You know we farmers are privileged to a lot of inside military intelligence. One of the benefits of being in the front line, so to speak.'

Dewey nodded.

'But the intelligence is pretty disheartening. What it amounts to is that the country is crawling with terrs and we are losing this war – especially since South Africa has cut off our ammo.'

He heaved a heavy sigh before he made his next remark. 'Rina and I have decided to quit Rhodesia. We've had enough. The risks have reached the point where they are overtaking the returns.'

Dewey studied Alan Forrester as he paused to light a cigarette. He was a lean, strong man, tanned and fit. Probably in his early forties. But his brown hair was greying and his face showed the lines of stress.

'It's like this,' Forrester continued. 'There can't be more than about 180 000 whites left in Rhodesia, including women, children and the elderly. Fifty thousand of us are in military service, either full time or part time, and that number includes our middle-aged, some of the elderly, a lot of the women and some of the children.

'How much longer can we go on like this, outnumbered ten to one and the whole bloody world against us, all for their various self-interested reasons? I don't know any other country in such a situation, unless it's Israel, but at least they have the United States behind them. Here we can't even get the Bright Lights anymore.'

'Bright Lights' was the name given to armed civilian volunteers from the cities like Salisbury and Bulawayo who spent weekends or longer periods on farms as night guards to enable farmers to rest.

Forrester sipped his brandy and took a draw on his cigarette. 'My eldest son, aged only 18, mark you, is in charge of a fortified labour camp near Chimanimani – the only white man living among 300 blacks, and that doesn't include the terrs around them. What that means is that each day we wait for bad news.

'Last week all my cattle dips were destroyed, which is one of the reasons for your operation today. What it comes down to is this: how much longer can so few hold out against so many?'

Dewey glanced at Rina, who was quietly sewing. She caught his eye and smiled. 'It's not me,' she said. 'I am prepared to stay. It seems such a pity to go. We have spent 20 years building this place up. There was just bush when we first came here. But it's Alan's decision. And of course I go where he goes.'

Alan grinned ruefully. 'This comes from marrying an Afrikaner. There's your typical Boer woman speaking. They were always the toughest.'

Then he grew serious again. 'What it comes down to in the end is the kids. What future is there here for them? And is it fair on them that as children they should grow up with guns in their hands, prepared to kill or to die? What do you think, James? You have seen more of Africa than we have.'

Dewey shrugged. 'In the end it comes down to the African leader you are stuck with. In the Congo it was a disaster. In Kenya, a semi-disaster. In Botswana we have seen that it can actually work out quite well.'

He paused to light a cigarette and exhaled thoughtfully. 'Here in Rhodesia, well ... I don't think the fat man, Nkomo, and his lot will count for much in the end. I think it's ZANU that we will end up with. That means the leader will be Robert Mugabe.'

'And what sort of leader do you think Mugabe will be?'

'I don't know,' said Dewey. 'He's a communist, so it's hard to say at this stage.' He paused for several seconds. 'We can only hope for the best.'

He departed soon afterwards after telephoning Judith in Salisbury to assure her he was well. He did not tell her about Robert Corley. Better to be with her when he told her. He declined Forrester's offer of a bed for the night. 'I'd better get back to the camp. I think that's where I'm expected to be,' he said.

Forrester drove him back to the tented camp beside the airstrip. 'Nice thing about the Selous Scouts being here is that you can drive safely, even at night,' Forrester said. 'If there's one outfit the terrs are shit-scared of and will keep away from, it's the Scouts.'

A sentry on the airstrip directed him to the tent that had been allocated to him, Cronwright and Titus. Cronwright was already in bed and snoring. But Titus was up, fully dressed and waiting for him.

'Bwana, I am pleased you have returned, for I have a thing of great wonder to show you.'

'Titus, please, I am tired.'

'No, Bwana, come with me, for this thing you may never see again.'

They stepped outside the tent and Titus raised his hand. 'What do you hear, Bwana?'

Dewey listened carefully and heard distant sounds of revelry. 'It sounds like a party.'

'That is so, Bwana. We must go to it for I believe this thing that I saw will now happen again.'

Protesting mildly, Dewey allowed himself to be led to the distant glow of a campfire.

When they reached it he saw a large number of Selous Scouts, most of whom appeared to be drunk, seated about the fire. A ginger-haired young man, his camouflage jacket unbuttoned, who appeared to be doubling as a bookmaker and a compère, was taking bets. 'The book is about to close!' he shouted. There was loud cheering. 'Closing, closing, the book is now CLOSED!' More loud cheering.

'OK,' said the ginger-haired man. 'Gentlemen, we present the one and only Tripod van der Merwe who, his batteries recharged and refreshed and made strong again by rum and Coke, will amaze you with his second and last performance of the evening!'

There was another burst of cheering and applause – and a gigantic man stepped into the firelight. He was stark naked.

He was well over six feet, slope-browed, jut-jawed and bearded in the way many Selous Scouts were. He was impressively muscled, but all attention was riveted on his penis, which was formidably large and left no doubt as to how he had acquired his nickname of Tripod.

Another, more lithe Scout, also naked but for a brief item of underwear, appeared before the giant holding up what appeared to be a tattered booklet. It was only after several minutes that Dewey realised that what was being displayed to the large man was the centrefold of a *Playboy* magazine.

'Now concentrate, Tripod! There's a lot of bucks at stake here!' yelled the ginger-haired man.

In response to the order Tripod beetled his brows and tensed his big muscles, scowling down at the *Playboy* centrefold, the bearer of which began to gyrate his loins enticingly and, presumably, helpfully.

Slowly, and to the accompaniment of loud cheers, Tripod's magnificent member began to enlarge and rise.

Whereupon his audience burst into song, chanting:

Tripod, Tripod, have you any cock?
Yes sir, yes sir, hard as a rock!
Here it comes, here it comes! One, two, three!
Up it goes, up it goes, big as a tree!

Finally, Tripod, apparently satisfied that he was fully extended, beamed at his audience. It was an awesome sight – possibly, as claimed by many, the biggest erection of its kind ever seen in Africa, if not the world.

Now the audience grew impatient. 'Quick! Quick!' shouted someone. 'Hang it on before he comes!'

Someone stepped forward swiftly carrying an AK-47 assault rifle and hung it on Tripod's erection by its bandolier. There it hung, splendidly supported, and there was a burst of applause.

'One up the spout!' demanded a loud voice at the back of the crowd.

The handler quickly removed the weapon, slipped a cartridge into the breech and hung it back on Tripod's pod. More cheering, and shouts of 'Full magazine! Full magazine!' – at which the handler again removed the rifle and clipped into it a full magazine after first holding it up to demonstrate that it contained all its rounds.

Tripod's overworked manhood now hung a fraction lower but remained eminently capable of bearing its load. The crowd roared their appreciation and stamped their feet.

'Fix bayonet! Fix bayonet!' they chanted.

The AK-47 was swiftly removed and its bayonet fixed into position. It was gently rehung on its throbbing peg – and remained there, the support upon which it depended now showing visible signs of levelling but still magnificently equal to its task. The applause was deafening.

'Oyez, oyez!' shouted the ginger-haired man. 'The book is now open for winners to collect!'

Dewey shook his head in amazement. It was impossible not to be impressed. He turned and walked back to his tent, Titus trotting at his side.

'So what do you think of that, Titus?'

'*Hau, Bwana, hau!*' Titus seemed lost for words, which was unusual.

An unmarked army Beechcraft came for them the following morning, landing at first light. It took off almost immediately, carrying Dewey, Cronwright, Titus, two RLI officers and a malaria-stricken Selous Scout.

It took them some time to get the old Peugot started after they landed at New Sarum airbase. As he drove home, picking his way through the incoming morning traffic, Dewey grappled with the usual mind-switch back to normality. He recalled he had two lectures this morning and hopefully Judith had succeeded in getting Merrington to stand in for him. Anyhow, he would make it back in time to handle the second lecture.

His mind wandered to his rose garden and he suddenly remembered there were new plantings waiting at a local nursery. 'Titus!' he said urgently. 'You must take the station wagon and go fetch the white Pascali rose bushes at Lomandi nursery to plant in front of the summerhouse tomorrow.'

Titus shook his head. 'Memsahib, she say she want Coral Sunset roses from Bwana Donaldson's farm for in front of summerhouse.'

Dewey was irritated as he always was when Judith and Titus bypassed him on gardening arrangements. He also knew Titus got a mischievous and gleeful kick out of it.

'White Pascali would look much better in front of the summerhouse!'

'Colonel Memsahib, she say Coral Sunset for in front of summerhouse,' said Titus in a tone of solemn finality. In such situations he always gave Judith superior rank so as to leave as little doubt as possible about the outcome.

Dewey sighed. His love of Titus was beyond denying. But at times like these he wondered whether he did not prefer him as a comrade-in-arms rather than as a gardener. As a soldier he never questioned an order.

12

The secret

For me the Zanzibar revolution was a story that began badly and ended well – so well, in fact, that at some universities and colleges where journalism is taught the story is mentioned occasionally as a case history or example of how good fortune can turn a doomed foreign assignment into a success. I suspect it also provides some light relief for the students.

It certainly underlines something anyone contemplating a career in journalism should know: that luck plays a major role in the success of a reporting assignment, but you have to go and find it. There is a motto on the crest of the badge of that famous fighting unit of the British army, the Special Air Services, that puts it well: 'WHO DARES WINS.' It could be put even better: 'WHO DARES MORE WINS MOST.'

The retelling of the Zanzibar story here gives me an opportunity to reveal a secret that I have kept ever since the event and that has, to some extent, troubled my conscience. So let me now, in the following pages, expunge myself of this guilt.

The revolution that turned Zanzibar into a blood bath in January 1964 took everyone by surprise. One moment it was a peaceful island in the Indian Ocean, fragrant with the scent of its clove plantations, steeped in the centuries of its colourful history and romantic in its palm-fringed beaches and the fascinating Arab-style architecture of its ancient town. The next moment it was a battleground upon which the most gruesome atrocities were taking place.

Yes, there had been race riots at various times in the years preceding the independence from its status as a British protectorate a

227

month earlier. But they had been of no great significance. Ethnic rioting is a standard feature of African life. The point was that there had been nothing so unusual as to indicate that a major uprising was around the corner.

Zanzibar lies 22 miles off the coast of East Africa, north-east of Dar es Salaam, main seaport and capital of what was then called Tanganyika, later to become Tanzania.

For hundreds of years Zanzibar was an island ruled and populated by Arabs who founded its spice plantations and used it as a staging post for their African slave trade. The slavers would set off from the island on their expeditions into the African mainland and return to Zanzibar with captured slaves to market them on the old site that still stands there to this day. The famous explorers Burton, Speke and Stanley all used Zanzibar as their starting base for their ventures into the interior. Britain acquired Zanzibar as a protectorate in 1890 but allowed Arab rule to continue under a sultanate.

When independence came in December 1963 there were about 40 000 Arabs living on the island. They owned most of the land and dominated the trade and commerce. There were 300 000 Africans, mostly plantation workers, manual labourers and fishermen. The Sultan of Zanzibar had a palace, a private yacht and a red Rolls-Royce, and lived stylishly. It certainly was not a situation that could continue indefinitely.

I was in Nairobi when the first BBC report of the morning carried a flash by Reuter that serious fighting had broken out on Zanzibar. The local time was 09:15. There was no time for discussion with London. I knew there was a flight leaving Nairobi for Dar es Salaam within the hour. I flung the essential things into a bag and telephoned the bank, where I made a pit-stop to pick up a wad of US dollars and East African currency. I knew already it was going to be that kind of story. Everything would be shot to hell or closed, including banks. Cash would be king.

I was in Dar es Salaam four hours later, as were several other colleagues. We fought to get on a flight to the island, but all scheduled flights had been cancelled.

We hastened to the offices of the two air-charter companies that operated out of Dar es Salaam, only to find the management crouched over radio broadcasts saying that rebels were in control of the Zanzibar airport and had warned that any approaching aircraft would be shot down. So no go.

We raced to the harbour in search of seacraft. A fast motor launch was capable of reaching the island in under three hours, but we found that the Tanganyikan government had ordered a ban on all departures to Zanzibar.

The growing number of press correspondents in Dar es Salaam – being supplemented by the hour by further arrivals from Nairobi, Johannesburg, London, Rome and elsewhere – were milling around in frustration. Zanzibar was only 22 miles away and we couldn't get there!

A few telephone calls from residents on the island had come out and by all accounts there was mayhem going on there, but accounts were confused. Ominously, telephone contact with the mainland went dead after a few more hours, and our only link thereafter was via a radio ham until that too came to an abrupt end. The British Embassy in Dar es Salaam seemed to have intermittent contact but was as uncooperative as usual in releasing information. ('Sorry old chap but everything has to go through London.') Then their link faded as well.

By late afternoon we had bits and pieces to file plus the latest news that a British warship was on its way to the island to protect the 300 British residents there, of whom little had been heard. But all news was second-hand out of Dar es Salaam. No one had yet managed to reach the island.

What was emerging now was the classic anatomy of a foreign correspondent's nightmare: to have the world's most important story of the moment blasting away just over the horizon and no way of getting there. To be holed up with colleagues – all of us well-trained piranha honed in the art of ruthlessly scooping each other – and not knowing who would get there first.

I happened to remember that about 40 miles north of Dar es Salaam was Bagamoyo, the ancient and derelict port through which the old Arab slavers used to ship their miserable human cargos by dhow from the African mainland to the slave marketplace in Zanzibar. Bagamoyo was now a fishing harbour and although dhows still operated there they did little else than bring in the daily catch.

The point was that Bagamoyo was even nearer to Zanzibar than Dar es Salaam, if only by a mile or two. Surely a fishing dhow could sail the distance in a few hours?

I set off by taxi to Bagamoyo in the late afternoon and by evening I was trudging the beach, even wading into the shallow surf, to plead with fishermen landing their catches, offering amounts of money that would have made the *Daily Mail* accountants shudder, to set sail for Zanzibar immediately. No one seemed interested. Some seemed to think I was mad.

It was dark before I got lucky. I was taken by a fisherman to a group of people in a mud hut in a foul alley some distance behind the harbour where we did business by the light of a kerosene lamp, watched, from the shadows, by various family members including an old crone who smoked a pipe and irritated everyone by offering advice in a cracked voice.

The fisherman who had guided me had disappeared and I was grateful for the presence of my taxi driver, who had stayed with me, mainly because I had not paid him yet. My own Swahili was not up to the occasion and I needed him as an interpreter. At one point he drew me aside and warned: 'These people are not fishermen. They are smugglers and could be dangerous.' I agreed they could be dangerous, but where else to go?

The key negotiator in the group was the boat owner and talking to him was disconcerting because he had no nose and a terribly scarred mouth, all of it possibly caused by one slash of a machete. The disfiguration impeded his speech, which didn't help the negotiations because he became vexed when misunderstood.

He wished to know what would happen if the expedition to Zanzibar resulted in the seizure or loss of his craft. I readily offered to buy the boat. After nearly an hour of wrangling we agreed on a price of 800 US dollars, which was a sizeable chunk out of the money I had on me. They wanted the money immediately but I refused and finally they agreed to accept half upfront and the balance on arrival in Zanzibar. We shook hands on the deal. His grasp was limp and brief. I felt I was saying goodbye to 400 dollars.

I was told to go and wait on the beach and my taxi driver, after taking me there and getting paid, fled gratefully into the night. I sat down wearily on the sand. It was not the best night of my life.

I had filed a second-hand story from Dar es Salaam and had achieved nothing else except to buy the *Daily Mail* a dhow. There would probably be trouble about that and I shuddered as it occurred to me that I had forgotten to ask for a receipt.

I looked about me but there was no electricity in Bagamoyo and the populace had long since gone to sleep. The village had disappeared into the night. All about me was pitch-darkness.

The night wind that comes off the sea on the East African coast had risen. The surf was crashing, the wind was moaning, the sand was shifting and the sand-fleas were beginning to bite. The tropical warmth of the day had receded and it was cold. Fatigue began to set in but there was no question of sleeping. What if Scarface and his men came to rob me of the rest of the money they knew I had? What if in the morning they did not come at all and I had no one to sail my dhow? What if the boys back in Dar es Salaam had found a plane or a fast boat by now and were on their way to Zanzibar? I spent the night worrying about whether I was going to be robbed, killed or scooped. I ate the remains of a chocolate bar and finished what was left of a bottle of soda water.

The dawn came and the dhows anchored beyond the surf took shape in the gathering light. I shuffled up and down the beach wondering which one was mine and where the hell my crew was. Just as I was beginning to believe that I had been well and truly conned, they hove into sight, trudging through the sand, carrying oars, boat hooks, buckets and other tools of their trade. If anything, they looked worse by daylight than they had looked by lamplight, but I loved the sight of them and my relief at their appearance was vast.

We waded out into the surf to the most decrepit of the dhows, an open craft about 30 feet long, and clambered aboard. The first thing we had to do was bale it out. Nevertheless I had a dhow and a crew and we were off to Zanzibar, the story adrenalin was beginning to flow again and I felt good.

But now a serious crisis arose. There was a faint cry from the shore and there, to my astonishment, stood John Monks of the *London Daily Express*. 'Piggy' Monks, as he was affectionately known in the business, was an Australian, and his words, in the jagged vowels of that nation, carried clearly across the sound of the surf. I couldn't pretend not to hear them.

'Any chance of a lift, mate?'

He was standing in the surf, an airline bag and cameras slung about his neck, typewriter in one hand and his shoes in the other. His trousers were rolled up above his pudgy knees. That's what irritated me more than his sudden appearance. He had taken his shoes off and rolled up his pants as though he took it for granted that I would invite him aboard.

Let me explain the situation to those unfamiliar with the great rivalries of Fleet Street. The *Daily Mail* and the *Daily Express* were – especially in the era of which I write – the fiercest competitors in the British newspaper industry. They fought for scoops on an eye-for-an-eye, a tooth-for-a-tooth basis. They strove to outbid each other in paying vast sums of money for world exclusives. Their reporters and foreign correspondents were expected to go to extraordinary lengths and do all that was necessary short of actually physically knifing each other in the back to get ahead on a story.

How, in these circumstances, could I now offer the *Daily Express* a ride in the *Daily Mail* dhow?

For years Monks and I had raced each other up and down the African continent and performed Machiavellian feats in our attempts to outdo each other on stories. Sometimes I scooped him and sometimes he scooped me.

On one assignment in the Congo we hired separate twin-engined Cessnas to race each other in the afternoons across Lake Tanganyika to file our stories from a tiny lakeside village in Tanganyika where the proprietor of the trade store, who was also the postmaster, operated a Morse key.

He had come to know Africa, its mysteries and byways, almost as well as I had, which was how, when all other hopes faded, he had also remembered Bagamoyo.

What now to do? Fleet Street rules were that I should refuse to allow him aboard and leave him to his fate.

But a perhaps surprising result of the years of our fierce competition and professional throat-slashing and eye-gouging had been the emergence of a great friendship between us. And we had already experienced one or two occasions where logistics or the sheer pressure of events had forced us into co-operation.

I was not sure that the present situation justified a shared expedition. His presence on the beach indicated that alternative ways to Zanzibar had not yet been found and I felt I was a nose ahead. But the sight of him stranded in the surf rang the bell of a kind of comradeship that in certain circumstances obliges one to say – screw the grand traditions of Fleet Street and all its editors.

So I decided to take him aboard.

But there remained an important consideration. 'I had to buy this fucking tub. Will you pay half the cost?' I shouted.

He didn't even ask what it had cost. 'Is the Pope a Catholic?' he yelled back (a convoluted Australian form of assent, fashionably in use at the time). He waded out towards us, holding his typewriter and cameras above the waves.

'Good on yer, mate,' he grunted as we hauled him over the gunwale.

Scarface and his men raised the tattered sail and we set off, creaking and leaking, for Zanzibar. The sun was a red orb above the horizon and by midday we were cursing it.

Scarface had four men to help him sail the dhow. This might sound over-crewed for a 30-foot craft, but a dhow is a cumbersome thing that hasn't changed in shape or style since the twelfth century, and it takes muscle to manage its heavy boom and clumsy sail.

There was no shade on the craft. Monks's hat, a silly straw thing that looked like fugitive headgear from a girls' high school, was blown overboard by a gust of wind and the crew understandably were disinclined to stop to fish for it. I had foolishly forgotten to bring a hat. I wrapped an old T-shirt about my head. Monks replaced his hat with a pair of used underpants. We looked a right pair of pricks.

I had also been thoughtless about provisions. John had two bottles of Coca-Cola with him and generously gave me one. The hot Coke made us thirstier than ever.

The crew offered us water from a battered old jerry can and I took a grateful swig from it. But Piggy declined. He had seen Scarface drink from it and was convinced that his ghastly facial scar involving the loss of his nose and upper lip was the result of syphilis, and he thought he might catch it. I tried to persuade him there was only one way to contract syphilis and that it was safe to drink from the can. But he steadfastly refused.

By noon the sun was hellish. John's very fair complexion was taking a beating. His face was breaking up like a road map before my very eyes.

The wind was against us as we tacked laboriously back and forth and it was clear that the trip was taking longer than expected.

There was a small triangle of shade on board formed by the shape of the bow and we took turns lying full length with our heads in it. The crew regarded our plight contemptuously and cursed as they stumbled over us to swing the boom and, at other times, to bail out the boat, using a large old Pyotts biscuit tin.

A new problem had arisen. Scarface had a small transistor radio on board and had begun to pick up broadcasts from Zanzibar where the rebels had seized the radio station. The hysterical outbursts came across in a mixture of English and Swahili, and a picture began to emerge. Someone, previously unheard of, called 'Field Marshal' Okello was leading the revolution and repeated warnings were issued in his name that any aircraft or ship that approached the island would be fired on.

Each time this threat was broadcast Scarface ordered our sail to be lowered and demanded an extra fee before progressing because, he said, we were sailing into a life-threatening situation. When he did this a second time we argued furiously and he actually began to turn back in the direction of the mainland until I conceded and paid another ransom.

I then, casually, offered to buy his radio. He seized on this gladly as another moneymaking opportunity and demanded an outrageous price for it, which I paid. As soon as he handed me the radio I threw it overboard. Monks said it was a stupid thing to do and he was probably right. But it did put an end to Scarface's blackmailing.

However, the tensions between us were still rising, Scarface and his crew were muttering among themselves and we were nervously wondering what they were going to do with us.

For a while we had been conscious of the scent of cloves and to our relief the low profile of the island began to take shape ahead of us.

But suddenly there was pandemonium among our crew. A motor launch was approaching us from the direction of the island and it was coming fast. It circled us and finally cruised up along-side. It was filled with an ungodly-looking bunch of ruffians armed with a variety of weapons ranging from machetes and shot-guns and pistols to AK-47s. All the firearms were levelled at us.

A man wearing blue jeans, a camouflage jacket and a dirty tur-ban and holding a sub-machine-gun, who seemed to be their commander, yelled something in Swahili. Scarface replied point-ing an accusatory finger at us. Whatever he was telling them, the message seemed to be that it was all our fault.

'Who are you?' demanded the commander, pointing his weapon at us.

I launched into a formal explanation but was interrupted by Monks. With the inspirational bullshit that seems to come to the aid of Australians at times like these he said: 'We are British reporters who have been sent for by Field Marshall Okello to tell the world about this revolution.'

The launch commander conferred with some of his mob. Then he ordered: 'Lower your sail!' and I think we all feared the worst. But they merely threw us a line and took us in tow. The old dhow plunged along in the wake of the launch at a rate of knots that threatened to tear it apart and in less than an hour we were in Zanzibar harbour.

'You wait here!' shouted the launch commander. Obediently Scarface and his men dropped anchor and there we rocked, about 300 yards from the shore.

We saw the launch tie up alongside the quay and its crew go ashore and disappear among the harbour buildings.

A lone sentry, a rifle slung over his shoulder, paced up and down the quay, watching us. There was no one else in sight.

There was no doubt the revolution was still in full swing. The sound of small-arms fire interspersed with the thud of heavier weaponry and the thump of explosions could be clearly heard. We could see a pall of smoke above the inner reaches of the town.

We waited one hour, two hours. The sun set and we knew dusk

was less than an hour away. Nothing happened. The sentry on the quay paced up and down. It began to dawn on me that no one was coming to get us. In the town the fighting rattled and boomed on.

I ordered Scarface to up anchor and dock alongside the quay. He refused and we argued in our usual tangled and broken mixture of Swahili and English. He drew a finger across his throat to emphasise that we would be killed if we did not obey orders and stay where we were.

But I was worried about John, who was seriously sunburned, feverish and beginning to look ill. I was also worried about what the consequences might be of doing nothing. We were exhausted, had no food and hardly any water and our crew were likely to rob us, maybe even murder us, if we slept. There was also the important fact that, although we had reached the story, we were still half a mile away from the action.

I began to take my clothes off.

'What are you doing, sport?' asked John, anxiously.

'I'm going to swim ashore to get some help.' I stood on the side of the dhow in my underpants.

'You're crazy, mate. That bugger on the quay will shoot you!'

'Let's hope not. And if you think about it carefully, we've got no option. We certainly can't spend the night here doing nothing.'

'And what am I supposed to do with these sods?' He indicated the crew.

'Try and keep them amused until I get back.' To avoid further discussion I quickly dived overboard and began to swim to the quay.

I nearly drowned because of two serious oversights. The first was that the tide was going out, so I was swimming against a current. The second was that I had underestimated my exhaustion. I had not slept for two nights, I had eaten very little and the day's exposure beneath a tropical sun in an open boat had taken its toll.

I had estimated the distance to the quay at about 300 yards and reckoned I was a strong enough swimmer to make it. But before I got halfway I was in trouble. The fatigue that seized me was frightening. It was as if a paralysis was setting in.

I had come quite close to another craft and I changed my direction to reach it. I managed to grab hold of its anchor chain and hung there to rest.

I looked back at our dhow. Monks was watching me anxiously. The crew seemed indifferent. One of them had hung his backside over the stern to take a crap.

I looked at the quay. The sentry had stopped pacing and was watching me. Ominously, he had unslung his rifle from his shoulder and was holding it in the crook of his arm.

I started to swim again. I concentrated on keeping the strokes even and co-ordinating my kicking and breathing. I counted the strokes and I think that helped. But eventually I lost count and, without doubt, if the quay had been another ten yards away I would not have made it. As it was I floundered through the last few yards and went under a couple of times.

I reached the quay and hooked my arm through a motorcar tyre that hung from a rope. Another tyre hung a few feet above it. They were buffers for vessels when they tied up alongside.

I could not move for several minutes. I was actually sobbing with exhaustion and relief.

Eventually, painfully, I began to climb up the quayside, tyre by tyre. Monks told me later that the sentry lit a cigarette and smoked it while he watched me. He didn't bother to tell me that there was a flight of steps a few yards to one side. There were barnacles on the quayside and I cut and scratched myself on the way up.

Finally I made it and rolled onto the quay in my Y-fronts, sodden and bleeding. The sentry put the muzzle of his rifle against my head and said: 'You're under arrest.' Fuck it, I thought. Shoot me if you like. I tried to say it but didn't have the strength to speak.

Actually he was quite kindly at first. He allowed me to lie on the quayside for several minutes while he finished his cigarette. Then he kicked me in the ribs, not ungently, and told me to get up. I couldn't manage it at first, so he helped me up. He then pointed at a small building nearby and nudged me towards it with the barrel of his rifle.

When we got to it he opened a door and shoved me inside, slammed the door shut and locked it. He peered at me through the window and grinned at me. I was his prisoner and he was beginning to like it. He strolled back to his position on the quay.

I was in a room with a desk and a chair behind it and I immediately flopped into the chair. I looked around me and at the books and documents on the desk. I seemed to be in a customs or harbour administration office.

I began to shiver. It was a warm tropical evening and the sea had not been cold. But I was wearing only a pair of wet underpants and sunburn, exposure, fatigue and reaction were beginning to set in.

Suddenly my attention became riveted. My God, I was looking at a telephone. To arrest a newspaperman and lock him in a room with a telephone was either a monstrous oversight or some kind of trap. I got up and looked out the window. In the fading light I could make out the sentry standing at his post.

I went back to the desk and looked at the phone again and thought about it. No, dammit, it couldn't be a trap. How could they have known I was coming to Zanzibar and how could they have known I would swim ashore? The dickhead on the quay simply hadn't thought about the telephone. Wow!

Gingerly I picked up the receiver and dialled zero. There was an immediate response. A frightened voice said in unmistakable Asian accents: 'Who is that please, I am asking you kindly?' He repeated the question in Swahili. I hesitated, and he said: 'Jambo?'

'I am from the *London Daily Mail*,' I said.

'But you are phoning from the harbour!'

'Yes, I have just arrived. Am I talking to the central exchange?'

'Yes, yes. I am being trapped in here since the fighting began during my shift. Without having food, you understand? I am having water. I am making tea. But I am having no food for two days. It is too dangerous to go outside. Can you help me?' He sounded deranged.

'I think you had better stay where you are and I will see if someone can get food to you. Meantime can you help me? Can you get me a line to London?'

'London impossible, sir. But I am now managing to make contact with Nairobi.'

I felt dizzy with excitement. I gave him the number of the *Daily*

Nation in Nairobi and in less than a minute I was speaking to its editor, John Bierman.

Good professional that he was John wasted no time on preliminaries.

'Nice work, you're the first one in. Have you got a story?'

'Yes – can you take a dictate and pass it on to the *Mail*?'

'Sure – and can I use it for the *Daily Nation*?'

'Yes. Are you ready?'

'Yep. Go-go-go.'

I dictated six paragraphs, sitting there in my wet underpants, mopping at my cuts and scratches with bits of blotting paper that I tore from the pad on the desk. I kept it short, knowing that in London they would be close to the first-edition deadline and that all they would want at this stage would be to lead joyfully with the fact that their correspondent had reached Zanzibar first. They would tag on whatever other bits and pieces they had from the news agencies.

Some time after I put the telephone down I thought of more to say and telephoned John Bierman again with another dictation. He had already passed on my first take and spoken to the *Daily Mail*.

'They're ecstatic,' he reported. 'They're jumping over the moon. You're Fleet Street's hero tomorrow!'

'Yeah, just for the day, of course.'

'True. But make the most of it. Hit 'em for a raise.'

I made a mental note of the advice.

I had hardly put the phone down when there was an uproar outside. The door was unlocked and flung open and John Monks was propelled into the room by the quayside sentry who was shouting at him in Swahili.

Monks, carrying my personal effects as well as his own, was in a foul temper and looked terrible. His face, scorched crimson and blotched by the day's exposure to the elements, looked like an Aztec sun worshipper's dream.

He flung our possessions on the floor and said: 'Tell this bastard to stop prodding me with his fucking gun!'

I tried to remonstrate with the guard in my limited Swahili and took the opportunity to demand our release.

'*Wapi Bwana Makuba Field Marshall Okello?*' I asked, hoping he'd understand I was asking for the highest authority. But he sneered at me and walked out, slamming and locking the door.

I got dressed, wincing at the touch of the clothing on my sunburn and cuts, while John told me of the miracle of his own arrival.

The outgoing tide had swung the dhow and another similar craft nearby around until they were bows onto each other, and good old Piggy, noticing that the other craft had a dinghy attached to it, had flung our possessions from the one dhow to the other and jumped across, and then transferred to the dinghy.

There was a hullabaloo from the Scarface mob that feared the consequences of what he was doing. 'One of them followed me onto the other boat and grabbed hold of the dinghy as I was pushing off,' said Piggy. 'I had to clobber him with an oar.'

There was now another hullabaloo – this time from outside our prison, and the door was again unlocked and flung open in anger.

This time it was the launch commander who stormed in, waving his sub-machine-gun, and boy, was he pissed off. 'I ordered you to stay where you were! You have entered the People's Republic of Zanzibar illegally. You are spies! You will now be taken to Field Marshal Okello!'

It sounded ominous. We were being taken to Field Marshal Okello, but maybe not, after all, for a friendly interview.

We were bundled out of the harbour office and onto the back of a truck, hemmed about by armed men, and driven through the town. In the headlights we could see bodies lying in the streets, and the smell of death, which pervades so swiftly in tropical places, was already fouling the air.

The rebel forces had made the radio-station building and its environments their military headquarters. The scenes in the courtyard were horrific. Prisoners were being interrogated, beaten, tortured and executed in one of the most gruesome excesses in savagery Monks and I had ever seen. Their screams rent the air and made normal conversation impossible. The sight of two white men, even though obviously under guard, gave some of those being held the impression that foreign intervention of some sort was at hand and people clutched at us as we passed, imploring help, until beaten back by guards.

Even wounded rebels were in despair. They lay in rows on the ground, crying for help, in some cases bleeding to death. There seemed to be no medical facilities or assistance for them.

Piles of loot, presumably from the shops and the homes of Arabs, lay strewn about the courtyard, ranging from household utensils to hi-fi and TV sets and, as Monks remarked later, 'anything shiny'.

Now thoroughly unnerved and fearing the worst, Monks and I waited, crammed at the head of a flight of stairs, stifled and sweating while our guards, dangerously excited by the tempo around them, pressed their guns into our ribs.

Finally the door before us was opened and we were pushed through into what had once been the office of the head of broadcasting. The launch commander and two of his henchmen came in with us. What we saw was not encouraging.

There sat one of the blackest Africans I had ever seen, made sinister by the fact that he was wearing a black military uniform with silver insignia. He sat with his black-booted feet on the table. This was Field Marshal Okello.

There was no paperwork on the field marshal's desk and no sign of maps or battle plans on the walls. He was clearly conducting the war off the cuff, so to speak. All that was on the desk was a half-eaten banana, an ashtray filled with cigarette butts, numerous empty beer bottles, a pack of Lucky Strike cigarettes with a back-up carton close to hand, and a telephone.

The field marshal, clearly a chain-smoker, lit up another Lucky Strike while he listened to the launch commander's list of our sins.

At the end of it he barked: 'Search them!'

'Sir, we have already ...'

'Search them again!'

They began with a body search as the field marshal smoked and looked on. There was a squawk from Monks.

'Don't touch me there!' He turned to me and implored: 'Tell this bastard to stop feeling my balls, mate.'

I sighed. Monks had a tendency to speak at times when silence would be the better alternative. 'Shush,' I said.

I thought I detected a slight flicker of amusement in the eyes of the field marshal. Perhaps this wasn't going to end too badly.

Then all hell broke loose. Examining our personal effects, they found, in Monks's bag, a Zanzibar telephone directory. It was the one I had used in the harbour office and John, always an alert operator, had chucked it into his bag in case it became useful later on.

But now it was held up as dramatic evidence that we were spies. Why else would we be carrying a Zanzibar telephone directory but to make secret contact with subversive and reactionary elements on the island?

The launch commander was putting his case against us like a barrister in open court when the telephone rang. Whatever business came over the line seemed to capture all the field marshal's attention. When he put the phone down he stared at us as if surprised we were still there.

'Get them out of here,' he said irritably making shooing motions with his hands.

'But, sir ...'

'Get them out of here!' screamed the field marshal with such loudness that we were pushed out of the office at a speed that gave the guards waiting outside the impression we were trying to escape and they pushed us back into the office. But another yell from the field marshal, who was turning out to be a real yeller, drove us all back out and we were hustled downstairs, past the mayhem in the courtyard and back onto the truck.

The launch commander, visibly discomfited, was now anxious to be rid of us. 'You are under house arrest!' he said. 'You will be held at the English Club!'

We couldn't believe our luck. There was air-conditioning at the English Club. There was a bar and good food and, although the sleeping quarters below always smelt like a public swimming pool, the rooms were comfortable and there were clean sheets.

But when we were offloaded there, it was to find that things were not as usual. About 200 of Zanzibar's 300 British residents had taken refuge in or been banished to the English Club. It was packed with elderly folk (who had come to Zanzibar for peaceful retirement, only to see their homes burnt down or looted in the past 48 hours) and various matrons and young wives whose husbands were diplomats or civil servants or commercial representatives. And of course there were children of various ages,

242

either screaming or running around wild. There was no electrical power which meant the air-conditioning was off too. The toilets were not working either.

There was controlled pandemonium. A large-breasted lady was walking around saying: 'Don't panic! Remember we're British!' The club secretary, an elderly man retired from the old Tanganyika King's African Rifles, who had lost an ear, lopped off with a spear in a skirmish with 'natives', was heard to tell her testily that no one was panicking. But he himself panicked when he saw us. He distrusted journalists, believing they always stirred up trouble, and wasn't there enough already?

We soothed him and he very kindly took John Monks to his own quarters to provide salve for his sunburn.

I took the opportunity to seek out the telephone in his office. There was now substantial news to report and I dialled the central exchange. The same Indian operator answered. 'I am still having no food,' he said. I reassured him I would get him help by morning and he put me through to John Bierman again.

I now had the corpses in the streets, the appalling scenes at the radio station, the meeting with Okello and the scenes in the English Club to tell about, and I dictated three wholesome purple pages of events and colour. The first edition, leading with my arrival, was already on the streets, but the new stuff would build up the story for the next four editions. The *Daily Mail* had a fat and complete story. Now I could sleep.

I figured it was time to tell Piggy that the telephone was working to Nairobi and that John Bierman, kindly staying late at his office, was standing by to take his story. He was understandably angry that I had not told him earlier, but was forgiving, as I would have been. He was still in time for the final editions of his newspaper.

We spent the night sleeping on the floor in the crowded club. We were so exhausted that it was more like going into a coma and we were unconscious until midday the following day, reviving to find that a lot was going on, for example, that refugees were leaving the club, stepping over our recumbent bodies. The frigate, *HMS Owen* and an American warship, the *USS Manley* had arrived to evacuate citizens of their respective nations.

The Sultan of Zanzibar and his family, who had fled in his private yacht, were picked up by *HMS Owen* at sea, and the frigate then took British evacuees aboard in Zanzibar harbour. The English Club returned to something like normal and we were able to get beds.

A departing British resident kindly gave us the keys of his car and we cruised about the town. We saw a wild gang of armed revolutionaries driving around in the sultan's red Rolls-Royce.

But an important promise had to be kept. We scrounged some stale rolls and a slab of cheese from the English Club and delivered it to the telephone operator at the central telephone exchange. He was so grateful that he wept on Piggy Monks's shoulder. He was a thin, middle-aged and bespectacled Zanzibari of Indian origin who dared not risk his life by venturing outside. We promised to bring him more food the following morning. Compassion and gratitude aside, it was important to keep him fed. He was our only line of communication to the outside world. He allowed us to file that day's dispatches from his office.

On the way back from that mercy mission we almost collided with the truck that had driven us to the revolutionary headquarters the night before and we were reminded that we were under arrest. We were chased back to the English Club and threatened with execution if we ventured out again.

At the club we found that Major Walters, the one-eared club secretary, had found food and a way of preparing it and we sat down blissfully and gratefully to a supper of bacon and eggs and fruit salad.

Meanwhile the news of our arrival by dhow had hit the wires and awakened the rest of the international press to the existence of Bagamoyo. They converged on the little old seaport like locusts, buying and hiring dhows wherever they could find them, giving the little seaport the best boost of prosperity since the days of the slave trade.

Dennis Neeld of Associated Press and his photographer, Mohammed Amin, were the first of the new arrivals, having found a dhow equipped with a motor. They were seized immediately on landing and placed under house arrest in the Zanzibar Hotel.

Jack Nugent of *Newsweek* arrived after a 20-hour trip almost as harrowing as ours and was seriously beaten up by revolutionaries when they searched him and found his American Express credit card, which they said proved he was a CIA spy. He was hauled off to be executed but was saved by the intervention of Fritz Picard, the American Consul, who had stoically remained at his post on the island.

Other foreign correspondents who arrived included Richard Beeston of the London *Daily Telegraph*, Clyde Sanger of the *Guardian*, Bill Smith of *Time Magazine*, Robert Miller of the *Toronto Globe Mail*, Bob Conley of the *New York Times* and Peter Rand of the *New York Herald Tribune*.

American correspondents were hated on sight, very badly knocked around at times and virtually imprisoned in the Zanzibar Hotel. British and other correspondents were more leniently treated and allowed to file stories via the local cable and wireless office that had reopened for business. But all dispatches had to be censored by – guess who? Our old friend the launch commander who appeared to be one of the few members of the new People's Republic of Zanzibar administration who could read. He used a loaded pistol as a paperweight and we had to place our dispatches under it gingerly when he raised it. He read each dispatch laboriously with a furrowed brow and crossed out everything he did not like as well as everything he failed to understand, which left very little of the stories intact.

Piggy Monks and I filed copy through the censor for appearances' sake, but filed our real dispatches at night through our friend at the CTO whom we kept carefully nourished with daily deliveries of food.

The fighting in the town had died down but slaughter continued in other parts of the island where young Communist revolutionaries murdered, maimed, tortured and looted at will. More than 5 000 Arabs were killed in the purge.

Meanwhile the political picture began to take shape. Field Marshal Okello disappeared as mysteriously as he had appeared on the scene. A semi-literate brawling ex-seaman called Abeid Karume, who called himself a sheikh – which he was not – proclaimed himself Chairman of the Revolutionary Council of the People's Republic of Zanzibar.

Tanganyikan troops arrived from the mainland to 'stabilise' the situation and Zanzibar was, in due course, enjoined with Tanganyika to form the new state of Tanzania under President Julius Nyerere.

It appeared that the revolution had, from the beginning, been planned and directed from the mainland.

On the third day after our arrival I had occasion to return to the wharf where I had swum ashore. My epic swim had received a great deal of publicity (not least of all from the satirical magazine *Private Eye*, which treated it with the usual irreverence) and is part of Fleet Street history.

It was again late evening but, as I looked out into the harbour, assessing where I had dived from the dhow, something seemed wrong.

The tide had again ebbed. I studied the scene in some puzzlement, seeing that some of the craft in the harbour had tilted onto their sides and that the water close to the quayside was so shallow that outcrops of coral were showing above the surface.

It was then that I realised what I have guiltily kept secret for all these years and what I feel I must now reveal to cleanse my soul. Although it had probably been necessary to swim the first 100 yards, for the rest, I could have waded ashore. If I had drowned, it would have been in about three feet of water.

13

Tractors in love

It was Izak the field foreman who knocked urgently at the back door at 6 o'clock on that cold and drizzly morning to tell me that my two tractors had made love during the night.

I studied him carefully. He did not appear to be drunk. Nor did it seem to be a joke. He was ashen-faced with fear. The eternal phrase, never far from the minds of all who farm in Africa, leaped into focus: 'Oh God, what now?'

'Tell me again, Izak,' I said, very patiently.

He took a deep breath. *'Die trekkers, baas. Hulle het genaai!'* (The tractors, boss. They've been screwing!) His fright was so real that I felt a tingle of unease creep up my own spine.

'Baas, kom kyk,' (Boss, come and see) he implored. I donned a jacket and a pair of rubber boots and trudged out into the grey dawn. The other workers were grouped under the old blue gum tree, looking badly upset. Even more disturbing, my manager, Amien Samaai, also appeared shaken.

'What's this all about?' I asked. Amien merely gestured at the tractor shed, the doors of which stood open.

I approached it cautiously – and there, indeed, was an astonishing sight. Our bright red Massey-Ferguson tractor was perched atop our pretty little blue Dexter vineyard tractor.

I contemplated this for several minutes. I walked around the lovers carefully. The Dexter, not surprisingly, was damaged. Izak, who had followed me into the shed, nudged my elbow and pointed to the burn marks of the tyres on the cement floor behind the Dexter. He made a significant, pumping sign with his closed fist, the thumb extended between the first and second fingers. He was indicating that the tyre marks were evidence of passion. I walked back to the nervous group under the blue gum tree, and asked: 'What are you expecting now – that they will become the proud parents of a baby tractor?'

No one answered. Sarcasm was not going to work. I knew I had to be careful. South Africa's Cape farm workers with their Malay-African origins, are superstitious people. If I did not resolve this problem they might leave the farm. I recalled what had happened when a neighbour employed a bogus witchdoctor to 'cast a spell' on the house of a worker he had fired but who had refused to vacate the dwelling. The entire work force had fled.

I addressed my manager in front of my workers: 'Amien, you told me last week you were having post-ignition problems with the Massey-Ferguson. What happened here is that after you parked the tractors in the shed for the night, the Massey-Ferguson must have been left in gear and while still warm self-started and climbed onto the Dexter. A tractor isn't a car. It doesn't stop when it bumps up against something. It goes into traction. It climbs.'

'That's right, baas,' chorused the men, relieved that at last I appeared to have grasped the situation. 'That's what we are telling you. The Massey-Ferguson fucked the Dexter!'

I gave up. I had to get outside help to disengage the tractors (none of my people would touch them) and the problem took a long time to go away. It has never been forgotten. In the mainly Afrikaner rural community in which I live, events like my fornicating tractors become part of the local folklore and I am still greeted with cheers, laughter and ribald inquiries when I visit the village co-op.

Running a wine estate while being a foreign correspondent is, I know, unusual and it's not an easy combination. It can be argued that I may have been a better journalist had I not been involved in farming and that I may have been a better farmer had I not been involved in journalism.

But the fact is that I always wanted to be both a journalist and a farmer and the only way to accomplish both ambitions was to do both. There is another reason: I needed the farming way of life as an antidote to my other life as a foreign correspondent.

The world of Fleet Street was always exhilarating, the challenges exciting and the work at all times immensely rewarding in its involvement with great events and interesting people. Yet it left a hole in my life. I had a need to be more than an observer: I wanted to be part of something that was normal, ordinary and sane, apart from being an observer of so much that was abnormal. Farming and the making of wine answered this need. To return to these things and the calm and friendship of a farming community between assignments was the fulfilment of my spiritual need.

It helped that I was 45 minutes away from an international airport and that I could leave my land in the care of a competent and trustworthy manager.

Even so the departures were often sudden and disruptive. One moment on a tractor in a vineyard or in a ditch repairing an irrigation pipe. Then would come the message in the celebrated Fleet Street jargon: 'REUTER SAYS FIGHTING OUTBROKEN MOZAMBIQUE STOP WANT YOU THERE SOONEST STOP HIT THE GROUND RUNNING.' That left five minutes for urgent briefing instructions to farm manager Amien Samaai, usually ending with the words, 'I'll phone you from the airport and keep in touch with you whenever I can after that.' Then picking up the ever-ready suitcase and typewriter and the race to the airport – to arrive in Mozambique seven hours later and plunge into whatever chaotic cocktail of warfare and political intrigue that was raging there – still wearing farm boots and oil-stained jeans but with a dinner jacket in the suitcase in the unlikely event it was needed.

Returning home required readjustment back to farm life, such as serious discussion with Izak, the farm foreman, on how best to deal with a poisonous snake in the vineyards. My method was to shoot it in the head with a shotgun. His method was to pick it up by the tail and crack it like a whip, thus breaking its back and enabling its venom to be extracted for sale to the local witch-doctor. My method, he insisted, was stupid and uneconomic and he offered to train me in doing it his way. But I was in no hurry to learn anything that involved touching a three-metre-long Cape cobra, so I declined, telling him I felt his method was cruel. I dared not tell him the real reason which was that I was scared, although I believed he suspected it.

As a journalist I often have to write about social problems. As a farmer I often have to deal with them. Like, for instance, the time we were in the vineyards harvesting when a cry came from the workers' cottages that Joopie's wife was going into labour.

I turned to the man concerned and said: 'Quick, Joopie, go to your wife, she is starting to have the baby.'

'I won't go,' said Joopie, hefting a basketful of grapes into the trailer.

'Good heavens, man, why not?'

'It's not my baby.'

Mustering two willing women from among the pickers, I hurried down to the cottages and we got Joopie's wife into the pick-up. I drove furiously to the hospital. 'Please God, don't let her have the baby in the truck,' I prayed. She had the baby in the truck. That was when I became a midwife. Later I returned to the harvesting and made a general announcement: 'Joopie's wife is doing fine. And, whoever's child it is, it's a boy.'

One evening, having something to celebrate, we invited friends to a black-tie dinner party. The event had reached the merry stage when there came one of those ominous knocks at the kitchen door. I went to investigate and found one of my workers there who said: 'Baas, come quickly because Frik the tractor driver is killing his wife, who is also killing him.'

A man killing his wife is bad enough news. But a wife killing a tractor driver is even worse because good tractor drivers are hard to come by.

I rushed out and thoughtlessly leaped into the nearest vehicle, which happened to be my new car. I drove to the workers' cottages and was met by an awesome sight.

A large bonfire was burning, around which swayed an inebriated mob, mostly my workers and their friends. All attention was focused on Frik, the tractor driver, and his wife, Gertie, who were circling each other. He had a knife and she had an axe. He had already cut her in the neck while she had gashed him on the forehead.

Infused with good red wine and adrenalin I rushed up behind Gertie, snatched the axe from her hand, threw it into the fire and handed her over to willing, if unsteady hands.

I then faced my tractor driver in the flickering light of the fire, me in my dinner jacket and black tie and he in a remarkable state of undress. He must have been attending a function of some importance because he had on a suit jacket and tie and was wearing his war ribbons, having in his youth served as a truck driver with the South African 6th Division in North Africa and Italy. But the dignity of all this was somewhat affected by the fact that he was trouserless, a state of limited attire in which his wife had found him in flagrante delicto behind one of the cottages with another younger woman of the farm – and which had led to the fight.

'Give me the knife, Frik,' I said.

'Come and get it,' he answered.

At which a silence fell over the scene as everyone present waited with interest to see how the 'Baas' would handle this situation.

Fortunately, Frik, very drunk, fell over at this point and with the help of some who were not yet totally drunk I was able to disarm him. Hurriedly we bound up his wounds as well as those of his wife and bundled them into the back of my car. But while I drove them to the hospital they began to fight each other again. By the time we got there all of us – and the beige leather upholstery of my new car – were covered in blood.

I returned to my dinner party. The guests began to disperse. I can tell you that nothing breaks up a formal dinner party quicker than when the host returns after a brief disappearance minus his black tie and looking as though he has been on the losing side in a barroom brawl.

One of South Africa's great historical events, the release of Nelson Mandela from prison, was a tough test of my dual role as a farmer and journalist. He was set free as we were harvesting and pressing our grapes which was, of course, inconvenient.

What was convenient however was that the Verster prison from which he was released was just down the road from the farm, so I was able to get the harvesting and pressing into motion for the day and then drive down to the prison and join the international press corps waiting for Mandela to emerge. When he did so in that famous scene, hand in hand with his wife, Winnie, clenched fist raised in the air, I flashed the message to London on my cell phone and raced off to the Cape Town city hall from where the great man was due to make his first public speech in 27 years.

Thereafter it was a hectic day, covering and filing the story from a press centre crowded with milling, yelling reporters and TV and radio correspondents.

At about midday I received a telephone call from Amien Samaai, my farm manager, to say that a vast fire had broken out in the valley and was sweeping down on our farm. From that moment the day became, for me, very complicated as I dispatched pages of the story in between receiving reports from Amien that the fire was getting closer and all harvesting had stopped to enable everyone to fight it.

In the late afternoon Amien phoned to report that the farm homestead was on fire. His call came through as I was speaking to the *Daily Mail* foreign editor, Peter Birkett, and I was holding both telephone receivers, one to each ear.

Birkett was saying: 'We want 500 more words on reaction to Mandela's release and we need it chop-chop.'

Amien was saying: 'The thatch is alight. We've got men on the roof tearing out the burning pieces and throwing them to the ground, but the whole roof may go at any moment!'

I said: 'Get the men off the roof. It sounds too dangerous!'

'What's that?' queried Birkett. 'What did you say?'

I realised I had spoken into the wrong mouthpiece. 'My house is burning down,' I explained.

'Jesus Christ!' said Birkett. Then an awful thought struck him. 'You're not going to leave the story, are you?'

The dilemma was already seething through my mind. What was I to do? Mandela's release was the story of the decade. But the farmstead was my home – it was also a national monument. What was it to be? The story or the house? Here was the moment of truth. What was I most – farmer or journalist?

I decided to stay with the story. 'You'll have the 500 words in half an hour,' I told Birkett. To Amien I said: 'Do your best. Save what you can. I'll get there as soon as possible.'

I left the office at 10 p.m. An hour later, when I reached the farm, the whole valley seemed in flames. But to my astonishment the house seemed intact, although all the furniture had been carried out and was piled on the lawn. My men had saved it at the risk of their lives and were still dousing it with hoses, pumping water from the swimming pool.

But the vineyards still had to be saved. I fought the fire with them until sunrise, slept for three hours and returned to Cape Town for day two of the Mandela story. I worked until midnight that night and drove back home to help fight the fire again. We suffered one scorched vineyard but saved the rest.

I thank the Great Editor in the sky that Nelson Mandela isn't released from prison every harvest time when my house is on fire.

14

A Rhodesian tea party

Dispatch to Newsweek *from the Rhodesian war, 5 May 1978.*

The alert crackled in just after sunup. 'Call sign 3 to Acorn. We have six terrs visual, moving away. Distance 300 yards.'

The duty officer put down the dog-eared copy of *Playboy* he was reading, got up languidly and moved to the radio. 'Acorn speaks. You are copied. Fire Force is coming. Maintain contact.'

He touched a button and a siren began a mournful bleat. Cursing troopers ran out of canvas shower stalls, latrines and tents, struggling into camouflage fatigues and grabbing their FN automatic rifles as they raced for their helicopters. Within minutes they were airborne. A signals corporal entered the operations tent and sat down in front of the radio.

The colonel, barefoot and wearing a T-shirt and cotton shorts, ambled out of his quarters and into the operations tent, peered at the map and radioed for paratroop reinforcements. 'I knew the bastards were there,' he crowed.

Then he settled down into a webbed camp armchair and rapped out the first order of the engagement. 'Fabian, bring tea!'

A black steward wearing a white jacket and white gloves appeared, tray in hand. 'Yes, sir, Colonel sir,' he said. 'Tea is served, sir.'

Another day of beating the bush for Rhodesia's elusive black guerrillas had begun.

The war in Rhodesia has escalated viciously in the past year, and it will probably become still more violent in coming months.

The Patriotic Front guerilla forces now total 20 000 men and by some accounts another 3 000 fighting men are being trained in nearby Tanzania. Hundreds of Cuban and East German cadres are advising the guerillas and Soviet-bloc arms are arriving in increasing numbers.

A fortnight ago Secretary of State Cyrus Vance and British Foreign Secretary David Owen flew to Salisbury to make a last-ditch plea that Rhodesia's leaders initiate talks with the guerrilla commanders. The answer came back last week. No.

Prime Minister Ian Smith and the moderate black leaders who share power in Rhodesia's transitional government offered only a somewhat one-sided proposal – a cease-fire and a chance to help establish a new black-majority government.

Meantime here, deep in the bush, Call Sign 3, the seven-man patrol that had made a contact and alerted the command base, now informed that they were losing ground on the quarry. 'They've split,' panted the patrol's field radio operator. 'Four are heading for the hills and two are going south.'

As we listened to the radio traffic at the base camp code-named Acorn the colonel grunted: 'If there's one thing these guys are good at, it's getting away. Tell the choppers to turn them.'

The helicopters fluttered in to head off the fleeing guerrillas, hovering just long enough to land their troops and a pair of tracker foxhounds. The baying of the hounds came in clearly on the radio.

'Tally-ho!' said the colonel and officers who had now gathered about him chuckled obediently into their teacups as the chase accelerated.

The signals corporal kept up a running description of the action. An ageing Dakota rumbled onto the scene, skimming just 400 feet over the treetops and 16 paratroopers low-level jumped from its open door.

'Super,' said the colonel. 'We should have them bottled up now. Fabian, more tea!'

'Yessir. More tea coming up, Colonel sir!' The steward hurried forward with a fresh teapot on the silver tray, along with pancakes, cream and strawberry jam.

The radio spluttered a mixture of static and voices.

'What're they saying?' demanded the colonel.

'It's the chopper command car, sir. They're reporting one visual. They're going in to cull him!'

The sound of heavy machine-gun fire came over clearly on the radio. The colonel selected a pancake from the tray and carefully spread strawberry jam on it with a silver-handled table knife, adding a dab of cream which he ladled from the silver cream dish with a silver-handled spoon. As he nibbled at the delicacy Fabian, the white-jacketed and white-gloved black steward, his face expressionless, poured fresh tea from the silver teapot, replenishing the delicate china teacups on the camp table.

The radio hissed and crackled again. 'They got him,' reported the corporal. 'We have a floppy' (a dead terrorist).

'Good-ho,' said the colonel, spreading strawberry jam and cream on another pancake. 'I say, Fabian, these are damned good pancakes. Compliments to the cook, please.'

'Yessir. I will tell him, sir.'

It was a cat-and-mouse battle and it dragged on into the afternoon. The colonel began to look bored.

But diversion came in the arrival of a light transport aircraft which landed on the nearby dirt airstrip. A lieutenant, bare-headed and carrying a kitbag and a boomerang emerged from the plane and strolled towards the ops tent.

'Well now,' said the colonel. 'If it isn't young Walters back from vacation! Welcome back, George. Where did you go for your hols?'

'Australia, sir. Nice country but a bit boring. Glad to be back. Do you need some help here?'

'Yes, but have some tea first … and what's that thing you've got there?'

'A boomerang, sir. Sort of Aussie secret weapon. You throw it at a kangaroo. If it misses it comes back to you.'

'What – the kangaroo?'

'No, sir, the boomerang.'

'Well, bugger me,' said the colonel, impressed. Can you show me how it works? Let's try it out. Maybe we can use it on the terrs.'

The colonel, the two majors and the lieutenant wandered out onto the airstrip, leaving the battle in the bush in the care of the signals corporal and Fabian, the mess steward.

The lieutenant demonstrated the use of the boomerang, and the colonel and then the others had a go with it. It whizzed through the air impressively but no one was able to make it come back. 'Even my golf is better than this,' said the colonel irritably.

Fabian, in his white jacket and gloves, came hurrying across the strip towards them. 'Corporal says please to come, sir.'

They strolled back to the ops tent. 'It did sometimes come back to me in Australia,' said the lieutenant, apologetically. 'It's a moody thing.'

The radio was emitting shouts, curses and sounds of battle.

The corporal said: 'We have a scene, sir. Looks like we've got more of them.'

The colonel walked to the map and stood looking at it, scratching his crotch. 'Shut that bloody noise off,' he said irritably. 'Now then, corporal, where exactly are they now?'

The radio operator donned earphones and silenced the radio so that he became the only recipient of its sound. 'Contact position two miles south-east of the Blackburn ranch, sir.'

The colonel chuckled. 'That should wake old Jack Blackburn up,' he said. 'What's the score?'

'Four floppies, two still on the run, sir. We've got 'em squeezed between our boys and the paras. Choppers are monitoring ... we should have them all soon.'

The colonel grunted his satisfaction and sat down in his armchair. 'Four out of six isn't too bad. Time to celebrate. Fabian! Bring whisky-soda!'

As the steward brought in scotch, soda and ice on a silver tray the radio operator reported: 'We've taken a hit, sir!'

The colonel sipped his whisky and made no comment. The radio operator listened intently and reported: 'It's a Fire Force casualty, sir. Chest wound, but he's alive.'

'Chopper must fly him to Fort Victoria, we don't want him here,' ordered the colonel, tersely. 'We only want the floppies brought in here. At times like this one needs only to gloat.'

Fabian appeared and, standing to attention, addressed the colonel. 'Lunch is served, sir.'

'Good idea,' said the colonel. And he led his officers to the mess tent.

At lunch the colonel waxed mournful over the fact that in the coming week he was due to update his parachute jumps. 'I hate jumping out of bloody planes,' he said, buttering a slice of bread, as if it was to blame. 'Saw a bloke Roman candle once. Never been able to get it out of my mind. It's not like jumping in a combat situation. In practice jumps you've got too much time to think ... it's all right for you young bastards who get a thrill out of it, but for old farts like me the romance has faded.'

The major seated on his left remarked respectfully, 'But you still seem to do it all right, sir.'

'Well, yes,' agreed the colonel. 'In the end I just say to myself – if I Roman candle today at least it'll solve a lot of problems, including the bloody overdraft, the alimony, the teenage problems arising from the first marriage and the divorce proceedings arising from the second marriage – and at the thought of it a great surge of relief and courage suddenly takes hold of me and away I go!'

A trooper entered the officers' mess tent and came to attention. 'Signals corporal says Call Sign Three reports all hostiles slotted, sir.'

'Well done!' said the colonel. 'Tell the corporal to copy Call Sign Three commander: 'Nice work. Good hunting. Come in for a shower and some nosh.'

He raised his wineglass. 'A toast, gentlemen. Let's drink to a good day's work – and to our queen, God bless her, although she loves us not.'

They drank and the colonel made a wry face. 'Christ! Fabian, have you given us Rhodesian wine again? This stuff makes me go paralysed down my left side.'

'It's all we have left, sir.'

'God, what's this army coming to?'

There was the sound of a helicopter approaching. 'They must be bringing in the floppies,' said the colonel, brightening up. 'Let's go and have a look at the crop.'

They strolled to the landing strip, glasses in hand, and watched as the bodies of six dead terrorists were dumped from the helicopter. An intelligence detail under the command of a sergeant began to photograph the dead men in the routine check for known terrorist leaders and searched their clothing for documents.

258

'Well, what do you think sergeant?' said the colonel, sipping white wine as he watched the search. The joviality had gone out of his voice and he seemed suddenly subdued in the way soldiers usually are in the presence of fallen enemy.

The sergeant, sitting on his haunches as he took notes, tapped his teeth with a pencil. 'They look a bit underfed, sir. Probably crossed the border several weeks ago and may have had problems revictualling. Wearing East German uniforms ... very dirty, very tattered.' He motioned at the captured weapons piled nearby. 'Their AKs are fairly new and in good shape, though. Most of them very young, don't you think? This one here looks like a teenager – maybe 16 or even 15 years old. And here's an odd thing, he's wearing football boots.'

'Football boots, hey,' said the colonel, dully. 'Well I suppose that means he couldn't have been all that bad after all.'

With a flick of his wrist he threw the dregs of his wine onto the ground and walked away.

Footnote:

1. *Lieutenant-Colonel Peter Rich, Officer Commanding the Rhodesia Light Infantry, the commander featured in the above dispatch, survived the Rhodesian war – as well as the parachute jumps he hated – only to die in London shortly after the war when the taxi in which he was travelling overturned in a collision at Heathrow Airport.*
2. *I was deported from Rhodesia after publication of the dispatch. The army complained its tone was 'too frivolous' – although in fact I descibed the events exactly as they occurred.*

15

The love bite

When I was sent to interview the Countess de Sales about her pet lioness I never thought it would bite me.

Of course living in Africa means that sooner or later something will bite you. The consequences depend on what it is and where you are. For instance a mosquito bite south of the Vaal River is no big deal. But a mosquito bite north of the Limpopo could mean malaria.

There are other options that cover a wide range of insects, reptiles and animals and the results could be anything from an irritating itch to an unpleasant death, sometimes in dramatic circumstances. I'm not even going to mention elephants that can stamp on you and a wide variety of other beasts that can gore you, claw you, or chew you.

In fact it's not as bad as it seems. Most wild things avoid people because their instincts tell them we are an unpleasant and dangerous lot. And we who live in Africa follow certain rules and precautions when we move among them just as one observes laws and takes care in negotiating traffic in London or New York. (Take it from me, you are at greater risk on the M1 in England than you are on a jungle trail in the African bush.)

So when I was assigned to visit the Countess De Sales on the Kenya ranch owned by her mother, Lady Kenmare, to write a relaxed social feature about her and her lioness, I welcomed it as a light relief from the increasingly grim routine of wars and politics.

It was the tail end of the Happy Valley era of Kenya, the 'White Mischief' days of Nairobi. We were savouring the last hurrah of

260

British colonialism when the black man was stirring but not yet fully awakened and the white man was hoping for ways to be found to cling, if only in part, to a life he had created among the hills and valleys of the loveliest land in the world.

The whites of Kenya were, in the main, prosperous farmers, big-game hunters and Sloane Rangers, including the wealthy social set, many of them nobility, who owned ranches in Kenya and houses in London. Lady Kenmare was of this ilk and her daughter, Patricia, would have liked, if it were possible, to take her lioness to London and walk it through Harrods on a gold chain. These amazing people were key players on a fascinating stage in the colonial history of Africa that has gone forever. They have dissipated or retreated as Africans reclaimed the beautiful land. Lady Kenmare returned to England. Her daughter, the Countess De Sales, now the Hon Mrs Pat O'Neil (Patricia Cavendish to those who first knew her) retreated to the very tip of Africa and now owns the fine Broadlands Stud near Somerset West, 40 miles from Cape Town.

I hired a Landrover and drove to the Kenmare ranch that long time ago in Kenya. It was situated on the Tana River – in fact the lioness had been named Tana.

The countess met me on the steps of her farm house. She was a striking woman, blonde, wearing riding breeches and boots and glowing from the exertions of her morning ride.

'Hullo there!' she called cheerily, slapping her thigh with a riding crop. 'So glad you could come. Lovely day, isn't it? Would you like some tea now or after we go and see Tana?'

Something told me to get the lioness part of it over with as quickly as possible, so I suggested we do Tana first and then have tea.

'Good-ho!' said the countess and I joined her in her own Landrover and we headed off out of the precincts of the ranch with its neat corrals and splendid looking horses and into the bush. After slewing and bouncing along barely visible trails for about ten minutes we came to an open glade.

'This is where we usually meet,' said the Countess De Sales. 'She usually hangs about the house but these days she goes walkabout a bit. Sort of call of the wild, I suppose.' She placed her hand on the hooter of the Landrover and gave three loud honks. We waited a few minutes. Nothing happened so she gave three more blasts of the horn. Another few minutes passed. Then the countess raised a forefinger. 'Ha!' she said.

Then I heard it too. It was an approaching sound that resembled the gallop of a pony. Then into the glade rushed the lioness.

'There she is, the *darling*!' exclaimed the countess. Turning to me she said, 'Come along – come and meet Tana!'

I got out of the Landrover reluctantly, and I'll tell you why. This was no lion cub. It was a lioness that was at least three-quarters fully grown. Now, I don't claim to be an expert on lions, but I have had many conversations with game wardens and others who do know them well. Later I was to meet George and Joy Adamson of Elsa fame and I would rate them as among the best authorities on lions ever known to me. The consensus among these knowledgeable people concerning lions was that as cubs they are delightful, but there comes a time when they are unpredictable. 'A lion can grow up in your care and be your friend for life,' George once said. 'The female might be more dependable, but nothing's in writing. It is never impossible that she will turn on you for reasons that are understandable or reasons that are not.'

So perhaps I might be forgiven and not thought churlish when I confess that I did not respond to the countess's introduction to her lioness by rushing forward warmly with hand outstretched. I advanced a few steps and waited.

The lioness was pressing up against the countess's right leg and rubbing her head up and down her thigh and the countess was stroking it. It was purring like a buzz saw.

Suddenly the beast took notice of me and advanced. The measured, prowling walk of a lioness is one of the most beautiful movements among wild life. It is at its most beautiful when it is intently curious – or when it stalks its prey. In my case I assumed, nervously, it was merely curious.

She came up to me and her great golden eyes were undoubtedly warm and lovely. She sniffed at my groin and I suppressed a shudder.

Then she reared up on her hind legs and placed her paws on my shoulders and I fell flat on my back. A lioness, I should have told you, is a heavy beast.

I lay prone beneath her, frozen with fear, not daring to move a muscle. She leered down at me and her breath was hot and foul. She sniffed at my ear. Would she tear it off? She sniffed at my throat. Was she about to rip it out?

'Goodness me,' exclaimed the countess, 'She certainly likes you!' Then she added: 'But lie perfectly still.'

The advice was superfluous. I was already as rigid as a corpse. The lioness was now sniffing my chest. To add to my concern the beast had begun to purr and was drooling. Why was she drooling?

'Tana really *adores* you!' trilled the countess.

Suddenly the lioness seized my left breast between her teeth. I nearly blacked out with the shock and the pain of it. Her purring was like thunder in my ears. I could feel the wetness of her drool through the thin fabric of my shirt and, what with my fright and the pain and the stench of her, this was getting beyond a joke.

'Tana is biting me!' I informed her through gritted teeth.

'Don't worry,' said the countess reassuringly. 'It's only a love bite. Just a little nibble ... she really likes you.'

A love bite. I looked up past the great head of the lioness at the blue sky of Africa and asked God if He could lend a hand with this situation.

My prayer was answered. The lioness suddenly released me and walked away, looking bored.

'There you are, you see?' said the countess. 'Nothing to worry about. She just wanted to have a little nibble. Come on, uppies now. Would you like some tea?'

'Yes, I think I would ... thank you.' I struggled a bit to rise and made it on the second attempt.

We got into the Landrover and as she started it she called the lioness. 'Come on, Tana, we're going to have tea!' We drove back to the ranch with the lioness loping along beside us. I had rather hoped we would be leaving it behind.

But Tana joined us for tea, roaming about the house and finally flopping on the living-room hearth rug where she lay, panting gently and watching us through half-closed eyes.

I asked the countess if I could use a bathroom and she showed me the way. There, in privacy, I opened my shirt and inspected the damage. There were livid welts on the left side of my chest, not quite bleeding. In the weeks that followed they turned into bruises that passed through exotic stages of colour before fading.

When I returned to the living room the lioness was asleep, stretched out on the hearth rug.

As she poured tea the countess said: 'I must tell you a funny story about a colleague of yours who also came here to write a story about Tana. We couldn't find her at first and he was sitting there exactly where you are now when Tana appeared in the room and came up behind him. He was bald and Tana happens to like balls and shiny things like that and she tapped him on the head with a paw. He turned around and looked up and saw her looking down on him. Do you know what he did?'

'No, tell me.'

'He fainted. We had to revive him with smelling salts. Don't you think that's funny?'

I said yes, I thought it was very funny. Poor sod, I thought. At least in my case it had been a frontal assault.

16

Sadly, the Snake

I don't know why we all loved him so much because he could be extremely difficult. I think it had a lot to do with his kindness. He was, without doubt, one of the kindest men I have ever met, but he hated being caught at it. He seemed to think it was a weakness that needed covering up. As a result, he was at his gruffest and on his most offensive behaviour when he was being kind.

For example, when he heard that Elias, the telex operator at the Associated Press office in Harare had lost a son in childbirth, he gave him $1 000 and said: 'Here you are. Go bury him. Take a week off, get pissed, and come back when you're sober.'

I know that looks bad in cold print. So to help get it into perspective let me analyse it. A thousand US dollars in those days in Zimbabwe was more than half John Edlin's monthly salary (it's John Edlin I'm talking about, by the way) and it was, at the current rate of exchange, about 40 times Elias's weekly wage. And when John said 'go bury him', he also meant 'bury your sorrow'. The advice to get drunk was also sincere. John Edlin's own remedy for everything was to get drunk.

John Edlin joined the Argus Africa News Service at the age of 22 and was posted to Ghana. Few reporters, if any, get a foreign posting so young, but Edlin lied about his age and his journalistic experience, and the AANS, being a South African news organisation, could not afford to be too choosy. Black African governments were no longer accepting South African passport holders and Edlin had a New Zealand passport.

He engaged the services of two beautiful young Ghanaians to be his housekeepers and his mistresses and lived like a prince. He confided years later: 'They stole my money and generally ripped me off and gave me the clap, but they were great girls.' When he left Accra he set them up in a furnished apartment of their own with rent paid in advance for two years and a 'golden handshake' of $1 000 dollars each.

It was in Accra that he set foot firmly on the devastating road to alcoholism. Because he looked even younger than he was he became known as the Boy Drunk. He rejoiced in the reputation that he had been thrown out of every nightclub and bar in Accra.

Matters came to a head when he had a fight in a bar with an Irish diplomat over the merits of Guinness versus a local beverage, basically of South African origin, called Lion Lager. The Irish diplomat was able to claim diplomatic immunity in the fuss that followed whereas Edlin lacked any such protection. He was deported and arrived in Johannesburg, dishevelled and still displaying a black eye and other signs of the Accra fracas.

He was hastily reassigned to Harare in Zimbabwe. He had become the problem child of the Argus Africa News Service but Wilf Nussey, editor of the AANS, went to great lengths to protect him. 'John was a pain in the arse,' Nussey recalls. 'The management wanted to fire him after that Accra affair. But he had a non-South African passport, he was unmarried and therefore highly mobile, and he was a good reporter. He was too valuable to let go. But we couldn't base him in Johannesburg. He just didn't fit into a corporate structure.'

So John Edlin went to Salisbury, as it was then known, to become the Argus Africa News Service representative in Central Africa. And in the 20 years that followed he became a celebrated journalist and a living legend.

He was one of only two newspapermen that I knew who could sit down before a typewriter, drunk, and write an absolutely lucid, accurate report. The other man, for the record, was John Ridley of the *London Daily Telegraph*. Both were heavy drinkers on an almost daily basis. The only difference was that Ridley never fell over, whereas Edlin sometimes did.

Edlin developed into a brilliant journalist. He was one of the rare kind who had a natural talent and never needed formal training. He wrote concisely, descriptively and colourfully.

He also acquired access to sources of information that became the envy of his competitors. His secret was a geniality and an engaging informality that cut through protocol and established behaviour with surprising results.

In a continent that seethed with political change and volatility he was on first-name terms with heads of state, cabinet ministers, opposition leaders and the leaders of rebel factions.

His most remarkable achievement in the field of contacts was a rapport with blacks that no other white journalist seemed to achieve. Black politicians will use and attempt to manipulate journalists as most politicians do. But their underlying dislike of white journalists was as a whole quite general, ranging from hostility towards those who wrote critically of them to contempt for those who toadied up to them or wrote patronisingly of them.

Edlin certainly pulled no punches in his news coverage and political writing. But he escaped much opprobrium because, whereas many whites pretend to like blacks a great deal more than they really do, Edlin genuinely liked them. They found in him a total lack of the racism they detected among most whites. For that they forgave him a lot.

He never forgot the name of a hotel receptionist or porter or telephonist he met in the many African territories he visited and he intrigued them by inquiring with interest about their families and astonished them further by never forgetting the names of their children. When a Zambian taxi driver casually told him that the greatest ambition of his teenage daughter was to meet the famous British prima ballerina, Dame Margot Fonteyn, Edlin, on his next visit, brought a video containing performances by Fonteyn and sought out the driver. 'Here you are, mate,' he said gruffly. 'Tell her this is the best I can do for her until she can make it to Covent Garden.'

He never patronised Africans and his kindness towards them was of the roughest kind. He teased them and insulted them with a total disregard for conventions and they found him uproariously funny, even when he crossed into doubtful territory.

'Barman!' he once shouted, introducing an embarrassed British colleague at the Muthaiga Club in Nairobi to the black staff. 'Bring whisky-soda for Big White Writing Bwana who come in big silver bird from land of Great White Queen!' The rasping Kiwi accents cut through the hallowed surrounds like a buzz-saw and old colonial members turned ashen and sank lower into their leather armchairs. But the African waiters collapsed with laughter.

He produced similar hilarity in the dining room at the New Stanley Hotel when he prodded an overdone steak with his fork and complained to the head waiter: 'C'mon Kirari, you're not tryin' to poison me just because I'm a fuckin' *muzungu* ('white man') are you?'

He had two nicknames. One was Shithead and the other was Snake. The former was generally used by those whom he offended while the latter, more popularly used, derived from a famous incident at Beira airport in Mozambique.

Edlin, reassigned to a more important story elsewhere, was anxiously trying to catch a plane at Beira but was held back at the security checkpoint because an electronic device, shaped like a large tennis racket and used for detecting forbidden metallic devices on passengers such as firearms and bombs, had indicated that he was carrying something suspicious.

Every time the instrument was passed over the frontal region of his pants it bleeped a warning. It was a gadget only recently introduced to the security police at Mozambican airports and the official operating it was not yet entirely familiar with its workings – but was beginning to suspect he had caught a hijacker. He called his superiors and Edlin was surrounded by a circle of policemen who insisted that he produce whatever offensive thing it was that he had secreted on his person.

Edlin angrily and accurately insisted that it was the metal fly buttons on his jeans that were causing the alarm signals, but the Mozambicans remained doubtful. Meanwhile the doors to the aircraft had closed and the aircraft was preparing to take off.

Finally, Edlin, driven into a paroxysm of Antipodean fury, dropped his trousers and his underpants and waved his penis at his tormentors, yelling: 'There it is, you stupid bastards. It's only the old one-eyed trouser snake – and yes it does get steely but only when it's hungry!'

Snake Edlin gave Wilf Nussey a lot of problems. When he discovered that Wilf's full first name was Wilfred he routinely called him Fred, just to annoy him.

Sadly, the Snake

When Edlin won an award for his outstanding reporting in Africa, Nussey arranged a luncheon in his honour in Johannesburg, attended by various Argus company directors and other dignitaries. Edlin was to make a speech, but unfortunately Nussey failed to monitor his intake of wine. So when Edlin rose to speak all he could say was: 'Ladies and gentlemen, I'm so sorry but I'm too pissed to talk to you.' He then resumed his seat and toppled slowly forward until his head rested on the sole meunière in his plate.

The Snake's career with the Argus Africa News Service did not last. But it did not come in the form of dismissal. Quite the contrary. The Associated Press of America had become aware of his prowess, although not his drinking habits, and offered him the position of Chief of Bureau in Harare to cover Central Africa and beyond.

As ever, The Snake excelled at his duties. But Associated Press was soon to become aware of his basic problem.

An important senior executive in New York came to visit the Central Africa bureau and in his honour Edlin arranged an elaborate cocktail party at his own home to which local politicians, other dignitaries and colleagues were invited. Everyone turned up except Edlin, the host. As professional caterers had been hired, the party got under way and everyone had a good time. But as the evening wore on, worried colleagues and guests asked each other with increasing frequency: 'Where's John? Has anyone seen John?' Suddenly, much later, just as guests were beginning to depart, someone yelled: 'Hey! HERE'S John!' And there he was, lying behind the couch in the living room.

The Snake, in the course of his duties, was a frequent visitor to Bulawayo, Zimbabwe's second-largest city. There he regularly stayed at the Holiday Inn where he was always welcomed as a popular guest even though the manager reached for the aspirin in the top right-hand drawer of his desk whenever he booked in.

He was especially popular with the mainly black staff, whom he, in his usual way, chaffed, insulted, bellowed at and over-tipped. They adored him. His arrival was always an occasion of great celebration that would have been envied by any film star or any politician running for high office. There was much shouting and laughter as reception staff and porters crowded around him, shaking his hand and exclaiming: 'Meester Edlin, he is here!'

During one visit The Snake returned to the Holiday Inn at one o'clock on a rainy morning after a night out on the town that had left him (as he later admitted) 'seriously pissed'.

There was a small gaming area off to one side of the entrance lobby in the Holiday Inn to where The Snake, as was his habit, lurched for a final whirl at the one-armed bandits. After feeding his last small change into the machines and yanking fruitlessly at their handles, he fell into a lift that took him to his floor where he bounced off the walls outside his room, fumbled with the door lock, finally got the door open and tried to make it to his bed. But it proved too far and he fell face down on the floor, still wearing his dank raincoat.

That was how the room-service waiter found him on bringing him his morning coffee at seven a.m. The waiter dropped the tray and the coffee to the floor with a crash and, clasping his hands to his face, cried out: '*Hau!*' He then ran out into the corridor shouting: 'Meester Edlin, he is dead!'

He ran all the way downstairs to the reception desk shouting: 'Meester Edlin, he is dead!'

The news hit the hotel like a cyclone. Horrified staff ran out of the reception office, out of the porter's lodge, out of the breakfast room, out of the kitchen and out of the laundry. They were joined by taxi drivers from the parking area and passersby from the pavement. They all milled around in the reception area clutching each other in grief and yelling: 'Meester Edlin, he is dead!'

They all tried to get into the lift, but of course could not. So they ran upstairs, panting and sobbing and wailing: 'Meester Edlin, he is dead.'

Down the corridor to his room they ran, milling about outside the open door and shrieking at the sight of the recumbent figure in the raincoat lying face down on the carpet. 'Meester Edlin, he is dead!'

Tearfully but gently the first to reach him turned him over – and tears turned to cheers as The Snake emitted a loud snore, followed by a whisky-laden belch. They flung wide the windows of his room and shouted: 'Meester Edlin, he is ALIVE!' Outside, people cheered and taxi drivers honked their horns.

In the mysterious way that such men achieve it, The Snake was very attractive to women. Possibly he evoked in them a protective maternal instinct, or it could have been his sheer wildness that some found appealing. Or perhaps it was his depth of kindness that, for some, hinted at a hidden message of security. It was unlikely that it was his looks. He was slightly built, a shade below average height, with light-brown hair and blue eyes that held an expression of deceptive innocence. Not a bad-looking guy, but then again nothing exceptional.

He had several affairs in the time I knew him. They tended to end badly. For a woman, life with The Snake must have been like riding a roller coaster through a brewery.

I recall one relationship with a Polish girl of aristocratic origin that got as far as an official engagement. She was a stunning-looking woman, but the combination of Edlin and a Polish princess was too rich a mixture to last. I cannot recall her name, but what I do remember clearly is that he was badly hurt by that one, so much so that he took sick leave and travelled all the way to Cape Town to talk to me about it. I gave him whatever comfort good mates can give each other at such times. But I had the feeling that I didn't help much as I had troubles of my own at the time. In the end I think it was Goose who really saw him through it.

I must tell you about the relationship between Snake and Goose because it sheds further light on the nature and character of what I believe to have been the real John Edlin.

Goose, by the way, is Angus Shaw, who succeeded Edlin as Associated Press bureau chief in Salisbury. The nickname was an Edlinesque abbreviation of his first name: Angus, Angoose – Goose. Get it?

Well, Goose met Snake in Paris while standing on a platform in the metro after an aborted love affair. He was standing on the platform staring at the rail track, and he could already hear the distant rumble as the next train drew near and feel the flow of air that heralded its arrival. Suddenly flat New Zealand accents drowned out the sound: 'Don't do it, mate. It'll make an awful mess and no one will thank you for it.'

He turned and saw a slightly built man in a raincoat watching him. 'Come and have a drink,' said the stranger. Goose accepted and later The Snake took him back to his hotel where they talked long into the night. 'What you need,' said Edlin, 'is some sunshine. It helps a lot in situations like this. So why don't we get out of this cold and Frog-infested place and you come back with me to Zimbabwe?'

'I haven't got enough money for that,' said Goose.

'No problem,' said The Snake. 'I'll stand you the airfare, lend you some bucks and give you a place to stay and a job in my office. For the rest of it you soak up the sunshine, give the sheilas a break, and it'll all come right.'

Goose regarded The Snake as his saviour and lived, gratefully thereafter, as his number-two man at the Associated Press bureau in Harare, Zimbabwe.

It was but a natural extension of his gratitude therefore to dedicate himself to the healing of the wounds caused by the encounter with the Polish princess. This involved many medicinal visits with The Snake to the bar at the Harare Press Club and other places of comfort to attend to his lament. Goose succoured The Snake, took him home at night and put him to bed, raised him in the mornings and drove him to work, and got him through each day until the lonely evening hours when he would again help The Snake to anaesthetise the pain with alcohol and listen and commiserate as The Snake poured out his sorrowful tale of romantic misadventure.

In these ways The Snake regained his strength and was soon back on his accustomed routine of rampaging through bars and filing brilliant dispatches.

But two years later he was in love again and this time he married the girl. She was the elegant and very lovely Marilyn Poole who had been sent to Zimbabwe to open a local office for a leading British publishing house. She was a woman of extraordinary beauty and sensitivity, worth more than 20 Polish princesses, and desired by all men who saw her. A cry of astonishment therefore arose at the news of the marriage. What could such a woman see in a wild card like Snake Edlin?

My guess is that, like many women who came to know The Snake, she found in him the hidden kindness and was touched by it. Possibly she also sensed in him the deep and mysterious torment that caused his drinking problem and it stirred her womanly protectiveness and an urge to help him fight his demons.

But the marriage began to show signs of strain – perhaps better described as signs of sadness – after a year or two. The problem appeared to be that Marilyn wanted to have a child but The Snake was curiously reluctant, possibly another indication of the serious currents of unhappiness deep within himself. She would, on occasion, within the circle of their closer friends, tease him about it. 'But I'm your baby!' The Snake would protest. She would gently agree that in a sense this was true, but that he was not the baby she really wanted.

Suddenly The Snake was assigned to a major story of international importance. It was the devastating famine that had struck Ethiopia.

His reports from the starvation-stricken regions of that country were among the finest he had ever written, and might well have been the high point of his professional life. But, quite dramatically, the situation in Ethiopia also destroyed his marriage and his career. And it revealed, in unprecedented depth and clarity, the abundance of the compassion within himself that he always strove to conceal.

The way it happened was that Edlin became traumatised by what he saw in Ethiopia. He could not cope, emotionally or mentally, with the harrowing scenes of human suffering and death caused by one of the worst crises of starvation that the world had ever known.

He was stricken by the plight of children, skeletal and glaze-eyed, too weak to suck at the moistureless breasts of their dying mothers. He grew desperate at the sight of vultures picking at the corpses of people left for dead by others too weak to bury them.

He translated the pain and suffering into words with all the skill at his command and dispatched them into the ether for whatever good they could achieve – and indeed they were published worldwide through Associated Press, and governments and humanitarian organisations were soon sending food shipments to Ethiopia and the Sudan.

But Edlin then found himself having to report the shocking facts that while people continued to starve to death the food shipments were being consumed or sold for profit by the Ethiopian and Sudanese armies responsible for distributing them.

The traumatic cycle of witnessing and writing of such events inevitably takes its toll and The Snake eventually returned, exhausted, from the provinces to the capital, Addis Ababa. There he went on a bender to cleanse his mind of all that he had seen. But when he awoke in his hotel room two days later, the nightmarish scenes in all their horrific detail were still with him.

He then did what, to the best of my knowledge, no other journalist on a reporting assignment has ever done. He sent a message to the Associated Press headquarters in New York requesting leave of absence and, without waiting for a reply, hired, at his personal cost, a warehouse in Addis Ababa and set it up as a refugee centre for starving children.

In a wild bid to lessen the suffering he had seen, he transferred all the money he possessed to Addis Ababa and raised more on appeal. He used the funds to buy medical assistance, food, blankets, clothing and vehicles, and began to transport orphans from the most hunger-ravaged regions to his centre.

He hired, harangued, appealed and begged in his efforts to staff his venture. In a country historically accustomed to episodes of mass suffering he was regarded by many as eccentric. But others rallied to his cause and the Edlin Centre bustled on, bravely supported in the main by a dedicated band of voluntary workers intensely loyal to The Snake.

Donations from the Ethiopian government, the United Nations, various embassies and other sources helped to keep medical assistance and supplies coming in. Enormous encouragement and promotional assistance came by way of a visit to Ethiopia by the saintly Mother Theresa who visited the Edlin Centre and blessed The Snake and his work.

The Snake, of course, never stopped drinking. He worked at a furious pace, saving the lives of children and exhorting his team to greater efforts, but frequently needed to refuel at nearby bars.

It became dangerous to drink with him, for anyone thus trapped often awoke, heavily hung over, in the Edlin Centre, thereto lured by The Snake while helplessly inebriated and now unable to leave until having completed a stint of voluntary welfare among wailing infants.

One might ponder the many deep possibilities that may have moved The Snake to embark upon his Ethiopian mission and theological conclusions may well be drawn. It might be argued that he had become a Divine instrument of some kind. But what of the cruel cost to him of all these good works?

For when the mysterious force that had interrupted his career abated and he quit the Edlin Centre as suddenly as he had created it (leaving it in the good hands of his co-workers), he returned to Zimbabwe after an absence of almost a year to find that Marilyn had left him for an Italian lover by whom she had become pregnant. The Snake's marriage was over. Unable to bear a child by him, Marilyn had resorted to bearing a child by another man while he was elsewhere saving the lives of thousands of other children. It was an odd situation and a sad one with a lot of room for understanding.

The Associated Press staff in Harare were startled when The Snake walked in, hollow-eyed and thin. He scanned the telex machines, flipped through the message clips and sat down behind his desk as though he'd been away for a mere few hours. 'Well then, Goose, what've we got for today?' he growled.

Later, as they drank beer in their established corner in the Press Club, The Snake grew maudlin. 'I dunno, Goose, I can't explain it. Ethiopia seems a long time ago now, and the missus has run off with another bloke and I have to ask myself: Was it all worth it? I dunno. Well, anyway, fuck it and let's get pissed.'

Goose sighed. It was going to be a long night. Probably many long nights.

It was not only the loss of Marilyn. The mood of his employers had also changed. They would have liked to have fired him for abandoning the story in Ethiopia, but the timing was too awkward. To have fired The Snake after he had been blessed by Mother Theresa would not have been good PR. So they wrote off his mission as a sabbatical.

But in truth they were irked. Correspondents were hired to report noble causes, not to create them. If The Snake had heretofore been regarded as something of a loose cannon, he was now viewed as a loose cannon with a lighted fuse of indeterminate length. What would he do next?

The Ethiopian government took a different view. They invited The Snake back to Addis Ababa to present him with an award for the fine work he had done in establishing the John Edlin Centre. But not even that seemed to help his deteriorating relations with his employers.

The Snake resumed his routine of filing good stories and getting drunk. But whereas in the past his drinking habits had been tolerated as fair exchange for good copy, his editors now chose to be critical. In short they now closed in on him.

He claimed they undermined his morale and destabilised him with the usual strategies: non-use of good feature stories on which much time and diligence had been spent, unreasonable queries about his expense accounts, waking him up late at night with silly questions that could have waited until the morning, sending other correspondents into his accustomed area of coverage without the courtesy of first informing him and, on occasions, passing him over for top assignments.

Inevitably the day came when The Snake, in an alcohol-stimulated rage, tendered his resignation. In the past, when he had committed such a rash act, they had soothed him and talked him out of it. But this time his resignation was accepted and The Snake was without a job.

For a while he flew aimlessly between London and New York, seeking other employment and whittling away at his severance pay. But he had reached his mid-forties, that sensitive time in the life of a foreign correspondent when editors begin to show preference for younger men able to leap in and out of helicopters more friskily with combat troops and still unwise and passionate enough to risk their lives to the utmost to get a scoop.

The Snake finally faced the truth that he might have reached the end of the road in the profession to which he had given so much.

He came to visit me on our family wine estate in Franschhoek, South Africa, where I was relinquishing my own ties with journalism and devoting time to the wine business.

The Snake offered to sell wine for us in Zimbabwe and Zambia, and it seemed a good idea. After all, it could not be denied that he had wide knowledge of liquor outlets throughout Africa.

So my wife, Jill, and I took him to dinner at Chez Michel's in Franschhoek to discuss it, and The Snake took along our wine brochures to examine while we dined. He was fascinated by a highly successful blend we had introduced to the market called Angels' Tears and bellowed: 'Angels' Tears! Now that's a real leg-opener! We'll get the sheilas hooked on that one!' Chez Michel is a small restaurant and his abrasive Kiwi accents ricocheted off the walls like cannonballs. People at nearby tables were looking at him nervously.

We had spent the entire afternoon wine-tasting and I had noticed that The Snake had swallowed everything he'd tasted. 'Sorry, mate,' he had apologised, 'but my taste buds are deep down in my throat.'

All might have been well had he not switched to double whiskies on arrival at the restaurant, as a form of aperitif. He chose goulash as his main course and when it arrived he fell into it, face down, and would have drowned had we not rescued him. We cleaned him up as best we could and carried him out, followed by the proprietor, fluttering his hands and saying: 'Don't worry about the bill. You can come back and pay it in the morning!'

The Snake returned to Harare – from where he telephoned to resign as our Zimbabwe and Zambia representative before actually having started – because he had just received an offer to work for the United Nations as an advisor in setting up a news agency in Senegal.

He departed for New York for two weeks of consultations after which I received a postcard from Dakar to say he had arrived, he was enjoying good French wines, but the beer was bad.

He communicated with me only once more after that. It was an international call from Dakar on a fuzzy line heavily laden and broken up by atmospherics. He was trying to tell me something, but I couldn't make it out.

Suddenly the line became clear and I heard The Snake saying, against a background of barroom noises, that the United Nations had not renewed his contract and was there any hope of any kind of a job in Cape Town? I was in the process of assuring him that I would make inquiries when I heard him say: 'Hang on a mo, some bastard here is trying to pickpocket me!'

The line then went dead. I waited for a reconnection, but nothing happened. Later in the day I tried to telephone him on the only Dakar number I had for him, but without success. I waited for a week or two for more news, but finally figured that he would call me once he was back in either Zimbabwe or South Africa.

But the next news, about a month later, was bad. Chris Munnion, the *Daily Telegraph* correspondent in Johannesburg, phoned to say that Edlin had collapsed, apparently drunk, in a Dakar nightclub, had been carried to his apartment and had been left there to dry out. When he had not reappeared for several days, someone had gone to check on him and had found him as he had been left, and seriously ill from what appeared to have been a stroke.

The New Zealand diplomatic mission in Dakar arranged for a medical rescue aircraft to fly in from South Africa and take him to a hospital in Johannesburg. Colleagues who visited him there found him in a coma. He revived briefly during a visit by *Newsweek*'s Mark Peters. 'He was unable to speak,' Mark reported. 'But when I held his hand he returned the pressure. He looked very ill and terribly, terribly thin.'

The Snake died a week later.

A month later, friends and colleagues hired the mess at the barracks of the Transvaal Scottish Regiment in Johannesburg where they held a wake for him and drank copious amounts of spirituous liquors in the way they knew The Snake would have liked.

Goose succeeded Snake as the Associated Press bureau chief in Harare and, as I write this, he still holds this position. Marilyn is African regional head of the publishing company she represents and now lives in Johannesburg. Wilf Nussey lives in retirement in Cape Town.

The John Edlin Centre for disadvantaged children still operates in Addis Ababa and is a fitting tribute to a man who truly cared about people.

17

Dr Banda's press conference

My friend John Monks, former foreign correspondent for the London *Daily Express*, always maintained that among the more dangerous assignments we had to cover in Africa were Dr Kamuzu Banda's press conferences. This was because Banda often flew into a rage and sprayed saliva over us.

Monks was terrified of Banda's saliva. He was convinced that Banda had syphilis and that the presidential saliva was therefore infectious. I went to great lengths on many occasions to persuade Monks that there was only one way of catching syphilis but failed to convince him.

The president was afflicted by a nervous tic that caused a muscle in the side of his face to twitch and it worsened when he became angry. The condition caused saliva to leak from the corner of his mouth and he dabbed at it repeatedly with a handkerchief. He was always accompanied by a large woman said to be his nurse whose duty was to provide medication when required. I never witnessed any evidence of this but she was always close at hand and her presence, together with the obviousness of the condition and Banda's insensate rages, did suggest a chronic illness of some sort.

Dr Banda was a short man who walked with a jerky, clockwork-like gait as though he needed to be wound up with a key each morning. He ruled Malawi for more than three decades as its dictator-president, wearing a dark suit, a black Homburg hat and dark glasses, and carrying an ivory-headed ebony walking stick in one hand and brandishing a white ostrich-feather fly-whisk in the other. That was the way he always dressed. No matter the climate we never saw him attired otherwise. And we hardly ever saw him without his dark glasses, even at night.

The press conferences were memorable affairs in which his personal bodyguards played a major role. They wore white uniforms with red pillbox-styled caps and their job was to eject from the conference those who might persist in asking undesirable questions. We called them the Ice-cream Men.

The conferences invariably began with the saliva problem. Syphilis or not, saliva was undesirable and no one ever wanted to occupy the front-row seats at a Banda press conference because they were within range. If the president lost his cool, as he usually did, his spray would come at you like a monsoon.

'Creates a bloody rainbow on a sunny day,' vowed Chris Munnion of the *Daily Telegraph*.

Banda could never understand, or pretended not to understand, why we hung back. 'What's the matter with you? There are empty chairs in front here. Why does no one sit in front? Are you idiots?'

It didn't take him long to identify John Monks as being especially obdurate on the matter. 'You! Yes, you! The fat one! Sit in the front row!'

But Monks would have none of it and shook his head.

'Get out! Get out!' screamed the president. 'Throw him out!'

The Ice-cream Men converged on Monks and frogmarched him out of the room.

I still have my notes taken at that press conference. Here are some extracts:

Banda: 'I have no statements to make to you. I did not even wish to talk to you because you are all writers of lies. It is YOU who have asked to see ME. I will answer questions, but I will not answer *stupid* questions.'

Ian Mills of *United Press International*: 'Mr President, is it true that you have received an invitation to visit South Africa?'

Banda: 'That is a stupid question!'

Mills: 'But Mr President, it has been reported ...'

Banda: 'Shut up!'

Ronald Legge of the London *Sunday Times*: 'Mr President, is it true that you are about to announce a cabinet reshuffle?'

Banda: 'That is none of your business!'

He was now getting worked up. His cheek was twitching and he dabbed at his mouth with a white handkerchief. His gaze behind the dark glasses seemed fixed at some point above our heads.

Ronald Legge, who was seated beside me, whispered: 'Any moment now Big Nurse will have to give him his shot.'

Donald Wise of the London *Daily Mirror*, seated on the other side of me, whispered: 'Watch what happens now. This one usually freaks him out.' He rose to his feet and asked: 'Mr President, do you have any comment to make on the increase of witchcraft in Malawi?'

Banda: (Twitch-twitch. Dab-dab.) 'Don't you talk to me about witchcraft! You're the people who burned Joan of Arc at the stake!'

Wise: 'But Mr President, in regard to Malawi's witchcraft ...'

Banda: (Twitch-twitch. Dab-dab.) 'Shut up! That's a stupid question! Get out! Throw him out!'

The Ice-cream Men entered, seized Wise by the arms, and frog-marched him out.

Soon there weren't many of us left and the conference ended with no questions having been answered.

Dr Banda obtained his medical degree in the United States, studied medicine further in Scotland and practised for several years in Liverpool. Educated by Scottish missionaries during his childhood in Africa, he remained close to the Methodist religion and became an elder of the Church of Scotland. On the day Malawi – formerly known as Nyasaland – became an independent nation he sang to his people his favourite hymn: *Bringing in the Sheaves*. Those familiar with this hymn will know that it has 135 verses. President Banda sang every verse, an achievement of endurance for him – and his people.

In the early years of his rule his general behaviour was commensurate with his position as an elder of the Church of Scotland. But eventually, as power corrupted him, he fell from grace. He became dictatorial, political opponents disappeared or died in mysterious circumstances and a large proportion of the wealth of Malawi flowed into his Swiss bank account.

When he reached his nineties his mental abilities began to fail him, power slipped from his grasp and when he died his people were not unhappy to see him go.

281

18

Black mamba

Detective Sergeant Basie Morkel, slightly late, came into the CID section at John Vorster Square police headquarters at a fast trot, carrying his old briefcase in one hand and holding a transistor radio to his ear with the other.

He was absorbed in the cricket commentary he was listening to and so did not notice the air of expectancy and suppressed excitement with which his colleagues watched him approach his glass-panelled office. Basie entered his office and stopped dead. There was a black man sitting at his desk, on the far side, in his chair. Let there be no misunderstanding on this, the black man was actually sitting in Detective Sergeant Basie Morkel's very own chair, the one he sat in himself when he worked at his desk. Let it also be understood that in the entire history of that chair no black man had ever sat in it.

So Basie stepped quickly backwards and looked up at the number above the door to confirm that it was his office. It was indeed his office. He spun round and looked at the detectives in the general office. The grins and smirks on their faces vanished as if by magic and their heads bowed down as they became suddenly absorbed in paperwork.

Basie stepped back into his office and looked at the black man who was now standing.

'Who the hell are you and why are you sitting in my chair?' demanded Basie.

'I am Detective Sergeant Bats Dhlamini. I have been posted here from Maritzburg and I have been appointed to work with you,' said the black man. 'I'm sorry I've been sitting in your chair but the one on the other side of the desk is broken.' He held out his hand. 'I'm pleased to meet you,' he said.

Basie ignored the offered hand and said: 'Get out of my office and wait outside.' He flung his briefcase and the transistor radio on his desk, stormed out of the office complex and into the corridor outside, and knocked on the door and entered the office of his superior, Captain Danie Reitz, in one swift movement.

'Captain, there's a kaffer in my office!' he said, breathlessly.

Captain Reitz sighed. 'Sit down Basie. Take it easy. Here, have a cigarette.'

'No thanks,' said Sergeant Morkel tensely. 'Why's he there?'

Captain Reitz lit a cigarette for himself, took a puff and studied Basie through the smoke. 'Listen, Basie, I was going to introduce you to Sergeant Dhlamini personally, but you were late this morning. As you know we have a transformation programme and the white and black divisions of the police force are integrating. Sergeant Dhlamini is the first to arrive in this office and I want him to work with you ...'

'Why me, sir?'

'Because you are my best detective sergeant and I want Dhlamini to get acquainted with things here fast. His record is good and he comes highly recommended.'

'Do I have an option in this?'

'No. It's an order. Make the best of it, Basie. It's a new government, a new world and a new way of life. Don't try and fight it.'

'Does he have to sit in my office?'

'Yes, until we can find him one of his own.'

Sergeant Morkel rose swiftly to his feet and left without another word, not quite slamming the door behind him but shutting it hard enough to indicate his displeasure. Captain Reitz sat looking at the closed door thoughtfully. Then he shook his head, shrugged and stubbed out the cigarette in his ashtray.

Basie found Sergeant Dhlamini waiting patiently outside his office.

Basie swept files and other papers off a small table in the corner of his office and said: 'That's your place. I'll get you a chair and a telephone ... yes, what do you want?' His inquiry was directed at a young detective who had appeared in the doorway.

'Sergeant, a body has been found in Sandton Mews Park. Captain Reitz says can you please check it out and take this ... and take this man with you. Flying Squad's there already.'

'Dammit man, why can't you go?'

'Captain wants you to go, Sergeant.' Basie cursed.

As they drove to Sandton Mews Park Basie put the car radio on. He did not want to talk to Sergeant Dhlamini and he wanted to listen to the cricket. The commentator said that South Africa was all out for 356 and Australia was already at 76 for two wickets.

'They're going to hammer us again,' said Sergeant Dhlamini. 'Our bowling's gone to pieces.'

Basie shook his head in disbelief. Not only had they given him a kaffer partner but it also talked cricket.

He leaned across Dhlamini and took a small leather-bound hip flask from the glove compartment. He pulled its stopper off with his teeth as he drove, letting it dangle by its silver chain. He took a swallow and re-corked it. He did not offer Sergeant Dhlamini a drink. Basie Morkel had been raised on a Northern Transvaal farm where whites did not eat or drink from the same utensils as blacks. There had been a very respectable old black preacher who used to call at the homestead for donations and whom his mother liked very much. She used to invite him to have coffee with her on the stoep, but always kept a separate cup, saucer and teaspoon in the kitchen for his use.

The body in Sandton Mews Park was that of a well-dressed, middle-aged white man. The District Surgeon, Dr Jan Dekker, was already there.

'What happened to him, Doc?' asked Basie.

Dr Dekker shrugged as he got up and stripped off a pair of rubber gloves. 'Seems to have been a heart attack. No outward signs of physical harm, except there's a double puncture here ... on the outside of his left hand. He may have run into a thorn bush.'

'Snakebite?' suggested Sergeant Dhlamini.

Basie Morkel and the doctor exchanged glances. 'Who's he?' asked Dr Dekker. Morkel made no reply. He seemed not to have heard the question.

'Sergeant Bats Dhlamini,' said Dhlamini, holding out his hand. The doctor hesitated a moment, then shook it perfunctorily.

'Well,' he said. 'It doesn't look unlike a snakebite, but I doubt you'll find snakes in this part of town. It's too civilised. Only snakes who live here are lawyers and stockbrokers. Ha-ha!'

Basie had been going through the pockets of the corpse and stood up with an open wallet in his hand. 'Name's John Riley Waterson. Lived in Bedfordview. Doesn't look like he was mugged. There's about 900 rands here.'

The Flying Squad officer butted in. 'We've had a missing persons report that matches this guy's description. And we think we've found his car, a BMW 535, down the road over there. Question is, what the hell was he doing in the park?'

Dr Dekker prepared to leave. 'Probably looking for a woman, or even a man. Or just stopped for a pee. Anyway, I'm off. Looks like a plain heart attack and I'll confirm it with you guys after an autopsy.'

Back at John Vorster Square Basie Morkel made his way to the washrooms for a clean-up. The entrance door bore a spanking new sign that said 'TOILETS'. The old sign that had been removed had said 'TOILETS FOR WHITE OFFICERS ONLY.' He went in, removed his jacket and washed his face and combed his hair, gazing moodily into the mirror as he did so. He had a pugnacious face and blue eyes that were set close together. His hair was thinning. His stocky build, once compact and muscular, had reached the stage where his gut was beginning to bulge over his belt. At the age of 31 it should not be happening yet, but Basie drank a lot of beer and, like many detectives, he ate irregularly and badly.

He was joined at the long line of washbasins and mirrors by Dolf Muller who, like Basie, was a sergeant, but had somehow been overlooked in the promotion line and was now 55, grey-haired and looking forward to retirement. They grinned at each other in the mirror.

'How's your new partner?' asked Dolf.

'Don't ask,' growled Basie and changed the subject. He didn't want to talk about it. 'How are you? I hear rumours that you're taking early retirement.'

'Ja, man. I'm getting the hell out of here. And if you want my advice you should get out too. They're looking for good cops in Canada.'

'Bugger that. I don't want to live in Canada. It's too cold. And why should I go, anyway?'

'Surely I don't have to spell it out for you, man. We were both due for promotion a year ago. We didn't get it, right? Now you've been given the job of babysitting a kaffer and training him up for the job they had in mind for you, you poor bugger. Next thing you'll find he will be promoted over your head. It's going to be Lieutenant Dhlamini instead of Lieutenant Morkel. Mark my words, that's what will happen. Well, I'm not going to wait around for that sort of shit. My son's got a farm in the Soutpansberg. I'm going to help him run it.'

Basie wiped his hands thoughtfully on a paper towel. 'Can't see that he's lieutenant material,' he said.

Sergeant Muller barked a short laugh. 'Do you think that matters?'

'Funny thing is,' said Basie, 'he likes cricket.'

They were startled by the flushing of the nearest toilet. The door opened and Sergeant Dhlamini emerged. He stood beside them and washed his hands.

'Speaking of cricket,' he said, politely, 'I hear the Aussies are 288 for four. Like I said I think we're going to get hammered.'

The two white men fled. 'Jesus,' said Basie in the passage outside. 'Do you think he heard everything we said?'

'I reckon he did,' replied Sergeant Muller. 'Which is another reason why I'll be glad I'm not around when he's a lieutenant.'

Shortly after he reached office the following morning Sergeant Basie Morkel received a telephone call from Dr Dekker. 'Basie, who did you say that black guy is who was with us yesterday?'

'Sergeant Dhlamini. Why?'

'Well, he was right about the snakebite. Waterson was bitten by a mamba.'

'A mamba? Yerra!' exclaimed Basie.

'We've identified the venom. He was bitten twice, on the hand and in the neck. We found the second bite behind his ear, just below the hairline. Cause of death definitely snakebite. There's enough mamba poison in him to have killed ten men.'

Basie put the phone down slowly. Sergeant Dhlamini, who had turned around at hearing his name, was looking at him gravely.

'How did you know it was a snakebite?' Basie asked.

'Just a hunch ... the bite mark on his hand and the expression on his face.'

'What expression?'

'Sort of strange look of terror, like he'd got a hell of a special kind of fright.'

Basie stared at the black man. He did not recall an abnormal look of terror. He'd seen the rictus, the contortion of facial muscles, but he'd seen that in many cases of death. Faced with death, people went into shock. It was a fact.

Bats Dhlamini was musing over the snake. 'A mamba ... in Johannesburg. It doesn't make sense.'

'There are snakes in Joburg,' said Basie.

'Cobras, yes. Ringhals, yes. Boomslangs, yes. But a mamba, no. That's a Lowveld snake. You find it in Natal, kwaZulu, Eastern Transvaal, Swaziland – even Mozambique. But not in Johannesburg.'

'How come you so sure? How do you know all this?'

'I'm from Natal. I'm a Zulu. I grew up among mambas.'

Basie grunted. 'Well, I've got to tell the captain this guy had the bad luck to get bitten by a snake in the park.' He trudged off to Captain Reitz's office and returned a few minutes later. 'Captain says people in the vicinity have to be told that snake might still be around. There's a primary school nearby and they must be told first. You go and draw a car from Vehicles Section and do that while I stay here and type up the report. Okay?'

'Okay,' said Bats.

'And tell everyone to be watchful without getting into a panic,' warned Basie. 'Last year when that circus python escaped into the sewage system we had people crapping in their gardens because they were too scared to sit on a toilet.'

When Sergeant Dhlamini had left Sergeant Morkel sighed with the relief of being alone in his office and switched on his pocket transistor radio while he typed the report of the accidental death by snakebite of John Riley Waterson of Bedfordview, Johannesburg. He heard, with despair, a summation of the test match. Australia had won.

Bats Dhlamini went methodically through the process of

informing the neighborhood of the possible presence of a mamba. The headmistress of the primary school was, understandably, the most anxious.

'What does it look like?' She was quite a large, matronly woman, and she removed her spectacles and rubbed her eyes in perplexity at what the presence of a mamba could mean to the children in her care.

'It could be up to three-and-a-half metres long,' said Bats. 'And it's actually not black. More a sort of dark olive-brown colour. I think you must keep the children away from grassy areas for a while.'

'Is it very poisonous?'

Bats hesitated, remembering Sergeant Morkel's advice to play it cool. But he decided to be frank.

'I have to tell you it is one of the most dangerous snakes in the world. It is very aggressive if it feels threatened. A child bitten by it would die within an hour. Anyone seeing it must keep well away and report it immediately. Please tell the children this while helping them not to get into a panic about it.'

He visited several nearby residences and two Sandton-style office complexes set in garden surroundings. Reaction to his information was varied, ranging from deep concern to wisecracks. But everyone promised to be vigilant.

He left until last the apartment block called Sandton Mews adjoining the small park and after which the park itself was named. It was there that he encountered the first surprise.

The elderly caretaker, like Dhlamini a Zulu, greeted him in the traditional manner. 'I see you!'

'I see you!' replied Dhlamini politely.

He listened carefully to Dhlamini's warning about the snake and promised he would inform all the residents. Then he added: 'This man who died, I know him. He did not live here but he used to visit here. He was here the night before he died.'

'Hau!' said Dhlamini. 'Who did he visit?'

'The woman in apartment 211. She was his girlfriend when her husband was away on long journeys with his work on the aeroplanes, which was many times. But on that night she refused to open her door to him.'

'Why not?'

'For two things. One was that the husband had found out that this man was his wife's lover, and there had been a big row with much noise and fighting. And the other thing was that he was drunk. He fell about, he was full of spit and he was so drunk he could not even speak properly. After she refused him he came to me here in the lobby and held onto my coat, making drunk noises. I pushed him outside and told him to go home and sleep.'

Dhlamini's mind was beginning to race. 'What happened then?'

'He went through the small gate that leads to the park. I watched him go. He was going to his car. He always left it on the other side of the park, never here, because he did not wish the husband of the woman to see it.'

Dhlamini was gently chiding. 'If he was too drunk to drive his car you should have called the police. You may have saved his life.'

The old man shrugged, his face expressionless. Saving the life of a stupid white man, whether from drunken driving or being bitten by a snake, was of no concern to him.

Sergeant Dhlamini went to the small gate. He saw two sets of footprints. One coming through the gate and one going out.

They were identical and he suspected they were Waterson's. It had not rained for several days and the prints were clear. It appeared no one else had used the gate entrance in the past 48 hours.

He went to the car and opened the boot wherein lay the bolted-in and locked steel box containing the shotgun and other items of police equipment that became useful on occasions. He took out the small Nikon camera and went back to the gate where he photographed the footprints after placing a ballpoint pen along-side the clearest one for measurement purposes.

Then he walked into the park, following the prints, noting that they became increasingly erratic until they ended where Waterson's body had been found.

He cast around for the incoming prints coming from where Waterson's car had been parked on the opposite side of the park and when he found them, followed them back to the small gate. The track appeared normal and straight until they reached a small copse of a dozen of so poplars planted and sculpted to enhance the appearance of the park. Here, suddenly, the tracks became confused into a jumble of imprints as though the man had staggered or leapt about. Then they resumed towards the apartments but with deeper heel imprints as if made by running.

Dhlamini had looked after his father's cattle as a child and like any other good Zulu herdboy had become a competent tracker – the alternative to having to face the parental wrath resulting from the loss of a cow. The trail he was now following made fascinating reading.

He went back to the poplar grove. It was quite evident that this was where Waterson had met the mamba. He looked about the area. It was also clear that the copse had other visitors at times. There were other footprints which also passed by the spot where Waterson seemed to have had his encounter, but he was able to identify Waterson's.

There was some mild litter lying about, including two empty beer bottles, a wilted condom, an empty cigarette pack and a length of sisal cord, one end of which was tied around the narrow trunk of one of the young poplars.

Dhlamini began to walk away, then stopped as an old memory stirred in his mind. Slowly, he turned and walked back to the tree with the sisal cord around it. He knelt on the grass and examined the cord closely, noting that the loose end had been cut. He took a penknife from his pocket and carefully cut the entire cord from the tree. When he returned to the car he took a plastic bag from the steel box in the boot, placed the sisal cord in it and sealed it.

He drove back to John Vorster Square and handed the camera film and the plastic bag containing the sisal cord to the forensic laboratory with an explanation and a polite request that he be allowed to collect the results early the following morning.

Sergeant Dhlamini then drove to Soweto, the big sprawling black township outside the city of Johannesburg. He needed to think and he wanted to do it in a more familiar environment.

He had arrived from Maritzburg to live in Soweto only a few weeks ago but had already discovered that Mama Cash's shebeen was one of the more congenial places in which to relax. He parked the unmarked police car outside the shebeen and locked it securely after first raising the engine cover and loosening one of the battery terminals. No point in getting an official vehicle stolen on his first day at work. The atmosphere there was bad enough as it was.

Inside the shebeen he sat down at a table amidst its cheery buzz and ordered a beer and one of the bang-on ripe mealie cobs dressed with the butter and herb sauce for which Mama Cash was famous. In the way he had seen other customers do it he stood the hot mealie on its end with the fork and stripped the mealie kernels off it with the knife. He forked up and ate the delicious mealie kernels first and then picked up the cob and sucked it dry of its tasty sauce. With a sigh he sat back, wiped his lips with a paper serviette and took a sip of the cold beer.

He ran the day's events through his mind. The difficulties with his white colleagues didn't bother him. Poor dogs, their day had come and they were running scared – scared for their jobs and their future careers under a black government. That was their problem, not his. But he supposed he should discuss his growing suspicions on this Waterson case with Sergeant Morkel as soon as possible. He suspected Morkel would deride him and he wished he had more to go on.

Then the idea struck him. He looked around. Mama Cash, shebeen owner, money-lender, friend to all in need, beloved of the people of Soweto, was sitting behind the till on her large and strong chair, especially designed to accommodate her great buttocks and substantial girth. Her 'kiri', the baseball-bat-sized club with which she kept law and order in her shebeen, stood in a corner nearby, within swift and easy reach.

Sergeant Dhlamini finished his beer and went to pay Mama Cash for his lunch. As he did so, he leaned close to her and whispered: 'Mama, please, I need a sangoma. Can you tell me where to find a good one?'

A smile split the broad, handsome face of Mama Cash and she chuckled. 'Aah,' she said softly. 'Only a few days in town and the boy needs a sangoma!' She drew a pad towards her and wrote down a name and address and gave it to him. 'He is a good one. He has helped me. I am sure he can help you.'

He found the address in a sleazy part of the township in a dusty street that smelled of woodsmoke and cooking and shrilled with the chatter of children and the yells of women who, in the African way, discussed matters with each other from either side of the street.

The sangoma's house bore the usual tokens – mysterious graffiti and the horned skulls of dead beasts. That the ancient art of witchcraft was in good financial health was indicated by the smart white Mercedes Benz 350 that stood outside the premises. Passers-by and the children playing in the street gave it a wide berth. Dhlamini parked directly behind it, confident that his own vehicle would be safe under the umbrella of its protection. A police car might be stolen in Soweto, but a witchdoctor's never, nor the vehicle next to it.

He was about to knock on the door when it was opened suddenly from within, and he cursed silently at the way it startled him. A comely girl in neat white nurse's overalls and cap stood there smiling at him. 'I saw you through the window parking your car,' she said. 'Welcome to Dr Matsula's rooms.'

She sat down behind a desk. 'Do you have an appointment? No. Well he still has two patients to see ... so if you don't mind waiting?'

He saw nobody in the waiting room and assumed patients waited alone in separate rooms and left by a rear exit in the discreet way some psychiatrists assisted the confidentiality of their patients. He sat down and stared curiously about him. There was a larger-than-life-sized black and white photograph of a wizened old man in a fur hat and a leopard skin cape on the wall behind the receptionist. Presumably Dr Matsula. A brown and white ox-hide shield with two spears positioned horizontally above it was situated on the opposite wall. There was also a colour photograph of a group of men in hats and cloaks of various furs and skins. Possibly a sangoma's convention. Or graduation class of whenever? Also prominently displayed was a colour photograph of Nelson Mandela.

He had never before visited the premises of a modern-day sangoma overlaid with the trappings of western culture. It was a long way from the days when the tribal witchdoctor capered, hideously attired in animal skins and feathers, in front of terrified folk and 'smelled out' a victim for execution. He caught the eye of the receptionist, smiled at her and almost expressed his thoughts, but realised in time that would have been a mistake. Respectable modern sangomas were offended by the term 'witchdoctor'. They saw themselves as medicine men and counsellors who cured the body and spirit and provided love potions and other 'muti' to ward off evil spirits. What was wrong with that? The sangomas who fell from grace these days and were called witchdoctors were those who cast evil spells to harm people and who committed murder, and who dealt in the body parts of children from which to prepare their 'muti'. As a police officer Dhlamini knew the line separating the two was sometimes obscure.

An hour and a half passed before the telephone on the receptionist's desk rang and she told him Dr Matsula would see him. 'You must pay me first,' she said, shyly.

'How much?'

'One hundred rands.'

He winced, but paid up, wondering how the cost of a visit to a sangoma was going to look to a police accountant.

Dr Matsula was considerably smaller than his photograph and sat cross-legged on a kaross, wearing his fur hat and leopard-skin cloak. Underneath it he was wearing grey flannel trousers and a pricey-looking pair of brown leather shoes. Apart from that, stepping from the westernised reception area into his consulting room was like stepping back into deepest Africa. Dhlamini almost reeled at the strong smell that filled the room – emanating from roots, bunches of dried herbs leaves, flowers, fynbos, grasses, and bottles of unidentified liquids and substances that stood on shelves around three quarters of the room. A gigantic fertility mask, its expression lecherous and topped by a rampant phallus, loomed above the sangoma. It was dramatised by the soft glow of a red light within, clearly a touch to impress or intimidate his clientele. Smoke rose from an incense tray in one corner of the room, its aroma fighting a losing battle with the odour of the herbal stocks. Whether intended or not, the transition from formality in the waiting room to ju-ju Africa inside was eerily effective.

Dr Matsula did not rise, did not even look at him. Sergeant Dhlamini sat down on the floor and crossed his legs. The sangoma still didn't look up, and said nothing. Dhlamini realised he was expected to speak first. He decided to get straight to the point.

'I am looking for the sangoma who sells poisonous snakes.'

'What sort of poisonous snakes?'

'Mambas.'

For the first time the sangoma looked up. His eyelids were heavy and drooped and the eyes beneath them slitted and reddened in the light filtering from the great fertility mask on the wall. 'Many sangomas deal in snakes. Their venom provides muti. But the mamba is a deadly and difficult snake. Very few sangomas would touch a mamba.'

'I know that. I wish only to know where I may find such a person.'

Matsula kept his slitted gaze on Dhlamini. 'Who are you?'

'I am Sergeant Bats Dhlamini. I am a police officer.'

The old man lowered his head and looked at the floor again.

'I do not discuss other sangomas and I do not speak to policemen.'

'A crime has been committed,' said Dhlamini.

Matsula made no reply. Dhlamini waited. The minutes passed. Matsula sat like a graven image and said nothing. Dhlamini sighed and began to rise to his feet to go.

'Wait,' said the sangoma. 'Do you wish me to throw the bones? You have paid for it.' Dhlamini hesitated, then nodded and settled back on the floor.Matsula reached for the calabash beside him and shook it. He then upended it so that its contents scattered on the floor between them. It was mainly bones, small bones, probably of animals, possibly of humans. Some were marked and coloured. There were a few curiously shaped stones, a copper nail and what appeared to be the incisor of a large animal, possibly a lion or a baboon or similar.

Minutes passed while Matsula studied the bones intently. So intently that Dhlamini grew apprehensive.

Finally the sangoma said: 'You are an ambitious man. The bones say you will have a successful career ... very soon your career will sing because of one who works in a place where they keep the wild beasts ... this person is of the people who have nine fingers.'

'What place where they keep the wild beasts?' asked Dhlamini.

Matsula scooped up the bones and replaced them in the calabash. 'The bones have spoken and now they are silent,' he said. He became still again, looking at the floor.

When Sergeant Dhlamini left the sangoma's house he drove immediately to the outskirts of Soweto where he had seen the tents and the signboards of Boswell's circus, a place where they kept wild beasts in cages. But no one there knew of anyone who had nine fingers.

Dhlamini drove despondently back to the city. He passed a newspaper poster which read: 'MAMBA KILLS MAN IN SANDTON' and another which said: 'KILLER SNAKE LOOSE IN CITY.' He sighed. So much for trying to avoid panic. The media had begun to promote it.

He was almost back at police headquarters when he was struck by a realisation so suddenly that he cursed and braked sharply, causing the driver behind to swerve outwards to avoid a collision – and to shake his fist at him as he passed.

Dhlamini looked at his watch. It was 4.30 and the evening rush hour had begun. They would be closing soon but he might just make it if he hurried. He reached for the blue flasher light beneath the dashboard, slapped it on the roof of the car and switched on the siren. Then he did a U-turn and headed for the Johannesburg Zoo.

If Dhlamini expected Sergeant Morkel to be derisive when he reported to him the following morning he was not far wrong. Morkel began by listening to him with a cynical smile. But whatever his faults and prejudices Morkel was a good cop. As the tale proceeded his expression changed to one of close attention. By the time Dhlamini finished Morkel was looking at him with grudging admiration. 'You've done good work, man.' The compliment was jerked out of him as though he had no control over it. A full meeting was set up in Captain Reitz's office an hour later.

'Okay,' said the captain, crisply, 'Yesterday it was a death by misadventure, now we have a murder inquiry, so let's go. Let's start at the beginning ... what do we have on the snake?'

District Surgeon Dekker, fresh from a crash consultation with a snake expert and with his own medical report in front of him cleared his throat and began: 'There are two kinds of mamba, Captain. The green mamba hangs around mainly in trees while the black mamba is a ground snake. Both are of the front-fanged variety, both have distinctive coffin-shaped heads and are equally venomous. But whereas the green mamba tends to be shy and avoids contact, usually only biting if handled, the black mamba is a highly nervous, unpredictable and aggressive snake. It will attack rather than withdraw and it is unusually muscular, which gives it an ability to rear up to two-thirds of its length. It's adult size is about three-and-a-half metres which means it comes at you at about eye-level. It moves fast and it strikes very fast. Its venom is virulently nerve-destroying and kills within an hour or two. Severe throat pain, nausea, imbalance, muscular pain, profuse salivation, sweat-ing and incoherent speech all occur within five to 20 minutes. Chest pain follows, then breathing difficulty occurs followed by total respiratory failure and death. It's a very nasty snake, Captain.'

'It sounds a real shit of a snake,' agreed the captain. 'And it was this type of snake that killed the deceased, right?'

'That's confirmed, Captain. Two bites. One in the hand, one in the neck. He would have died as I have described.'

'Thank you, doctor.' The captain waved his cigarette at Bats Dhlamini. 'Okay, Bats, Basie here tells me you've done some deep digging on this case. Let's have your report.'

Dhlamini felt a quick surge of pleasure. The informal use of his first name together with Sergeant Morkel's in the presence of this gathering was a subtle indication that he had earned professional respect. He opened his notebook. 'Captain, the deceased, John Waterson, made frequent visits to Sandton Mews. He was having an affair with a lady in apartment 211, Mrs Rosalie Albertyn, whose husband, Frans Albertyn, is a South African Airways pilot who is often away on international flights. He is away on a London flight at present, due in tomorrow morning.

'The husband found out about the affair and there was a bad scene, lots of shouting. It was heard by several people in nearby apartments. Albertyn was heard shouting at Waterson, apparently over the telephone, to stay away from his wife. It seems that after that Mrs Albertyn ended the affair but Waterson continued to attempt to visit her, even though she refused to open the door to him. He always parked his car in a side street on the far side of Sandton Mews Park and walked to the Mews along a path that runs through the park and, at one point, it passes through a small clump of trees.

'The night before he was found dead, Waterson visited the apartment again and appeared to be drunk. After Mrs Albertyn refused to open her door, Waterson went to the caretaker in the lobby and fell up against him, grabbing him by the lapels. The caretaker, believing him to be drunk, ejected him from the building. He said Waterson was so drunk that he was drooling and mumbling and he could not understand what he was saying. As we know, Waterson was found in the park the following morning, dead from snakebite.'

Sergeant Dhlamini looked up at those present. 'It is my belief that Waterson was not drunk on that last attempt to visit Mrs Albertyn. He had already been bitten by the mamba, and what the caretaker mistook for drunkenness was, in fact, the effects of having been bitten by the snake. Waterson was asking for help, but he was already so much affected by the venom that he failed to make himself understood.'

Captain Reitz cocked an eyebrow at Dr Dekker. 'Possible, Doc?'

'Entirely possible, I suppose ...' conceded Dekker, spreading his hands. 'It fits in with the symptoms of imbalance, salivation and incoherent speech. And I have to tell you something, Captain. We found no alcohol in Waterson's blood at the autopsy.'

The captain frowned, shaking his head. 'But even so, where's the murder in all this? Bats, you are far out on a limb, you know. What are you trying to tell us, man? That Frans Albertyn turned into a snake and bit his wife's lover?'

Sergeant Dhlamini ignored the jibe. 'Listen to this, Captain,' he said, producing a plastic bag with the sisal string inside it. 'I got this back from forensics this morning. I found this cord tied around one of the trees in the park. Forensics have identified two tiny scales on it as reptilian. Yesterday I followed Waterson's spoor across the park to the Mews apartments where he was thought to be drunk and back to where his body was found. On the way to the apartments his tracks followed the path past the tree where this cord was tied and the soil showed a lot of disturbance. From there Waterson's spoor indicated he was running. On the way back from the apartment, where he was crossing the park obviously with the intention of getting back to his car, the spoor showed he was staggering, until he collapsed where he was later found dead.'

Dhlamini drew a deep breath before making his next statement. 'It's my conclusion, Captain, that this snake was tied by its tail to that tree to kill Waterson – by someone who knew that he would pass by it. What supports my conclusion is that Waterson was bitten twice. A mamba tends to strike once – it is not its habit to repeatedly strike or savage a victim. But if it is tied up like a dog and therefore furiously angry and cannot move away, and its victim is probably falling about, the snake is likely to strike again and again.'

They were staring at him. There was a long and embarrassed silence. The captain played with a pencil, tapping its lead point softly on the desk in front of him. 'Now that's a novel way of knocking somebody off,' he said, carefully straight-faced. He shot a look at the district surgeon. 'Doc, you ever had a case of a guy murdered by a snake tied by its tail?' Dr Dekker shook his head.

'It's happened before,' said Sergeant Dhlamini quietly.

'Oh? When?'

'A long time ago, Captain. My grandfather once told me how witchdoctors used to predict a man would die by snakebite and then tie a black mamba to a tree on a path known to be used by the victim. A mamba used in such a way would be a very angry snake. It would strike at whoever came near it, and would later be released and removed by the witchdoctor – whose reputation as a prophet of death would grow mightily.'

The captain leaned forward. 'Listen Bats. I respect the folklore and appreciate all the work you have put into this investigation. But we cannot go into court with a murder charge based on fables. I can see where you're coming from. Okay, we've got a jealous husband and a dead man and a snake. But unless we can connect all three with evidence we're going nowhere. And dammit, man, let me tell you something else. If I caught someone screwing my wife I might also contemplate murder, but sure as hell you wouldn't find me buggering around with a mamba, trying to tie it to a tree, hoping it'll take a bite at my wife's boyfriend. What do you think a defence advocate will make of what you are saying, hey? We'd be laughed out of court!'

'I am not saying Frans Albertyn put the snake there himself. He would have found a person who does that sort of thing.'

'Oh? And how would he have found such a person?'

'The same way I did. By going to a sangoma.'

'Aha!' said the captain. 'I was wondering when we'd get back to the witchdoctors.'

Sergeant Dhlamini was patient. 'Captain, it's the sangomas who know these people – the snake people. They buy venom and snake parts from them for their muti.'

'Christ!' said the captain. 'Snake people ... snake parts for muti.' He lit a cigarette. 'And you are saying you have found a suspect?'

'Yes.'

'Where?'

'The Johannesburg Zoo. His name is Rufus Ngwena. He works in the snake pit there.'

'How did you identify him as a suspect?'

Dhlamini hesitated. He would have liked to tell the captain how Matsula the sangoma had thrown the bones which had pointed the way to a nine-fingered man in the place where the wild beasts are kept – and where he had found Ngwena, a nine-fingered member of the Fingo tribe of the Xhosa people, who amputated the small finger of the left hand of every child when born. But he feared the captain might not be able to handle any more folklore and fables, as he had put it. So he limited his reply to: 'Well, sir, he is the only snake man in Johannesburg who works with mambas.'

'At the zoo?'

'No. It's the only snake they don't keep there. Too dangerous. But his fellow workers at the zoo tell me he has a pair in his private collection at his home in Soweto.'

'What else?' asked the captain. He was beginning to sound more relaxed as the discussion ebbed back into a world he could understand.

'There's his record, sir. He was arrested in Port Elizabeth in 1973 for placing a Cape cobra in a man's bed. Got five years for attempted murder. In 1979 he was charged with illegal possession of a firearm. Got six months. In 1984 he was jailed for two years on a charge of witchcraft. Publicly put a curse on a victim. She was later bitten by a puff adder in her hut, but survived. It was alleged, but could not be proved, that Ngwena placed the snake there. He has sangoma status, but he's known to be one of the bad ones.'

Captain Reitz nodded. 'Now we're getting somewhere. Where's the bastard now?'

'He hasn't been at work for three days. I called at his house last night, but there was no response when I knocked.'

'Bad sign, he may have gone into hiding,' said the captain. He turned towards Sergeant Morkel. 'You've been bloody quiet all the time, Basie. What do you think of all this?'

'Sergeant Dhlamini is playing a hunch sir, and my own hunch is that his hunch could be on track. But, like you say, we still don't have connecting evidence. For example, it could be argued the snake trap was set for someone else – or just a sick joke at the expense of anybody who came by. We have to establish that there was communication between Frans Albertyn and Ngwena.'

'So what now?'

'We talk to Albertyn and his wife – and we find Ngwena.'

Captain Reitz nodded. 'Right, saddle your horses and get going!'

'Albertyn is away on a stopover London flight,' said Dhlamini. 'He gets back into Joburg tomorrow morning.'

'Okay, so we'll talk to his wife in the meantime,' said Sergeant Morkel. Then he frowned. 'Listen, meantime what about this bloody mamba? Do we assume it's still slithering around in the vicinity? I've had the press onto me again this morning. They're carrying on as though it's our pet snake.'

Dhlamini shook his head and pointed at the sisal cord. 'That stuff was cut,' he said. 'The mamba didn't free itself. So it's my guess Ngwena came back for it, and that could account for other footprints I found at the scene. He wouldn't want to lose it. It's a valuable snake in terms of what it can do for him and what he can get just by extracting and selling its venom.'

'One wonders how the devil *he* manages to handle it,' said Dr Dekker.

'Courage and a very special ability with a long pole and a loop,' said Dhlamini. 'As a matter of fact if you can somehow get its head covered, perhaps by a sack, it goes quiet and you can shove the rest of it in quite easily.'

'Nice to know that,' commented Sergeant Morkel, sourly. 'Let's bear it in mind.'

It was Basie Morkel's idea to visit Mrs Rosalie Albertyn after 10 p.m.

300

local time – which was 9 p.m. London time – to ensure that flight SAA 288, flown by Captain Frans Albertyn, was already airborne. 'I don't want her telephoning him in London to tip him off that we are onto him,' Basie said. 'The less he knows until we grab him the better.'

Mrs Albertyn was understandably upset at the late-hour visit. She had already gone to bed. 'Can't you cops visit at decent hours?' was her spirited reaction.

She was a petite, slender woman, pale-skinned and dark-haired with large brown eyes of the soulful kind. Basie Morkel had no difficulty in understanding how men were attracted to her.

She set out to be unhelpful from the start. 'No, I don't know if my husband had any contact with a Mr Ngwena or any other black man. Yes, he did threaten John Waterson over the telephone but certainly had no intention of killing him.'

Finally she said: 'Look, Sergeant, I'm devastated at the death of John Waterson. But my husband and I are now trying to repair our marriage and I want to put this all behind me. I don't want to answer any more questions. If I have to, I will only do so with an attorney present!'

Back in the car Basie Morkel said: 'Tough little bitch. We're not going to get very far with her.' He reached for his hip flask and took a swig. He slid a sideways look at Dhlamini and seemed as though he would like to offer him a drink, then changed his mind and put the flask back in his pocket.

Frans Albertyn was arrested the moment he stepped off Flight SA 288 from London. The arrest and questioning of suspects was an area in which Basie Morkel excelled, and with Albertyn he aimed for maximum impact. He met the pilot on the tarmac at the foot of the steps leading from the aircraft and showed his police badge, holding it up high, ignoring the shocked reaction of other flight crew. He said loudly: 'Captain Frans Albertyn? I am Detective Sergeant Jacobus Morkel of the Criminal Investigation Department of the South African Police – and this is Detective Sergeant Bats Dhlamini. We are taking you into custody in connection with the murder of John Waterson.' He had arranged for immigration and customs officials to accompany him to the aircraft and had them clear Albertyn's arrival on the apron. He was then bundled into a police car and Basie ensured that it sped all the way to John Vorster Square with its siren howling.

Dhlamini sat in front with the uniformed police driver and Basie sat beside Albertyn. Within minutes he knew they had their man. Although it was a cool morning Albertyn was sweating. Innocent people, if arrested, usually ask questions. Albertyn said nothing.

On arrival at John Vorster Square he was taken to an interrogation room and the door was slammed shut on him. Morkel and Dhlamini observed him through the two-way mirror for half an hour, carefully noting the man's body language. Albertyn sat silently on a chair, staring blankly at the table in front of him. Then, suddenly, he buried his face in his hands and sat like that for a long time.

When Morkel and Dhlamini entered the interrogation room Morkel made a point of bursting in noisily and slamming the case file on the table before sitting down. Dhlamini remained standing, leaning against a wall. Morkel flipped the switch on the tape recorder and, locking Albertyn's eyes into his own baleful stare, he intoned: 'April 26, 1994, 10.45 hours, present Frans Albertyn of 211 Sandton Mews, Johannesburg, with Detective Sergeants Morkel and Dhlamini.'

Morkel hunched his shoulders and leaned forward, his eyes still fixed on Albertyn. He had played hooker for his high school XV and, later, for his rugby club. The look he now fixed on the murder suspect was the same with which he had always engaged opposing hookers in the vital instant before the scrum enmeshed – a brutish, malevolent stare under lowered eyebrows, the eyes slightly squint in their concentration. He now went straight for the jugular, with a short, knife-like verbal thrust: 'You hired an assassin to use a poisonous snake to murder your wife's lover, John Riley Waterson!' he snarled. He pointed to the mirror on the wall, revealing its secret dramatically and lied: 'Through that two-way mirror, ten minutes ago, the killer, Rufus Ngwena, identified you as the man who hired him to kill John Waterson! He will tell it to you to your face in court!'

Frans Albertyn cracked open like a boiled egg slapped with a breakfast spoon. 'I didn't ... I'm sorry, truly sorry ... he wasn't supposed to kill him. I only wanted him frightened. Oh my God ...' He buried his face in his hands.

Sergeant Basie Morkel stood up, looked at Sergeant Dhlamini, and inclined his head at Albertyn. 'Okay, Bats,' he said. 'You do the necessary. He's all yours. You earned him.'

Bats stepped forward. 'Frans Albertyn. I am Sergeant Bats Dhlamini. I am arresting you for the murder of John Riley Waterson.' And he informed him of his rights, after which he was led away to a cell.

'Come on,' said Basie. 'Let's get the other one. You know where he lives. We'll take your car.'

As they drove off Basie whipped out his flask and took a quick swig to brace himself for the task ahead. To make sure he was well primed he took another nip. He didn't offer the flask to Dhlamini.

When they arrived outside Ngwena's house Morkel ordered Dhlamini to stop further on so as to be out of sight. As they got out he said: 'You said in your report that this guy's been on a firearm rap,' he said. 'We're not taking chances.' He drew his pistol and checked the magazine.

Dhlamini opened the boot of the car and extracted the shotgun. Morkel frowned. 'Is that necessary?'

'Yes,' said Dhlamini, firmly. 'I was the worst handgun shot at police college. I'm happier with buckshot.'

They walked to Ngwena's house and Dhlamini examined the door, looking for the tiny twig he had inserted where it met the frame. It was still there. 'He's not here. The door hasn't been opened since I was here last.' Nevertheless he knocked. There was no response.

Morkel examined the cheap lock. It didn't look strong. 'Break it open!' he said.

Dhlamini hesitated. 'We don't have a search warrant.'

'Too bloody bad. Break it open!'

Dhlamini stood back and smashed his heel against the lock. It snapped and the door crashed open. Morkel cocked his pistol, stepped inside and moved to the left, panning the room swiftly with his firearm. Dhlamini released the safety catch on the big 12-bore shotgun and followed, stepping quickly to the right.

'Yerra! What a stink,' said Morkel holding his nostrils. 'Something's died inside here.' Then he saw the body on the floor near the window. It was a black man, lying with his head turned to one side, dried spittle on his cheek, his face contorted in the rictus of death.

Morkel bent down to examine the body. 'Jeeslike, this could be our friend Ngwena. Looks like he might have been taken out by his own mamba.' Even as he uttered the words he realised the significance of what he was saying and straightened up with a chill of fear trickling down his spine.

'Basie, look out!' yelled Dhlamini. Morkel spun around and for a fraction of a second saw the snake as it was about to strike him. It had reared up to two-thirds of its length and its head was level with his own. The head then disappeared simultaneously with the deafening blast of the shotgun and became distributed about the room in small pieces, some of them sticking to the walls. The rest of the snake ended up in a corner, writhing, twitching and coiling.

Morkel staggered outside where a curious crowd was gathering. Dhlamini followed him out, still holding the shotgun. They both leaned, panting against the wall.

Morkel wiped the sweat from his face with the sleeve of his jacket. 'Thanks, hey,' he gasped. 'Thanks for shooting straight.'

'First time I've ever shot straight,' said Dhlamini, taking out a handkerchief and wiping his brow.

Morkel dug into his hip pocket, hauled out his flask and took a long pull. He looked at Dhlamini for a couple of seconds, then thrust the flask at him. 'Have a dop,' he said.

Dhlamini accepted the flask, drank from it and handed it back. Morkel put it to his lips and drained the rest.

They radioed for assistance and stayed until the body of Rufus Ngwena was removed – along with the cages of snakes found in a shed behind the house. In one of the cages, on its own, was another mamba.

When they returned to headquarters Morkel went to the toilets and washed his hands and bathed his face. He dried himself on a paper towel and was combing his hair when Sergeant Dolf Muller entered and joined him at the washbasins. He looked carefully into the toilets to ensure they were alone.

'You hear the news about our headquarters?' he asked. 'No?

Well, they're changing the name. No more John Vorster Square. I suppose they're going to give it some kaffer name. They're also going to abolish military-style ranks. We're going to become constables and inspectors and chief inspectors – like those guys in the health department who check on drains. Well, bugger them. They can do what they like. I'm getting out of here. And you, Basie? How's the partnership going?'

He managed to pronounce the word 'partnership' with a sneer.

'When are you actually retiring, Dolf?' asked Morkel, returning his comb to his pocket.

'End of this month.'

'I wish it was today,' said Morkel as he turned to go. 'Because you're beginning to piss me off.'

Muller stared after Sergeant Morkel as he left, slamming the door.

'Well, well,' said Sergeant Muller, turning and addressing himself in the mirror. 'Well, well, well.'

19

Getting it wrong

Harvey Ward met me at Salisbury airport with the telex from London in his hand. It said: 'MAYDAY MAYDAY NEED URGENTEST 600 WORDS ON ANYTHING FOR HOLE IN MAIN FEATURES PAGE YOU'VE GOT NINETY MINUTES REGARDS FISHER FOREIGN.'

There are problems with this kind of message where you are expected to pluck a story out of thin air. One is that it's not coming only to you. It's been sent out to every correspondent in the field. For some reason a feature has been pulled out of the foreign section of the paper at the last moment and it's one of those rare occasions when there's nothing on hand with which to replace it. The features editor panics and runs to the foreign editor shouting: 'Help!' The foreign editor throws out a net far and wide by messaging all his correspondents throughout the world. They then haul in the net to see what they've got and use the best.

Because foreign hacks are an insecure lot who need the reassurance of being published frequently, most of those messaged will strive to hit the jackpot by grabbing at whatever facts, colour, romance or drama they can find to write and send in 90 minutes. Some great reputations have been made in this way. On the other hand, within such scrambling lie the seeds of error.

Personally I don't like writing fast. It makes me tense. American reporters were always better at it than us Fleet Street hacks because they simply slammed over the facts to rewriters who cleaned it up for them and checked for accuracy. (I have a framed poster of one of the old-timers in his shirtsleeves, necktie undone, wearing a press card tucked in his hatband and a pencil-thin moustache above his evil grin as he purrs into a telephone: 'Hiya, sweetheart,

306

gimme rewrite!') Fleet Street on the other hand has always expected its reporters to deliver fully composed, well-written stories needing only to be brushed up by sub-editors. That ain't so easy, sweetheart. Not in 90 minutes.

So when Harvey gave me the telex I groaned a little. 'When did this arrive?' I asked.

'Half an hour ago.'

'So we've got 60 minutes left?'

'Yeah.'

'Shit.'

'Yeah.'

After that we ran out of words.

I was still in my formative years on the foreign reporting staff of the *Daily Mail* and I was anxious to please. But how and where was I going to find the subject matter to write and send a 600-word factual article in 60 minutes?

Harvey watched me sympathetically. Then he said: 'I've got an idea. Tell passenger services to hold your luggage and meet me in the bar. Bring your typewriter.' I did as I was told, mystified but hopeful.

When I got to the airport bar Harvey had already ordered two beers and was sitting at a corner table. I sat down opposite him, expectantly.

'Listen,' said Harvey. 'Let's send them the story about the spider men of the Okavango swamps.'

'*The what*?'

'The spider men of the Okavango swamps,' said Harvey, patiently. 'Have you never heard of them?'

'No.'

He sighed at the tedium of dealing with my lack of experience of Africa's best-known secrets. 'OK, listen. As you know the Okavango swamps have been diminishing in area over the past three decades as the deserts to the north expand and the rivers that feed the swamps run dry.'

'Uh-huh.'

'Well, this has led to a sharp reduction in the fish resources in the swamps, especially in the northern region where these people, who are fisherfolk, live. This means that their traditional food supplies have virtually come to an end and they are starving to the extent that they have become terribly emaciated, so much so that they look spiderish.'

'Uh-huh.'

'In fact they no longer have the strength to launch and paddle their canoes,' Harvey said. He took a thoughtful sip of his beer.

'So how do they eat?' I asked.

'Well,' said Harvey. 'The one advantage of their emaciated state is that it makes them so light that they can run across the giant water lilies on the swamps, spearing the odd fish that still remains here and there. But it's touch and go.'

I studied Harvey Ward carefully. It's hard to measure bullshit in Africa. In Britain, for instance, if someone told you that a strange group of one-eyed beings had been discovered in north Wales with parasols growing out of their heads and that it was due to global warming, you wouldn't rush headlong into believing it. But in Africa so much that is believed turns out to be untrue and so much that is unbelievable turns out to be true that one hovers frequently in a state of doubt. As the old Romans discovered: '*Ex Africa semper aliquid novi.*' (Out of Africa there is always something new.)

'Harvey, have you actually seen these spider men?'

He hesitated for the briefest of moments. 'Fleetingly,' he replied, studying the beer level in his glass. 'Was up there on safari. Saw them but they ran away ...'

'Across the giant water lilies?'

'Yeah ... very shy people.'

'What's the name of the tribe?'

'Buggered if I can remember offhand,' said Harvey. 'Anyhow you've got space for only 600 words and' – he looked at his watch – 'you're 35 minutes from deadline.'

He was right. All around the world, from New York and Buenos Aires to Hong Kong and Moscow, *Daily Mail* correspondents were cancelling lunch appointments, quitting theatres, abandoning breakfasts or rolling out of bed, depending on which time zone they were in, to beat the 90-minute deadline. I was in danger of losing out.

So there in the corner of the bar at Salisbury airport I hauled out my typewriter and we swiftly wrote the story of the spider men of the Okavango swamps. I worked in further details as Harvey recalled them, like how, advantaged by their weightlessness, the spider men strove to achieve alternative food sources by darting up trees and chasing monkeys.

I put through a collect call to London from a public telephone in the airport hall and dictated the story to an intrigued copytaker. Harvey then drove me to the hotel where I took him to dinner.

Let me tell you about Harvey Ward. He was a former South African welterweight boxing champion and still looked the part. He was a compactly built, superbly fit man with a very short-back-and-sides haircut, a tough mouth and what I suppose could be called machine-gunner's eyes. I would not have liked to have met him in a boxing ring, even if only to get his name and address.

We had known each other for a long time – since our high-school days when he was school boxing champion and earned a lot of respect and hero worship from those of us who were a little younger than him.

Harvey became a cadet reporter for the Cape Town *Argus* after he left school and ended up as news editor of the group's Rhodesian publication, the *Rhodesia Herald*, which was when I met him again. He was also the *Daily Mail*'s stringer (local correspondent) and as such would assist me when I visited Rhodesia.

He was an ardent supporter of Rhodesian premier Ian Smith and eventually resigned from the *Rhodesia Herald* (and gave up the *Daily Mail* connection) to become Director of Information in the controversial Smith government. He became totally committed and used to give weekly political commentaries on Rhodesian television that were full of passion, fire and brimstone. Still a boxer at heart, he used to emphasise points in his fast delivery with restrained punches and jerky movements of his head and shoulders, as if manoeuvring around an opponent. A cruel way of enjoying his commentaries was to switch off the sound.

But before he became a propagandist Harvey enjoyed a high reputation as a journalist and news editor and was considered especially knowledgeable on Central African history, especially the era of Cecil Rhodes and the great Matabele chieftain, Lobengula. He frequently wrote colourful articles in the local press about this period and revealed to me that he was writing a biography of Lobengula, although I do not recall it ever being published.

Schoolboy hero worship extends to some degree into adulthood and this, together with his wide, if romantic, knowledge of the local African culture and history, was what tipped me into accepting his information on the spider men of the Okavango swamps in those pressured moments at Salisbury airport.

The story was a great success. The cable I received the following day said: 'MULTITHANKS YOUR EXCELLENT SPIDER MEN WHICH WELL DISPLAYED STOP EDITOR SENDS HIS PERSONAL CONGRATULATIONS REGARDS FISHER FOREIGN.'

I passed a handsome credit to Harvey for his assistance and took him out to dinner again where we preened ourselves on a job well done.

But two weeks later came another kind of message. I was still in Rhodesia when it arrived. It said, coldly: 'EDITOR HAS RECEIVED FOLLOWING LETTER CONCERNING YOUR SPIDER MEN STORY STOP NEEDS YOUR COMMENTS FORTHWITH FISHER FOREIGN.'

The letter was from a district commissioner in Bechuanaland (now Botswana), at that time a British protectorate in which the Okavango swamps were situated, and he seemed very upset.

'Never in my 30 years in Her Majesty's Colonial Service have I ever read such utter balderdash,' he wrote. 'I am well acquainted with the Okavango swamps, which are in my area of jurisdiction, and I have never been aware of these spider men, nor am I aware of the circumstances from which they emerge ...' The letter continued at length in this vein and ended with an embarrassing invitation to me to visit Bechuanaland and show the whereabouts of the spider men – and, while I was about it, point out the giant water lilies.

I hastened down to the *Rhodesia Herald* editorial offices where I found Harvey at his desk typing a story. I said: 'Harvey, we've got a problem here!' and showed him the letter.

He focused his machine-gunner's eyes on it and read it with his fighter's jaw out-thrust. Almost imperceptibly he went into the crouch of a cornered boxer.

'Yaah!' he said. 'These bloody district commissioners ... all they do is sit on their arses and write this sort of crap. What do they know about the real Africa?'

20

Coming home

The first thing that Stephen Bretton's wife told him when he landed at Cape Town airport was that she wanted a divorce. It was not entirely unexpected. She had been threatening to divorce him for more than a year.

But this time there was something different about it. For one thing, she met him at the airport. That was unusual. He was usually left to find his own way home. It was a lot different in the old days when she used to meet him at the airport on his return from every assignment with kisses so passionate that fellow travellers used to stand and stare, or nudge each other and wink. And the realisation that she was not wearing panties under her thin skirt would alert him that she expected sex on the way home, and they would turn off the highway on the N2 between the airport and the city for an urgent surge of lovemaking in the back seat of the car.

That was a long time ago. The long absences on news assignments and the disruptions of social and family life had taken their toll. Even when home, the exhaustion and distraction of intense news stories that ran for days at a time with their bombardment of telephone calls into the late-night and well into the early-morning hours kept him tense and preoccupied and left her resentful.

She had become especially bitter over the interrupted vacations, taking the understandable view that in the light of all else a holiday, at least, could be considered sacrosanct. The last one had been a disaster. Returning home after a three-month absence, spent mainly in the ever strife-afflicted Congo, he had taken his long-overdue leave and they had piled the children into the car and driven up the coast to Plettenberg Bay and checked into an hotel on the beach. They had set off immediately for the farthest corner of what was a long near-deserted beach. An idyllic beach, in fact. They were both instantly aware of its healing potential and for the first time in many months they held hands. The children were ecstatic and rushed ahead of them, joyfully, into the surf.

After their swim they sat on the sand. Stephen, who was facing the distant hotel, was the first to see the approaching figure of a porter from the hotel. He was carrying a yellow envelope. Vanessa saw the expression on Stephen's face and turned. Glumly, they waited as he trudged towards them.

She gazed stonily seawards as he opened the envelope and extracted the telegram. It said: 'ASSOCIATED PRESS REPORTS FIGHTING EASTERN CONGO WANT YOU THERE IMMEDIATELY STOP HIT THE GROUND RUNNING REGARDS FISHER FOREIGN EDITOR.'

He sighed.

'I suppose it says "hit the ground running",' she sneered.

'Yes.'

They gathered their belongings and hiked back to the hotel to check out. The children ambled disconsolately behind them. 'Why do we have to go back now, Daddy?' whimpered his eight-year-old daughter, Susan. His ten-year-old son, Alan, said nothing. He rarely complained. But he hung his head and kicked the sand as he walked.

Vanessa turned on him. 'Why don't you just tell them to screw off, Steve? Why don't you say no, just for once!'

'I can't do that.'

'But dammit, Steve, aren't we entitled to a life of our own just sometimes? Why does it have to be you? Why can't someone else go?'

'Because it's my story.'

She tossed her head. 'That sounds like crap to me!'

Susan began to weep. 'Stop fighting!' she pleaded.

It became evident, soon after their marriage, that Vanessa would not be happy as the wife of a foreign correspondent. Stephen had explained that it would be tough. She had brushed his doubts aside, seeing only the romance of it. But as the first months passed and the loneliness and the frustrations set in, the marriage began to deteriorate. The arrival of the children helped in some ways but in others it did not. Vanessa was a woman who needed the support of a husband at home. The scenes and rows began. The suspicions grew. She was convinced that he was being unfaithful to her on his assignments. He began to suspect that she was having affairs while he was away. The desperation of their love and the children kept the relationship going. But the pressures rendered it increasingly derelict.

Stephen was now returning home after six months in Vietnam, often in circumstances which had made it impossible to communicate with his home. Dramatic and professionally stimulating as the assignment had been he had suffered, throughout, the realisation that it was probably the death knell of his marriage.

She was waiting for him in the arrivals hall and her aloof loveliness affected him as it always did – choking him with the emotions of the past, saddening him with the problems of the present. She was as lovely as ever – tall, blonde, striking in black designer jeans and a green sweater of the clingy kind that did its duty by her figure and matched her eyes.

But her expression was cold and distant and when he tried to kiss her in greeting she turned her face away.

The drive to the city was icy and her declaration was blunt. 'I'm suing for divorce, Steve. You'll get the papers this week. Meantime we've moved out. The house is in my name so it'll make no legal difference. When you find a place we'll move back in.'

'Where are you staying?'

'With Hilda.'

'Ah, Hilda.' He knew her friend, Hilda Farley had, for a long time, been urging her to move out. Hilda, large and authoritative, had never liked him, and she was the sort of person who would relish breaking up a marriage she disapproved of.

'I want to see the children.'

'You can see them tomorrow. Collect them about ten o'clock. Have them back by two o'clock.' She added, waspishly: 'They might not recognise you, of course. Five months is a long time.'

So that was how it was going to be. Access rights already

313

prescribed, even if not yet legally, by Vanessa. And probably Hilda.

She switched to another tack, springing it on him suddenly. 'You came in on an Alitalia flight from Rome. Why did you come back via Rome again? There are much more direct flights to here from Saigon. You've got a woman in Rome, haven't you?'

'No, I have not. And as you are divorcing me and have obviously taken legal advice, I am not going to answer any of your questions.'

She drove him the rest of the way in silence, dropped him at the deserted house and drove away without another word.

When he called to fetch the children the following morning Vanessa was not there and Hilda, smugly in charge, informed him unnecessarily, 'She's with her attorney.'

He took the children to the wharves in the old part of the harbour because he knew it was a place they liked, and they wandered among the smaller ships and fishing craft tied up there. Their welcome had been as effusive and affectionate as ever, but now they seemed withdrawn.

It was Susan who opened the subject in her usual forthright manner. 'Mummy says you and she are getting divorced. Hilda says it is because you are bad.'

'And what did Mummy say about that?'

Susan paused for recollection. 'Mummy didn't say you're bad.'

'Well then, I think you should rather pay attention to what Mummy says, not Hilda.'

Alan said: 'Dad, does this mean we are not going to see you anymore?' He tried to disguise the tremor in his voice. 'Hilda says ...'

'Pay no attention to what Hilda says!' said Stephen sharply. 'Of course you will see me again. I know I have been away a lot and I'm really sorry about that. But people like journalists, airline pilots and sailors often have to go away a lot.'

Both children nodded slowly as they pondered the logic of this.

Stephen added: 'In fact you'll probably see more of me. I'm going to ask my editor to let me stay at home more.'

It was Susan, as usual, who zeroed in on target. 'Maybe you should have asked him that before,' she said.

The divorce summons arrived the following day, delivered to

him at home by a deputy sheriff. Stephen read it through, not understanding much of it until he came to the financial demands. He swallowed hard and arranged a meeting with his attorney, Max Stenner.

Max sighed as he read through the summons. 'She's using Simon Figg as her attorney,' he said. 'That's a pity.'

'Why?'

'Figg's an egotistical, pompous prick who's also a jackass.' (Max ignored protocol in describing colleagues when with clients who were also personal friends.) 'Parades himself as a champion of women. Conflict divorce is a big thing in South Africa these days and Figg sees himself as a specialist. He watches too many American law movies. Problem is he's become the sort of lawyer women go to when they want revenge or big settlements, so you're in for a tedious time. He'll try and take it all the way to court and he'll try and build up the costs. Be prepared for lots of nasty correspondence and allegations. They'll try and make you out to be a bad father, a wicked husband and, generally speaking, a shit, in the hopes of frightening you into a large settlement or influencing a court. And you may find people stalking you or trying to break into your house. So don't leave anything lying around that may be useful to the other side.'

'Good God, this is ridiculous. Can't we just try and settle?'

'Obviously we'll try. If she were using a different kind of attorney it would be reasonably easy. But I rather think it's going to be difficult.'

'So what do we do?'

'You leave it to me. I'll put in the application to defend the action and I'll handle Figg and deal with all his odious preliminaries. I'll refer back to you when necessary. In the end it will come down to the money and, as we see here, they're asking for a lot. So what I am going to do now is arrange for a meeting with a senior advocate of my acquaintance who I believe will be helpful in advising us on strategy. If it goes to court you'll be needing an advocate anyway. Meantime, try and forget it. Work as usual, relax as much as possible. Go on enjoying the kids. Don't get involved in discussions about the divorce with Vanessa. That could result in comebacks. I'll call you soon about the meeting.'

Stephen didn't find it easy to forget the divorce proceedings. Vanessa now had the backing of a divorce committee comprising Hilda, a few other close friends and her mother who had flown in from Johannesburg to render support. Vanessa was on a high in her role as the wronged wife fighting for divorce rights and he detected coolness in certain mutual friends, indicating the divorce committee had been at work.

'It's part of the usual quagmire,' Max Stenner told him. 'Don't let it worry you. As Norman Mailer once wrote, you don't really get to know your wife until you meet her in a divorce court. The same sort of thing can be said about friends.'

The children, however, with the wisdom children often show in times of crisis, seemed to succeed in maintaining a balance in their affections and loyalties to both parents. But they were understandably showing signs of stress. Susan was demonstrating unusual emotional behaviour and Alan's marks at school were dropping.

Stephen's editors were outstandingly supportive. Experienced in the pressures on their foreign correspondents and guilty in the knowledge that many of their broken marriages and other domestic difficulties were the result of their work, they strove to make amends at times like these.

Stephen received a telephone call from John Hanley, editor-in-chief of his newspaper. 'Stephen, I'm so sorry to hear the bad news,' he said. 'You must let us know if there is anything we can do to help. Meantime, take time off. Spend it with the kids ... and whatever happens I hope it's for the best. Just know we are all thinking of you.'

Max Stenner called to say that a meeting had been set up with Advocate Abe Krakowsky in his chambers. 'It'll be a working lunch,' said Max. 'He's in court morning and afternoon but has very kindly made time for us.'

Stephen was impressed. Everyone knew Abe Krakowsky. He was a senior counsel widely regarded inside and outside the legal profession as heavy artillery, and had featured prominently in some major criminal and political trials. How had Max persuaded him to become involved in what to him must seem a mundane divorce action?

When Stephen arrived at the chambers of Advocate Abe

Krakowsky SC, Max Stenner was already there and the advocate was poring over his divorce summons. A matronly secretary was serving tea and salmon sandwiches.

There was another person present, a tousled-haired young man in a crumpled suit whose tie looked as though it had been put on in a hurry and whose reddened eyes suggested slow recovery from a hangover. He fidgeted quite a lot, sometimes running a fore-finger around the inside of his collar and twitching his head about as though his neck was tense.

Max said: 'Stephen, meet Advocate Krakowsky, and this here is Advocate Henry Tucker.' Advocate Tucker rose and shook hands. Advocate Krakowsky, a tubby man, grey-haired and avuncular, was absorbed in the divorce summons and merely gestured Stephen into the remaining empty chair opposite his desk without raising his head. He had come to the analysis of Vanessa's plea for alimony where her household needs were detailed, and muttered: 'Last week I was arguing constitutional law in Namibia and here I'm involved in the price of tomato sauce.'

When he came to the last page of the document and finally looked up, Krakowsky said: 'Has everybody got tea and sandwiches? Okay, let's proceed.' He looked at Stephen for a few seconds, sizing him up, and smiled. 'Listen Stephen – can I call you Stephen? – okay, listen. I'm due back in court in an hour, so we don't have much time. Can I give it to you straight?'

'Yes, of course,' said Stephen.

'All right. If there's no hope of reconciliation, take my advice and get through this quickly. Be generous. Let her have the house, give her the furniture and the pots and pans, give her the car, let her keep the jewellery and anything else you have given her and exactly one half of whatever other assets you may have. Cut yourself free and start a new life. You're young enough to do that.

'On the question of alimony and child maintenance, work out with Max here what's reasonable and stick with that. They'll try hard for more, but don't give an inch.

'You can never anticipate precisely how a court will rule. But most judges, on the question of alimony, take the view that what a divorced wife should get is what she needs, not necessarily what she wants.'

He gestured at the divorce papers. 'Apart from the legal formalities, that's a load of hogwash.' He then pointed to a file that lay beside it. 'And these letters which your wife's attorney has been sending to your attorney complaining about various aspects of your behaviour recently, like buying your children too much chocolate when you have access to them, would have rendered even my late Labrador helpless with mirth.'

Advocate Krakowsky leaned back in his chair and folded his hands across his ample midriff. 'Sit tight, Stephen. They'll talk very tough, but may well cave in at the door of the court – *ad valvas curiae*, as we call it. If it goes further than that the court will have regard to the fact that your wife's discontent with the marriage is justified due to the nature of your work. But in the end it comes down to the money. That is where your generosity on assets will impress the court and stand you in good stead with your resistance to the excessive demands for alimony and maintenance.'

A gentle cough came from the direction of Advocate Tucker. 'Ah yes,' acknowledged Advocate Krakowsky as if he had just become aware of his colleague. I won't be representing you in court. You can't afford me. So Henry here, who often assists me, will be looking after you. He is eminently suited to your kind of case. And I'll be available for advice if at any time needed.'

The divorce case of Bretton vs Bretton came before the Cape Supreme Court two months later. The generous concessions recommended by Advocate Krakowsky had been made and the excessive alimony and maintenance demands rejected. Simon Figg and his team had been informed there would be no further negotiations. Their subsequent communications had been ignored.

With a strategy thus well defined Stephen Bretton became more relaxed over the outcome of the divorce. He was left only with the worry about Advocate Henry Tucker who appeared to be alarmingly eccentric. The case required a number of pre-court conferences to which Tucker invariably turned up late, unshaven and looking as though he had slept in his clothes. Once they had found him asleep on the couch in his office, wrapped in his court gown. The meeting had to be delayed while he shaved, gargled, swallowed pills and combed his hair.

Max Stenner went to lengths to reassure Stephen. 'Don't worry about Henry, popularly known in the profession as Silvertongue,' he said. 'He may seem a worry now but he very much comes together in court. You'll see.'

Silvertongue, he explained, would under normal circumstances have been appointed a State Counsel by now, entitling him to the letters SC behind his name. 'He's brilliant in court,' he said, 'but everyone's a little afraid of his unconventionality. He comes to work on a Harley-Davidson and at nights he plays the saxophone in a jazz band at the Green Dolphin nightclub on the waterfront.'

Signs of Silvertongue's unconventional court style began to emerge as soon as the Bretton divorce hearing began. The opposing counsel was an Advocate Quincy Mundell, short of stature but upright of bearing and pedantic of speech. His dark hair was parted neatly in the middle and arranged carefully each side of his head. As he began his introductory address, Silvertongue rose on a point of order and Advocate Mundell resumed his seat.

'My lord, I wish to draw to the court's attention that my learned friend is wearing brown boots,' said Silvertongue.

Mr Justice Fenner Conway, grizzle-haired and lizard-like, raised his eyes from the papers on the bench before him and peered over the rims of his spectacles at Advocate Mundell's footwear. Simon Figg, seated beside his advocate, peered downwards. So did Vanessa, who was seated beside Figg.

The Clerk of the Court, seated below the bench, also took a look, leaning slightly to one side to get a better view. The policeman standing just within the door of the court shifted his position a step and looked at Advocate Mundell's feet.

'Of what interest is it to the court that Advocate Mundell is wearing brown boots?' inquired Judge Conway.

Silvertongue seemed surprised at the question. 'Merely that my learned friend is wearing a dark suit, my lord. One does not wear brown shoes with a dark suit and one must ask if it is fitting that such lack of taste is acceptable in your lordship's court?'

A titter ran through the court and Mundell shot a venomous look at his colleague.

The judge replied dryly: 'Mr. Mundell's appearance is acceptable to the court. Please sit down, Mr Tucker.'

'As your lordship pleases,' said Silvertongue with a disapproving frown. He'd achieved his objective, though. Vanessa was being represented by a shabby lot. Her advocate wore brown boots in court. The judge may not care but Mundell was visibly rattled.

Vanessa herself was produced as the first witness. Her loveliness lit up the gloomy panelled surrounds of the court and the judge sat back to take a good look at her. There was little doubt that she enhanced her case just by being there.

Brown Boots Mundell (which rapidly became his nickname among the defending team) took her through the agony of being married to Stephen Bretton. She held a small handkerchief to her eyes as she described the loneliness and despair of raising two small children virtually as a single parent, while knowing that her husband was living an exciting life and, in between, flying first class on airlines and 'living it up' in five-star hotels.

Throughout her testimony Silvertongue sat going through his customary routine of playing with a pencil, tugging at his collar and twisting his neck as if to release his tension.

When he rose to cross-examine her he was very charming. 'You smell very nice, Mrs Bretton. I can pick up the fragrance of your perfume from here. What is it called?'

Judge Conway looked up sharply and Brown Boots began to struggle to his feet to object. But Vanessa answered demurely: 'Chanel Cinq.'

Silvertongue beamed at her. 'And the scarf you are wearing ... so elegant. Yves St. Laurent, is it?'

'No. Versace.' Vanessa's reply was more reserved this time and she glanced at her advocate.

Brown Boots leaped up. 'I object to this questioning, my lord. Where is it supposed to be heading?'

'Either drop it or get to the point, Mr Tucker!' said the judge.

'As your lordship pleases,' replied Silvertongue silkily. 'Meantime I would like the witness to look at these newspaper clippings.' He walked over to the witness stand and handed a sheaf of news clippings to Vanessa and handed copies of them to her advocate and to the judge.

'Now, Mrs Bretton,' said Silvertongue. 'Would it be correct to say these clippings are published news reports written by your husband and dispatched to his newspaper?'

'Yes,' replied Vanessa, turning the clippings over one by one.

'Would it be correct to say that they are, almost without exception, reports of combat situations in which the writer would have been exposed to some danger?'

After a long pause in which she studied the clippings in more detail, Vanessa replied: 'Yes.' The judge and her lawyers were also sifting through the pile.

Silvertongue lifted one clipping from the copies in front of him. 'Including one, I see, in which he was arrested by Congolese soldiers, badly beaten up and arraigned for execution until rescued by United Nations troops?'

'Yes.' The reply came a little breathlessly.

'And here is one dispatched from Vietnam, from a place called Con Thien, from which it is clear that Stephen Bretton, your husband, along with several other correspondents were in dire danger for several days and almost lost their lives. In fact one journalist was killed and several others wounded. Do you see that report?'

'Yes ... I have read it before.'

Brown Boots was on his feet. 'Where is all this taking us, my lord?'

'I was about to ask Mr Tucker that very question,' said Judge Conway. 'Mr Tucker?'

'Please bear with me, my lord. We are almost there.'

Silvertongue shuffled through the file in front of him until he came to Vanessa's list of needs upon which her financial demands were based. He looked up and spoke quietly: 'Mrs Bretton, the court has heard you describe your loneliness and despair while, as you put it, your husband lives an exciting life and travels first class on airlines and lives in five-star hotels.

'But these published dispatches before the court tell of a man doing a difficult job in highly dangerous and exhausting circumstances, much of it at the risk of his life. Is it too much to ask that he be conveyed to what might be his death in comfort, and in between being beaten up and nearly killed he takes his rest in five-star hotels when they are available?'

Vanessa was silent.

'Well, Mrs Bretton?'

She shifted her stance in the witness box. 'I suppose so.'

'Thank you, Mrs Bretton. And I see here that you require alimony for, among other things, to continue your regular membership of the Health and Racquet Club, regular attention at the Mount Nelson beauty and skin care salon for facials and massage, weekly visits to a hairdresser, membership of the 100 Club which I understand is a ladies luncheon club and I see that you drive the latest top-of-the-range VW Golf. If I may say so, Mrs Bretton – wow! And would you not agree that you are living at least as fine a life as your husband is trying to live in far more difficult circumstances – except that his costs are being borne by his newspaper, while he has to pay yours out of his salary? And this is what you want increased?'

Vanessa did not reply and this time Silvertongue did not bother to press for an answer. 'I have no further questions,' he said. He sat down, rested his chin on his chest and appeared to go to sleep.

Vanessa's team then called to the stand a psychiatrist, Dr Ibrahim Banjee, who gave evidence at length to the effect that Vanessa was in state of severe stress and clinical depression and therefore would not in the foreseeable future be in a fit state to consider any form of employment. This was, Max whispered in an aside to Stephen, to ward off any possibility that the court would reduce her alimony claim by her income-earning potential. She held a degree in social science that gave her competence in several fields of work.

Silvertongue, who was slumped in his chair with his chin on his chest, did not raise his head during Dr Banjee's evidence. He appeared to continue dozing and remained in this position when the evidence was concluded.

'Advocate Tucker, do you wish to question this witness?' asked Judge Conway, peering at Silvertongue irritably over his spectacles. Max Stenner nudged Silvertongue who appeared to awaken with a start and greeted the witness jovially.

'Oh, hello, Dr Banjee! Nice to see you again. Are you giving evidence? Will it be the usual – the old 'can't-work-because-she's-too-depressed' kind of stuff?'

Brown Boots leaped to his feet. 'Objection! I object, my lord! This is outrageous!'

The judge hammered the bench with his gavel. 'Order! Order! Advocate Tucker, you will withdraw that remark and you will stop making a mockery of this court!'

'If he really didn't hear the evidence he can't cross-examine!' bawled Brown Boots.

Silvertongue shot back: 'It doesn't matter whether I heard the evidence or not. I make a practice of never cross-examining this witness anyway.'

Judge Conway gavelled them all into silence. 'Dr Banjee, you may step down. We will adjourn for today and trust that the morrow will find sanity restored. Advocate Tucker, please see me in my chambers!'

It didn't take long for the news to spread. The *enfant terrible* of the Cape Supreme Court had been carpeted again.

The following morning's session began with an apology by Silvertongue for his behaviour of the day before. With that out of the way he called Stephen Bretton to the witness stand. He led Stephen in a swift presentation of his income and financial position to show that he could not afford his wife's outrageous demands and left it at that.

Stephen was then at the mercy of Brown Boots who rose and began a ponderous line of questioning, clinging doggedly to the theme that he was a blackguard who enjoyed a licentious lifestyle that consumed funds which would otherwise be better applied to meet his wife's alimony claim.

'It appears, Mr Bretton, that whenever you return from an assignment, wherever it may be in the world, you fly back by way of Rome. Can you explain that?'

Stephen paused. He looked thin and vulnerable in the witness box, slightly stooped from the years spent crouched over a typewriter. Wearied by the emotional strain of the past several months, he occasionally conceded a nervous gesture, adjusting his spectacles or smoothing his rebellious brown hair away from his brow.

'Well, Mr Bretton?'

Stephen cleared his throat. 'Rome is an airline crossroads, one often changes flights there.'

'You seem to answer hesitantly, Mr Bretton. Are you being evasive?'

323

Stephen felt a surge of resentment. 'There's an old Zulu proverb that says one should walk carefully around a snake,' he said.

Judge Conway shook his head. 'Advocate Mundell is an officer of the court, Mr Bretton. You cannot call him a snake.'

'I was merely quoting a Zulu proverb, sir ...'

'We will not debate the route you took via the Zulus to apply the insult. You must apologise to Advocate Mundell.'

'I apologise.'

Brown Boots looked smug and hitched his gown. 'Now, Mr Bretton, tell the court why you always come home by way of Rome.'

Stephen hesitated again.

'Answer the question, Mr Bretton,' ordered the judge.

'Well, you see, my lord, there's an excellent restaurant in Rome called Alfredo's. They make the finest fettucini in the world. Stopping off in Rome to visit Alfredo's and enjoy a plate of fettucini and listen to the violin music there is a little luxury I treat myself to whenever possible, especially after a rough assignment. It relaxes me. Helps me to relate to the normal world again. Sometimes my flight connection allows me only about four hours to get a taxi into the city, eat at Alfredo's and get back to the airport in time. But it's worth it.'

There was a bemused silence in the court after Stephen had spoken. The judge, chin on hand, was looking at him thoughtfully.

Brown Boots spread his arms wide in shock and turned to the court at large. 'Well now, listen to that! You always fly home via Rome so that you can have some pasta! And at whose expense do you dilly-dally thus, may I ask?'

'At my newspaper's expense.'

'And do they know that you fool around like this?'

'I don't know. Maybe. It's never really come up. The charges go on my expense account. They've never queried it.'

'Well now,' said Brown Boots, his thumbs under his armpits as he shot a swift look at the Bench to ensure that this iniquity had his lordship's full attention. 'It's a bit wicked, isn't it, free-loading on your expense account like that and taking a little holiday in Rome to eat pasta while your family, having not seen you for several months, awaits you at home. I'm sure your wife would rather have had you home for dinner. And would not your newspaper company consider it dishonest?'

'I doubt it.'

'You *doubt* it?' Brown Boots surveyed the court in amazement. 'It certainly sounds dishonest to me, as I am sure it does to his lordship and all the rest of us here.'

'Well, I think yours is a different world, Mr Mundell.'

Brown Boots gazed around the courtroom again in mock astonishment. 'Oh? His lordship and everyone else here live in a different world, do we? Can you explain to us the difference between your world and ours?'

Judge Conway, now leaning back in his chair, had placed the tips of his fingers together and was watching Stephen over the rims of his spectacles. Even Silvertongue had lifted his chin from his chest and was watching him. Vanessa was leaning forward as she watched him. Stephen sighed and addressed the court feeling as though, indeed, he was conversing with the denizens of a different planet.

'Well, in my world there are times when one works for periods like three days without sleep – driving, running, hiding, writing, battling with communications, surviving – even to the point of actually trying to stay alive. You see a lot of violence in my world. You see a great deal of death. You see gruesome things that can hardly bear discussion. I know things like that seem pretty remote and mundane when discussed in a place like this. For it to mean anything it has to actually happen to you ... I mean, to see the body of a child killed or maimed in battle is ... well, it's something that tends to stay with you. I think it's for these reasons that one seeks a respite to leave as much as possible of it all behind and prepare yourself for the return to normality. I don't think I'm the only one who feels this way. I know a colleague who on his way home seeks out the city producing the best available symphony concert and goes there to listen to music. I have another colleague who checks into an hotel for three days and gets drunk. People have different needs, I suppose ... In your world, after a hard day in court you may need to stop off at a pub or a club on the way home to have a drink. In my world it usually takes a little more than that. I think most newspapers who employ foreign correspondents understand this and it rarely becomes the sort of issue you have raised here.'

There was a silence after he had finished. Judge Conway maintained his posture, his fingertips still pressed together. But his lizardy eyes moved slowly away from Stephen and came to rest on Brown Boots.

Stephen glanced down at Silvertongue who slowly closed and opened one eye. He looked at Vanessa and wondered why she seemed sudddenly pale.

For a moment Brown Boots looked like a man who had mislaid something. But he recovered his composure quickly, glanced around the courtroom in a quick assessment of reaction and cleared his throat. 'Ah yes, well ... be that as it may.' He scratched busily among his papers. 'On the question of such light relief from your work routines as you have described, Mr Bretton, I would like to introduce to the court one of your notebooks ...'

Silvertongue was up like a hissing cobra. 'Objection! I have not seen this notebook.'

'I have had copies of its pages made for you, your client and for his lordship,' said Brown Boots, silkily, and he started handing sheaves of photocopies to all concerned.

Silvertongue continued to protest. 'This is a civil, not a criminal, case, my lord. He can't produce evidence like rabbits out of a hat!'

'Nevertheless I shall allow it,' said the judge, inexplicably.

Silvertongue looked shocked and sat down. He whispered to Max Stenner: 'Where did they get their hands on that?'

Max shrugged. 'I don't know. I warned Stephen not to leave things lying around.' He glanced across at Simon Figg who had a smug 'now-we've-got-you-bastards' look on his face.

'We have heard much from Mr Bretton today about his horrifying experiences and how he seeks relief from them,' Brown Boots began spitefully. 'Let us now examine some of his other forms of recreation and the money he spends on them. My lord, I wish to refer to the section of the notes I have labelled as page 14A where you will see ...'

'Objection!' snapped Silvertongue, rising. 'This persistent questioning about money spent by the defendant when on assignment is irrelevant. There is no way plaintiff can rely on his newspaper's expense account for alimony.'

'Objection overruled,' said the judge. 'I'd like to hear about all money spent. I will then decide what is relevant.'

Silvertongue sat down gloomily and Brown Boots resumed. 'As I was saying, my lord, on the page I have labelled 14A in Mr Bretton's notebook containing various notes pertaining to the war and other events in Vietnam you will see the words 'Vicki's Bar' and that it is underlined. Below that heading are what appear to be the names and ages of two young women, 'Kia 17' and 'Mia 23'. Now, Mr Bretton, kindly tell the court who these women were whom you appear to have met in Vicki's Bar, presumably a place of recreation somewhere in Vietnam and what your relationships were with them?'

Stephen replied coldly: 'It has nothing to do with women. Those are casualty figures. Kia, as you have called it, is actually an anagram, KIA – killed in action – and the figure 17 is no one's age. It is the number of American soldiers who were killed in that week. Mia, as you have called it, is MIA – missing in action – and 23 is the number of soldiers missing in the same week.'

Brown Boots was taken aback, but struggled on manfully. 'And what, if we are to believe what you are telling us, has this to do with Vicki's Bar?'

'Vicki's Bar, in the Da Nang press centre, later renamed the Vicki Chapell Press Centre, was where correspondents gathered not only for relaxation but for press briefings. Vicki Chapell was a well-known and much admired American correspondent who was killed in Vietnam and the press centre – and its bar – were named after her.'

Judge Conway who had been paging through the notebook interrupted dryly. 'Advocate Mundell, I notice elsewhere in Mr Bretton's notes the figure 6 alongside the name – or initials – KIA. So unless you intend to infer even more serious impropriety on Mr Bretton's part perhaps you should discontinue this line of questioning.'

Suddenly there was a commotion as Vanessa jumped up and ran out of the courtroom. The court sat in silence as the rapid staccato of her high heels faded into the distance down the corridor.

'Well,' said Judge Conway, 'we seem to have lost the plaintiff. We may as well adjourn until tomorrow morning.'

That night, as Stephen finished the sort of makeshift evening meal that men separated from their wives prepare for themselves, there came a knock at the door. When he opened it Vanessa stood there.

They looked at each other in silence for a few seconds. He could see that she had been weeping. 'You shouldn't be here,' said Stephen. 'Your lawyer wouldn't like it.'

'I've fired him,' she said. 'Steve, I want this horror to stop.'

She came inside and put her arms about his neck and laid her head on his chest. 'I'm sorry, I'm sorry, I'm sorry. Stephen, can I please stay here tonight?'

Stephen met with Silvertongue in his chambers the following morning and they were joined by Max Stenner who confirmed he had received a call from Simon Figg to say that he no longer represented Vanessa. 'He sounded pissed off,' said Max with satisfaction. 'And I reckon Mundell can't be feeling so good either.'

'So what's it to be?' asked Silvertongue. 'Do I sense reconciliation in the air?'

'In a sense yes, in another sense no,' replied Stephen. 'We feel a lot for each other, but we've agreed that what it comes down to in the end is that no sane woman who wants a normal life should be married to a foreign hack. So we've decided to go ahead with the divorce but in a more civilised way, without the likes of Simon Figg. Vanessa has accepted the terms and wants Max here to draw up the papers for us and for you to steer it through the court. For the future, we'll take our freedom and focus on ways we can make it up to the kids.'

'Well, I'm sorry to receive the instructions,' said Max. 'But if you're going ahead with it, it's the best way for it to happen.' He rose to his feet. 'I'll get on with it then.'

After he had left Silvertongue took a half-empty bottle of whisky and two glasses out of his drawer. 'Let's have a snort,' he said. 'I want to wipe out the memory of the look on Brown Boots's face when he heard KIA wasn't a whore but a casualty figure.'

'It's ten o'clock in the morning!' protested Stephen.

'I've never been able to understand the connection between

time and drinking whisky,' said Silvertongue. He raised his glass. 'To happiness, in whatever form it comes – and for starters, why don't you come down to the Green Dolphin tonight and listen to some jazz? Barney Moletsi's going to be hitting the piano, Garth Pizzy's on base, Charlie Mondisi's on drums and I'll be playing sax. You wanna come?'

'Yes,' said Stephen. 'I'd like that.'

21

The rugby match

Dispatch to the Washington Times, *9 September 1986*

The bar in the Picardie Hotel in the town of Paarl in the Western Province of South Africa is not exactly the cultural centre of the community. But it is a place where national issues of great importance are frequently debated with both eloquence and vigour – so much in fact that on occasion the debaters move outside into the High Street so as to address each other in more robust fashion.

It is on occasions like these that the police sometimes join the debate, whereupon the venue switches once more, this time to the charge office and cells of the Paarl Central Police Station.

The final speeches are usually heard in the Paarl Magistrates Court where the magistrate gives the final ruling on who was right. Invariably he rules that the police were right.

It was here, in this vibrant forum of the Picardie Bar, that one, Johannes Vermaak, a railway shunter of honest repute, entered dramatically and announced the shattering news that the town's elite white high school, Paarl Gymnasium, was going to play the Paulus Joubert coloured high school at rugby.

There was a long pause of total silence as the shock of this intelligence seeped into the embalmed minds of the Picardie assembly. All around the bar pints of Lion beer and tots of Old Buck gin and Commando brandy paused on their way to parched throats – in itself a rare interruption in the Picardie Bar.

Then Frans Esterhuizen, a farmer, shouted: 'Jee-sus Christ. You mean our boys are going to play Hottentots?'

Dirk Malan, a long-distance lorry driver, said: 'They'll also be playing coolies. They've got coolies at that Paulus Joubert school.'

'But at least they won't be playing Kaffirs, they've got no Kaffirs there,' said Bokkie van Jaarsveld, an agricultural implements salesman.

Bokkie van Jaarsveld was regarded as the liberal of the Picardie Bar, and his comment was ignored.

'Well,' said Frans Esterhuizen, grimly, 'this is something I've got to see.'

Everyone agreed that this would be a rugby match not to be missed.

As the news reached other parts of town it drew similar reactions of surprise, some of them more sophisticated than in the Picardie Bar and some of them even less sophisticated.

By and large the reaction was disapproving. At best is was doubtful. 'I know things are changing in this country,' said a middle-aged lady in Checkers supermarket, 'but isn't this going too fast?'

To understand more easily the nature of this doubting it should be known that Paarl is a very conservative town. It is where the Afrikaans language was first formed and spoken, and a monument to the language stands proudly on a nearby hill to remind all of this important fact.

The town is white-walled and beautiful, situated among vineyards. Its rural, mainly Afrikaner community would like to keep it white-walled and beautiful – and white.

That a white and a coloured school had decided, among themselves, to play rugby together was disturbing to this tranquillity – and proved once again that there was dangerous liberalism in learning and books.

It was true that multi-racial sport had arrived in South-Africa, but it was not yet acknowledged in Paarl, sacred shrine of the language of Afrikanerdom.

For these various reasons a large crowd came to watch the rugby match between Paarl Gymnasium and Paulus Joubert High School last week.

Dr Danie Craven, grand chief and high priest of South African rugby was there to give his blessing. 'This is a breakthrough to a better South Africa,' he said. But old Paarl residents shook their heads sadly. Oom Danie van Niekerk, aged 80 and who had hoped to reach his grave without seeing such a terrible thing, said to his younger brother, Oom Johannes van Niekerk, aged 77: 'Yerrah, Yerrah, Jan, what has become of our town?'

Oom Johannes scowled. 'It's all this damned television from America,' he said.

The Picardie Bar debating society was there, with pint flasks in their pockets and prepared to be nasty, but feeling inhibited under the cold-eyed gaze of several members of the Paarl police force who came to stand purposefully close to them.

Elders of the Dutch Reformed Church, dressed in black, watched the scene with folded arms and narrowed eyes, intent on reporting back to God.

The coloured spectators who came to support and cheer for the Paulus Joubert team stood separately from the white spectators.

The coaches of the two teams spoke last anxious words to their players. 'If I hear any of you call any of them a Hottentot or a coolie, I'll beat his brains out,' said the Paarl Gymnasium coach.

The coloured coach of the Paulus Joubert team told his boys: 'By inviting us to play them, these honkie Boers are behaving nicely – so no kicking or swearing at them. Now take off your boots, I want to make sure no one's got a knife in his sock.'

The match was watched mainly in silence, although cheerleading teams from both schools worked valiantly at infusing some gaiety into the scene.

Privileged by years of better training and facilities, the white team began to pile on the score, and some white spectators smiled or nodded cynically.

The Picardie Bar contingent made snide comments.

Then, quite suddenly, a centre three-quarter on the coloured side found a gap in the Paarl Gymnasium defence and streaked through in a weaving, storming run. He ran like a person obsessed, as if pouring all his energy and determination into this one feat of excellence.

His brilliant burst took him 40 yards and within five paces of the try line before he was pulled down.

The crowd – all the crowd – went mad with delight. In that

instant the great South African love of rugby, which is more important than religion, more important than politics and knows no race barriers, eliminated all prejudice and made the crowd as one.

In that one electrifying moment apartheid was forgotten and South Africa moved a little further out of the shadows here in Paarl where Afrikanerdom has its roots.

'Yerra, Jan, but these Hottentots can play rugby,' said Oom Danie van Niekerk.

Which summed up an unfamiliar feeling among many of those present that perhaps such games were not a bad thing after all.

22

Sarah Barrell

Sarah Webb Fairbanks Barrell was blonde, long-legged and lovely. She also had intelligence and courage. Not surprisingly, she was highly successful in her career as a photojournalist.

She spoke in a low-pitched voice, slightly tinged with a Southern drawl. She took care to keep it low-pitched at all possible times, because otherwise it became kind of squeaky. If you wanted to analyse her meticulously – as men sometimes tend to do when they put a beautiful woman under a microscope – you might say that she had everything going for her except that sometimes she had a squeaky voice.

But Sarah had so much going for her that her voice didn't really matter. In fact, had she contrived to find a way of going through life without uttering a word, it would hardly have been noticed.

She was six feet tall and lissom and walked with the sexy lioness-like tread of the ramp model she once was, all of which, of course, dramatised her beauty. When she entered a restaurant men stirred like startled gazelle.

She was tough. Very tough. She had to be. She was competing in one of the world's hardest professions and had got there by a bruising, knockabout route.

In the small American town in which she was born and bred she had been seduced by a teacher at the age of 14 and become pregnant, which had required an abortion.

She ran away from home to become a model, at which she did remarkably well, until led into vice by the chief executive of her agency who hired her to become a plaything at parties for his friends in the advertising industry.

This led her to become a highly-paid call-girl, working a beat around New York's top nightclubs and five-star hotels.

She once asked me: 'You ever hear this shit about me once having been a whore?'

I was silent as I fumbled for an answer. She laughed and said: 'Yeah, well mostly it's just gossip or nastiness, like when I scoop someone or won't sleep with someone. But as a matter of fact, it's true.'

And she went on to tell me, in her soft, Southern drawl, about her three years as a high-class hooker, sometimes laughing as she worked through the anecdotes.

'It wasn't all bad,' she said. 'I actually remember times that were fun. And I met a lot of interesting people – and some famous people. And the money was good. Some girls I knew in the business made enough bucks to invest and retire on. The trick was to know when to stop. I think I got that right. I began studying photography in my spare time and I quit when I had enough saved to buy cameras and an air ticket to Rome and to give me a lifestyle there while I took a course in fashion photography.'

An affair in Rome with an Italian news photographer took her to Vietnam where she accompanied him on an assignment. That was the beginning of her career as a foreign correspondent, as a writer who illustrated her dispatches with her own photography. Soon photo-features by Sarah Barrell, distributed to major newspapers and magazines through a leading photo-agency, became a known product in international journalism. In career terms, she had arrived.

When her Italian boyfriend returned to Italy, she stayed in Vietnam and commenced a relationship with a well-known television correspondent reporting the Vietnam saga for a major American network. It was in Saigon that I met her, briefly, for the first time.

Sarah moved on to the Cambodia story with her new guy, but broke up with him in Phnom Penh during a row in the Inter-Continental Hotel that became legendary in international press-corps recall. She threw his typewriter, electronic equipment and clothes out of an upper window of the hotel and he responded by, in turn, throwing out her cameras and clothing. Colleagues and other hotel residents sunbathing beside the swimming pool below had to take cover as the sky rained cameras, tape recorders, jeans, T-shirts, jockey underwear, panties and brassières.

Sarah left on an assignment to Cairo after that and from there moved down to Johannesburg, which was where we met again. She moved busily around southern Africa and began to focus on the then Rhodesia, the lead story in the region at that time. She became fascinated by Africa, as so many first-time visitors do. 'I love this place,' she told me once. 'I feel my destiny is here.' She was not wrong about that.

Her visits to Rhodesia became increasingly frequent until she finally moved her base from Johannesburg to Salisbury, as it was then known. The attraction of the place for her was understandable. It had some of the familiar elements of Vietnam: an ongoing war being fought by an army of big, suntanned, attractive men; a resident press corps covering a permanently high-profile story; with the added excitement of other correspondents, cameramen and photographers coming and going. Lots of action, lots of news, lots of parties, lots of fun. All the things, in fact, that Sarah was good at and loved.

There were some problems. Sarah, as I have already indicated, was no ordinary woman. Inasmuch as her extraordinary good looks proved a valuable asset in some aspects of her work, in other ways her attractiveness was a distraction and even caused offence.

War is a serious business and military commanders don't like having their troops distracted in combat situations by the presence of film-star-quality blondes.

In Vietnam – in fact in any American war theatre – tolerance of female war correspondents was about as broad as you could get. Officers in the field cursed at their arrival but none would dare go so far as to object, so long as they didn't do anything silly and so long as they didn't insist on separate latrines in situations where it was difficult to provide them.

I can recall an intense, dark-haired girl in Vietnam representing a Greek ethnic publication in the United States who went to pieces in a nasty situation and insisted on tearfully cradling the heads of wounded marines. She was quickly flown out.

In truth, though, most of the women correspondents I have

worked alongside have been highly professional people, in some instances outpacing some of us males in performance and sheer courage.

Sarah Barrell was certainly in this upper echelon. Well established as a war correspondent, she also knew the score on the finer points and she worked hard at keeping a low profile: she wore no make-up on military assignments and did her best to keep her blonde tresses unobtrusive under whatever headgear the army provided.

But she just couldn't help her femininity. Even in camouflage fatigues, flak jacket, steel helmet and paratroopers' boots, she looked like she was modelling military wear for *Vogue* magazine.

It was more of a problem in Rhodesia where, to begin with, the military didn't want any truck with journalists, and access to the combat zones was strictly limited. It was a smaller but no less vicious war than Vietnam's – whites were fighting for their very survival. It took me six years to breach the protocols and get an assignment to a combat situation – after which I was deported because it was felt I had written about it in too light a vein.

Sarah was taking pictures and reporting from the front line within weeks, to the fury of the long-established resident press corps – and of course the inevitable conclusions were drawn. It could only be because she was trading sexual favours.

'Yeah, yeah, I know,' Sarah sighed when she heard the gossip. 'I've heard it all before. Why don't these creeps learn that you don't have to sleep with the general to get a good army assignment? You only need to be nice to him.'

Not, she would remark in aside, that she was above using the ultimate feminine strategy to achieve a really worthwhile objective. 'After all,' she would reason, 'if you got it, why not use it?'

Her arrival in Salisbury certainly disturbed the resident international and local press corps.

The Rhodesian war had been going on for more than ten years and the Salisbury reporters had become an insular and clubbish little community. It had entered that stale phase that afflicts all press corps when a story becomes old. The coverage had become lethargic and had reached the point where correspondents tended to help rather than compete with each other. Recognised old hands who came and went were welcomed, but newcomers tended to be excluded from the inner circle of shared information.

This was always a dangerous policy because every now and then a feisty new arrival would feel snubbed and adopt the 'Screw you bastards, I'll show you!' attitude, work hard at finding an exclusive angle and scoop everyone to smithereens. There would follow cries of dismay from wounded hacks as they rushed from bars, leaped out of swimming pools or extricated themselves from between the moist thighs of women and rolled out of bed to respond to angry call-backs from irate editors. It was certainly the quickest way for a newcomer to be invited onto the circuit.

Sarah Barrell didn't want to be on the circuit. She was a loner who had never cared for pack journalism. 'You run with the crowd, you might never get scooped, but you might also never get a scoop,' she used to say. Which was true enough.

Thus she was destined to become unpopular among most of her colleagues in Rhodesia.

It wasn't just her work style. It was also her appearance. One would expect that a tall, beautiful blonde would enjoy instant popularity. This is not necessarily so.

Women hated her from the start. Female colleagues felt outgunned and, in general, women didn't like the way their menfolk looked at her.

Male colleagues tended to be intimidated by her. For one thing, she spoke their language, even down to the usual much-used four-letter words, and she was inside their heads, knowing what they were thinking when they looked at her, cynically aware of what they were saying about her behind her back. It wasn't that she had second sight. It was just that in her short life – she was 31 years old when she came to Africa – she had done more and seen more than most men twice her age, and she had become wise beyond her years.

It disconcerted most men that her approach to them was very similar to their own approach to women. She would stand a round of drinks at a bar and, if she wished to, she would set out to seduce a man of her choice for a one-night stand with the self-assurance of a practised philanderer.

I always had the impression that Sarah shuffled men like cards.

She would cast aside those who bored her or who did not attract her and focus her interest on those who appealed to her. She seemed to have a liking for two types: dark, intense men and those who were big and rugged. She liked men in uniform and she preferred tall men, an understandable preference of most tall women.

She did not care for frivolous advances and she hated being touched if she did not want to be touched. Her reaction to being imposed upon could be devastating.

One of her first affairs in Rhodesia was with a captain of the Selous Scouts (the Rhodesian Special Forces) called Mike Donnelly. She was sitting in a lounge at the Meikles Hotel when a slightly inebriated member of the press corps placed a friendly hand on her knee.

'Please don't do that,' said Sarah, coolly. 'Otherwise I'll have to ask Mike here to hit you with his cock.'

One of Africa's more distinguished correspondents, a physically small man, also made the cardinal error of fondling her publicly during the cocktail hour at the Salisbury Press Club. She looked down at him almost sympathetically and said: 'Aw gee, Chris, you'd just like to go up on me wouldn't you?' Turning to her companion she said: 'I can't stand horny little people, can you? Let's get outta here.'

Physical demonstrations of affection are part of southern Africa's way of life, and it could be said that Sarah was being over-reactive. But it probably had a lot to do with a part of her life she wanted to forget.

Whatever the case, it added to her growing unpopularity among the hacks on the Rhodesia story. She began socialising less with the press corps and more with the military and the robust farmers who comprised the irregular forces of the army. In this way she also gathered information and opportunities that enabled her to scoop her colleagues quite frequently, which eroded her popularity still further.

There's nothing bitchier than a bunch of aggrieved journalists – and I'm referring here to bitches of both sexes. References to Sarah Barrell became coloured by comments on her origins, her past history and the alleged ways in which she acquired her exclusive stories.

They nicknamed her Sarah Dum-Dum, derived from the worn-out cliché that because she was a blonde she must be dumb. But dumb she certainly was not. The army and police, as it turned out, thought she was a lot brighter than the rest of us.

A PATU (Police Anti-Terrorist Unit) commander told me: 'She showed us she could strip and reassemble an AK-47 rifle as well as an American M.16. By the time she left us she could also strip and assemble an FN. She could even do it blindfolded. She also knew how to operate an RPG. I've never met another journalist who could do all those things. Write about it, maybe. Do it, no.'

Rhodesia may have ended up as just another war assignment in Sarah's eventful life, had she not fallen in love.

'This is *it*!' she wrote to me in a long letter. 'I have never loved like this before. It makes me realise that all the other times may have been a preparation for this, to help me know the value of what I have now.'

The focus of her new passion was Major André Dennison, a company commander in the Rhodesia African Rifles, well known in Salisbury journalistic circles, who had proved himself in many combat situations to be a fine soldier and an outstanding officer.

It was an affair that could have emerged from the pages of a romance novel: she the tough, worldly-wise blonde war photo-journalist and he the dashing soldier whom she had accompanied professionally on several of his combat missions until he was wounded, after which she helped to nurse him back to health. On assignments she carried a .38 pistol given her by Dennison for her protection.

Rhodesians were a small community thrown together and tightly knit by their tribulations and war of survival where most people knew or knew of everybody else, and their affair became much talked about. It broke up Dennison's marriage and quite naturally people took sides, not least of all among the more garrulous members of the press corps.

I received one more ecstatic letter from Sarah. She and André had taken an apartment in Salisbury and were living together. After the war they would get married and buy a farm. Rhodesia was to become the end of her rough and wild road through life, and would become her home.

I had come to know Sarah Barrell well enough to know that there was a side to her that was seldom revealed to the very tough and cynical world in which she moved. She revelled in her experiences, her success in journalism and the excitement of it. She drank deep of the action and the romance. She was rightfully proud of the international reputation she had carved for herself in what was still, essentially, a male-dominated profession.

But there was a soft core to her that was very carefully guarded by an exterior that allowed close friendship or intimacy only on her terms. It was the inner essence of womanhood that persists in most ambitious and career-motivated women no matter how much obscured or relegated. In Sarah's case it did not lurk even close to the surface, but glimpses of it sometimes showed in contact with children or animals.

I recall an occasion when we were seated beside a swimming pool, and a little girl from a nearby group toddled up to her and stood before her, sucking a thumb and gazing at her with the wide-eyed look with which very small children sometimes appraise strangers. Sarah, who was reading, lowered her book a fraction to meet the stare. After a few seconds, intrigued, she removed her sunglasses, whereupon the child leaped straight into her lap. Curiously, neither of them had spoken a word.

I think Sarah was driven by certain events in her childhood, and undoubtedly her subsequent life and her work satisfied a hunger for adventure and for life itself. I believe that in André Dennison she had truly found the way to her secret goal: marriage and much else that women hold dear.

But it was not to be. Once again Africa took its toll. Dennison was killed in a shoot-out with guerillas near Fort Victoria. It had been a night operation and, tragically, in the darkness, he had been shot by one of his own men.

The incident left Sarah grief-stricken, isolated and lonely. She attended André's funeral, but family members and friends formed a protective circle around his wife and excluded her from the graveside.

Her life had become centred on André Dennison and, once he had gone, she had few people she could turn to for support or consolation. Rhodesia, her home-to-be, had again become just another foreign country in her tumultuous life.

Every meal a banquet, every night a honeymoon

She telephoned me in Cape Town a few days after the event. She was alone in her apartment. She sounded subdued and shattered in spirit, but spoke calmly.

I tried to console her as best I could, speaking on a long-distance line from 2 000 miles away.

Had I known that hours earlier she had visited a local attorney where she had made a will directing the sale of her cameras and leaving the proceeds and all else she owned to André Dennison's regiment, I might have realised what she had in mind and been able to do something to stop it.

A few hours after she telephoned me – it could have been the last call she made – she shot herself with the pistol Dennison had given her. She was 33 years old. What a waste.

23

Sons of Africa

On a warm evening on the beautiful island of Mauritius the anguish of the darker side of Africa that until then I had come to know only as an observer and a reporter visited me in one dreadful personal blow. I received a telephone call to tell me that my elder son, Michael, had been killed in a terrorist bomb attack.

I am not going to dwell on the shock and the pain of that moment and the hours and days that followed. Death in some form or other visits all of us in time and, when so many have lost sons and daughters in the violent conflicts that have swept the world throughout history, no man can claim precedence for the loss of his own. It is strictly a personal and a family matter.

In Africa, where life is cheap, death is a frequent visitor. The tempests, the plagues, the pestilence, the wars and the conflicts are many and various and the violence is pervasive. As a reporter accustomed to covering such events I learned to deal with it. Yet, of course, none of this prepares you for the moment when it happens to you.

I was on assignment in Mauritius for *Newsweek* magazine to interview the newly elected prime minister, Anerood Jugnauth, when the news came. The interview was scheduled for the following morning. Two things enabled me to carry out the task. One was a kind of numbness, I suppose of shock, that somehow placed me outside myself, leaving me with the strange sensation that what had actually occurred was happening to someone else and I was merely witnessing it. Each time I tried to grasp the fact and absorb it, something blanked my mind out as though a switch had been flicked. It enabled me to get through the interview, write the story in a mechanical sort of way and dispatch it. It was not the best-written interview of my career but I accomplished it. I then informed *Newsweek* of what had happened and booked the first available flight home.

The other enormous source of help was my colleague, photographer Mark Peters, who was accompanying me on what was his first assignment for *Newsweek*. Mark himself was no stranger to death and the effects of it (he was a veteran of the Rhodesian war) and his quiet sympathy and support and the efficient way in which he swiftly took over organisational aspects of the assignment gave tremendous relief. It was the beginning of a long and valued friendship.

I remember, too, the extraordinary kindness of the hotel staff and the Mauritian authorities. Communications between Mauritius and South Africa in those days were desultory and the hotel and the Mauritian government's Department of Communications kept a telephone line to Cape Town open throughout the night for my exclusive use. It was only weeks later that I came to realise I had not even been charged for it. Kindness of this sort is usually found only in a small country or community. In addition to which Mauritians happen to be especially nice people.

I arrived in Johannesburg where I was met by my wife who had flown up from Cape Town. I was also met by a reporter from a local newspaper who asked me: 'Can you find it in yourself to forgive what has happened?'

It seemed an odd question and, as part of my emotions at that time had built into an intense anger, I replied: 'No, I cannot.' Then, quickly realising it was the sort of reply that could be played around with in news copy and in headlines, I added: 'How can I forgive anyone when I don't know who did it and why?'

But it soon emerged, according to the police (and later confirmed by an ANC spokesman in Lesotho), that the explosion that had killed my son was the work of the African National Congress, at the time a banned organisation whose attempts to liberate South Africa from apartheid rule included terror attacks on the civilian population.

An explosive device had been placed in a trash disposal unit in a corner of an elevator in the Cape Town Centre, a multi-storeyed office building on the Cape Town foreshore. The bomb was timed to explode at a few minutes after 5 p.m. It was intended for members of the President's Council, whose council chamber was on the top floor of the building and whose daily meetings usually ended at 5 p.m.

As it happened the President's Council sat in a late session that day and it was an empty elevator into which my son stepped, alone, on a much lower floor where his office was situated. The bomb exploded as the elevator was descending and the wreckage and its sole occupant plunged to the bottom of the lift shaft.

A large number of people attended Michael's funeral and, as a family, we were greatly assisted in our grief by the condolences and support received from friends, colleagues and others in South Africa and abroad.

All that was left now was to handle the pain and the questions. For the pain had arrived. The numbness of shock that had enabled me to function in Mauritius had receded and the heartache had taken over.

The loss of any child is a disaster like none other. The fragments of memories and images pursue you long after you have learned to live again. And the loss of a son, perhaps most especially the first-born, is an eerie thing. It is as if your life force has been stopped.

In the weeks that followed Michael's death a constant refrain ran through my mind – words I had learned at high school by the Afrikaner poet, Totius, who, in a lament following the death of his own child, wrote:

My kind is dood!
Dit brand soos 'n pyl in my,
Die mense sien daar niks nie van
En die Here alleen Die weet wat ek ly.

(My child is dead!
It burns like an arrow in me,
People see nothing of it
And God alone knows what I suffer.)

In the months that followed I could not walk through the vine-yards on our farm and I left them to the care of others. Michael had walked with me through them so often that I could not, for a long time, bear to be there on my own.

I was also disturbed by the agonised grief of my eldest daughter, Catherine, for whom Michael had been a very special brother. They had needed to be a family to each other in the early years of my longest foreign assignments. And it was Catherine who, in my absence in Mauritius, had been called upon to identify her brother's remains.

With the pain came the questions. Why Michael? Why in a building occupied by more than 3 000 people did he have to be the one who walked alone to the waiting death? He was not political. He was dedicated only to his family and his work.

He was married and the father of a newborn baby son. He had always been a child of singular grace, quiet and conscientious, loved and liked by all who came to know him. He was a student when he died, very much part of the new emerging age of computer technology, while also working for a firm of consultant electronic engineers. On the day he died he had written a national examination. His professor wrote to inform me that he had achieved the highest mark in the country.

Why, so often, does Africa take the best and the brightest in its bloody maw? It must be a question frequently asked by so many who have grieved as I was grieving.

Michael's death occurred at a time when hosts of other young men were dying. Young white men sent to Namibia and the border of Angola to fight for the doomed apartheid regime. Young black men quitting South Africa via secret routes to join the liberation movements to fight the white regime. Blacks seized in their homes and imprisoned, sometimes never to be seen again. White teenagers in Rhodesia, graduating from high school, not yet old enough to shave, yet handed guns to fight and fruitlessly give their lives to preserve another white government doomed to extinction. Young black Rhodesians training in Russia, China, Algeria and elsewhere to return and fight and die for black rule and the creation of the independent state of Zimbabwe.

The blood of Africans spilled ever more and ever further

throughout a continent that seemed to have an insatiable lust for killing. The wars and revolutions raged on in Angola, Mozambique, Congo, Uganda, Sudan, Zanzibar, Somalia, Nigeria, Chad, Ethiopia, Kenya, Tanzania. And the worst was yet to come – the genocide in Rwanda and Burundi and the barbaric massacres in Sierra Leone and the recruitment of child soldiers to become adolescent murderers in West Africa.

It was a pan-African horror scene across which I had passed back and forth, doing my job of reporting it, never ceasing to wonder at the enormity of death in Africa, a continent so bloodthirsty that it destroyed life in great swathes, in ways so terrible and in circumstances so tragic, at times so bizarre.

Parts of it had already touched me personally: the death of my friend, CBS television correspondent George Clay, shot through the head in the advance on Stanleyville by mercenary troops at the height of the Congo war. And the deaths of other close friends as I have described in earlier chapters: Howard Lawrence whose life we tried to save by taking him to a forbidden casualty ward reserved for whites only; Sarah Barrell who shot herself when her Rhodesian soldier lover was killed in action; John Edlin who, driven by his demons, finally died after collapsing in a Dakar nightclub. Those were my friends.

Now Africa had taken my son.